Milliamperes

contents of case (with bandages)

contents of Desk

Medicine on desk

McCuen chisels

Small chisels

TELEPHONE 1613.
OFFICE OPEN AT ALL HOURS.

2 –

Crile, Dr.

To Professional Services

1 Clamp

forward | 1411 | 75

50

1 00

2 00

50

2 00

17 | 50

5 00

17 78 10

2 00

Cleveland O. Apr 10 1891

... duration of seventeen hundred

... $17.00 dollars I have this

Drs. H. E. Buets and G. W. Crile

... Chattels instruments and other

... contained in brick house and

... at No 380 Pearl St

... marked exhibit A attached

... sale.

C. H. Wood

Administrator of Frank J

To Act As A Unit

The Story of The Cleveland Clinic

CONTRIBUTORS

Muzaffar Ahmad
George H. Belhobek
Alexander T. Bunts
Sharon J. Coulter
George Crile, Jr.
Fawzy G. Estafanous
Carl C. Gill
Joseph F. Hahn
William R. Hart
Shattuck W. Hartwell, Jr.
J. Michael Henderson
Hilel Lewis
Floyd D. Loop
Maurie Markman
Daniel J. Mazanec
William M. Michener
Douglas S. Moodie
Richard Rudick
George R. Stark

To Act As A Unit

The Story of The Cleveland Clinic

Third Edition

John D. Clough, M.D., Editor

Library of Congress Cataloging in Publication Data

Main entry under title:

To act as a unit.

    Bibliography: p.
    Includes index.
[DNLM: 1. Cleveland Clinic. 2. Ambulatory Care
Facilities—history—Ohio. WX 28 A03 C6C6t]
RA982.C62C558   1985   362.1′1′0977131   84-24049
ISBN 0-9615424-3-8

". . .to act as a unit": The Story of the Cleveland Clinic   ISBN 0-9615424-3-8

© 1996 by The Cleveland Clinic Foundation. Copyright under the Uniform Copyright Convention. All rights reserved. This book is protected by copyright. No part of it may be reproduced, stored in a retrieval system, or transmitted in any form or by any means, electronic, mechanical, photocopying, recording, or otherwise, without written permission from the publisher. Made in the United States of America.

To the Memory of the Founders

FRANK E. BUNTS, 1861 – 1928

GEORGE W. CRILE, 1864 – 1943

WILLIAM E. LOWER, 1867 – 1948

JOHN PHILLIPS, 1879 – 1929

TABLE OF CONTENTS

ILLUSTRATIONS

PREFACE TO THE THIRD EDITION

Publication of the third edition of *To Act as a Unit: The Story of The Cleveland Clinic* coincides with the 75th anniversary of the founding of The Cleveland Clinic. The first edition, edited by Alexander T. Bunts, M.D., and George Crile, Jr., M.D., was produced in conjunction with the Clinic's 50th anniversary in 1971. The second edition, edited by Shattuck W. Hartwell, Jr., M.D., appeared in 1985 at the time of the dedication of the Crile Building, then known as the A Building. These milestone events are only a few of the high points of the Clinic's illustrious history, and it has truly been an honor and a labor of love for me to have the opportunity to review and update the continuing saga.

Structurally the book is similar to the previous editions. I have divided it into three sections, namely: "The Early Years," covering the events leading up to the founding of the Clinic and the period before the establishment of the Board of Governors; "The Board of Governors Era," beginning in 1955 and continuing to the present; and "The Divisions and Centers," a series of short histories of these professional units of The Cleveland Clinic. As Hartwell notes in his introduction to the second edition, much has been retained from the first edition, edited by Dr. Alexander T. Bunts and Dr. George "Barney" Crile, Jr. Other contributors to that edition included Dr. A. Carlton Erstene (affectionately known to those of us who were residents in that era as "The Ace"), Mr. James G. Harding (who played a very sweet trumpet in the Clinic's old dance band, The Arrhythmias), Dr. John Beach Hazard (the dignified and highly respected gray eminence of pathology), Dr. Fay A. LeFevre (first chairman of the Board of Governors and everyone's father figure), Dr. Irvine H. Page (the discoverer of angiotensin), Mr. John Sherwin, Sr. (one of the most dedicated trustees the Clinic has ever had), Dr. Carl E. Wasmuth (second chairman of the Board of Governors and the only one, as far as I know, who kept an adding machine on his desk, presumably for use during salary negotiations with the staff),

Alexander T. Bunts, M.D., Neurological Surgery, 1928–1962 (co-editor, 1st edition)

Dr. C. Robert Hughes (a longtime favorite in clinical radiology), and Dr. Walter J. Zeiter (a physiatrist-turned-educator, loved and respected by the residents of the day).

Additional contributors to the second edition included Dr. F. Merlin Bumpus (Page's protégé and the second chairman of the Research Division), Dr. Victor G. deWolfe (LeFevre's successor in vascular medicine, one of the last of the old-time doctors who still believe in house calls), Ms. Mary Rita Feran (the *Cleveland Clinic Quarterly*'s venerable managing editor for many years), Dr. Stanley O. Hoerr (who struck fear into the hearts of the residents), Ms. Carol M. Tomer (keeper of the Archives), Dr. William S. Kiser (the third chairman of the Board of Governors), Dr. William M. Michener (a pediatric gastroenterologist whose heart was always in education), and Dr. William L. Proudfit (clinical integrity and professionalism personified). Sadly, many of these outstanding members of the Clinic family have passed away, including Bunts, Crile, Ernstene, Hazard, LeFevre, Page, Sherwin, Bumpus, Feran, and Hoerr. It is to their memory and to the memory of the founders that this volume is dedicated.

Although this is the third edition in the *To Act as a Unit* series, a precursor volume called simply *The Cleveland Clinic Foundation*

George Crile, Jr., M.D., Department of General Surgery, 1937–1968
(co-editor, 1st edition)

appeared in 1938. This book was written by Ms. Amy Rowland, longtime secretary to the senior Dr. Crile. She recorded much of the information included in the first two chapters. Interestingly, she had little to say about the disaster, and this material was, for the most part, assembled by Dr. Alex Bunts. Some aspects of the Clinic's history have also been recorded by Dr. Robert E. Hermann, Dr. Ray Van Ommen, and Dr. Paul Nelson in *Medicine in Cleveland and Cuyahoga County 1810 - 1976*, published by the Academy of Medicine of Cleveland in 1976.

In the second edition of *To Act as a Unit*, the Board of Governors era was included in a single chapter (chapter 6), but the duration of this period now exceeds that of the pre-Board era (chapters 1-5). I have, therefore, split the post-1955 material into four chapters, coinciding with the administrations of the four chairmen of the Board of Governors. New sections on pediatrics (chapter 11), Centers of Excellence (chapter 14), nursing (chapter 17), and Cleveland Clinic Florida (chapter 20) appear in Section III. Finally, I have added an Epilogue with some general information about the trustees, governors, and staff at the end of Section III.

I am grateful for the assistance of Ms. Holly Strawbridge, who provided valuable editorial assistance. I am also indebted to all the

Amy Rowland

contributors who got their material in on time; to my long-suffering secretary Ms. Barbara Davis; and to many who proofread the manuscript, including especially Ms. Marilyn Wilker, Mr. Jack Auble, Mr. Gene D. Altus, Dr. Floyd Loop, Dr. Ralph Straffon, Dr. William S. Kiser, and Dr. Shattuck Hartwell. As with the previous editions, the Clinic's archives have been invaluable, and our two archivists, Ms. Carol Tomer and Mr. Fred Lautzenheiser, have dredged up endless amounts of minutiae (as well as some gargantuae) and all the pictures for this book. Dr. Robert D. Mercer provided considerable help with the chapter on pediatrics. Finally, I must express my appreciation to my wife Mary, who (a) put up with me during this effort, (b) did not grumble too much, and (c) went through the manuscript with a fine-toothed comb finding many errors, which I have hopefully corrected.

John D. Clough, M.D.
November 30, 1995

Shattuck W. Hartwell, Jr., M.D., Director of Professional Staff Affairs, 1974–1986
(editor, 2nd edition)

FOREWORD

This third edition of *To Act as a Unit* commemorates our 75th anniversary as an international health resource.

Our vision is to develop distinctive competencies in every specialty, to provide comprehensive care and satisfaction for all patients, and to attain a worldwide market base for specialty medicine. As we enter the 21st century, our integrated health care delivery system is prepared to meet the changing market and to realize that vision. Across Cleveland we have developed a unified provider strategy comprised of satellite facilities, collaborative hospitals, independent-physician organizations, and strong payer relationships. Our operation in Florida has matured and advanced, and it will soon be the site of a unified campus.

We are acknowledged as one of the country's best hospitals, and we are consistently cited among the 100 best managed hospitals in America. The key to such success is our staff of outstanding physicians and scientists, who educate, conduct research, and provide exceptional health care. As the number of the physician staff has grown — from approximately 400 to 700 in the past 10 years alone — our expertise and renown have likewise grown. Our commitment to both science and education, as well as to the care of patients, has been constant throughout 75 years of continual growth and will continue in the future. The years ahead will see us produce a superlative science and education institute, a cancer center, and a free-standing eye institute. These activities will add great value to science, education, and patient care.

People from all parts of the world and from all walks of life turn to us in times of illness and wellness. The Cleveland Clinic has become, in effect, an enduring public trust to which we consider ourselves accountable, as temporary stewards of a tradition of excellence. This update of *To Act As A Unit* offers a detailed account of the people, events, facts, and philosophy behind The Cleveland Clinic's formation and emergence as one of the greatest health care systems in the world.

Floyd D. Loop, M.D.
January 11, 1996

Section I

The Early Years

THE FOUNDERS

Dr. Frank E. Bunts

Dr. George W. Crile, Sr.

Dr. William E. Lower

Dr. John Phillips

ONE

THE FOUNDERS

*People are what they are
because they have come out of what was.
Therefore they should bow down before what was
and take it and say it's good — or should they?*
 — *Carl Sandburg, 1936*

On August 27, 1918, Dr. George W. Crile (known as George Crile, Sr.), who at the time was with the Lakeside Hospital Unit in France, wrote in his journal:

"What a remarkable record Bunts, Crile and Lower have had all these years. We have been rivals in everything, yet through all the vicissitudes of personal, financial and professional relations we have been able to think and act as a unit."[1]

This sense of cooperation and unity, shared by three of the four future founders of The Cleveland Clinic, made it possible to create the group practice model that still forms the basis for the institution.

Dr. Frank E. Bunts was the senior member of the three surgeons who had been so closely associated for many years before the founding of The Cleveland Clinic. After a brief career in the Navy, he attended medical school for three years at Western Reserve University and graduated in 1886 as valedictorian of his class. After a year of internship at St. Vincent Charity Hospital in Cleveland, he entered the office of Dr. Frank J. Weed, then Dean and Professor of Surgery at the Wooster University Department of Medicine, Cleveland, Ohio.

---

[1] An important source for *To Act as a Unit* was *George Crile, An Autobiography*, edited with sidelights by Grace Crile (1947). Crile was the author of 650 publications including several books.

1

Offices of Drs. Weed, Bunts, and Crile at 16 Church Street, 1886–1889
(artist's drawing)

Crile was born in 1864 on a farm in Chili, Ohio. He worked his way through Northwestern Ohio Normal School (later known as Ohio Northern University) in Ada by teaching in elementary schools. After receiving a teaching certificate, he was appointed Principal of the Plainfield (Ohio) School. Soon his interest turned to medicine, mainly as a result of his contacts with a local physician who loaned him books and with whom he visited patients. Some of the events of this period are related in his autobiography, among them exciting details of "quilling" an obstetric patient by blowing snuff through a goose quill into her nose. The sneezing that this induced led to prompt delivery of the baby. In 1886, Crile enrolled at Wooster and after two years obtained his M.D. degree with highest honors.

Crile served his internship at University Hospital[2] under Dr. Frank J. Weed, and after that he joined Bunts as an assistant to Weed in his large office practice. Then, tragically, at age 45 and at the peak of his professional career, Weed contracted pneumonia and died. At that time, Bunts was not yet 30 years old and Crile was three years younger. Crile expressed their feelings as follows:

"Wearied by loss of sleep, worry and constant vigil, we left Doctor Weed's house on that cheerless March morning and walked to Doctor Bunts's for breakfast. In our dejection, it seemed to us that

---

[2] Crile described the origin of University Hospital (not to be confused with University Hospitals of Cleveland, established in 1931) in his autobiography. "In 1882, three years before I first came to Cleveland, Dr. Weed and the group of associates who had revived Wooster Medical School, having no hospital privileges for their students except for the county poorhouse, established University Hospital in two old residences on Brownell Street 'in juxtaposition,' as the catalogue stated in a high-sounding phrase, to Wooster Medical School. This simple hospital had a capacity of perhaps thirty beds."

Bill of Sale
From Estate of Dr. Frank J. Weed
to
Dr. Frank E. Bunts and Dr. George Crile[3]

Small brown mares (Brown Jug and Roseline)	$125.00
Small sorrel horse (Duke)	100.00
Bay horse (Roy)	75.00
Top buggy	50.00
Top buggy	50.00
Top buggy, very old	10.00
Open buggy	20.00
2 Cutters, one very old	20.00
4 sets single harness	20.00
Lap robes	15.00
Miscellaneous articles in barn	3.00
Shed, old stoves, battery, etc.	50.00
Articles on stand	20.00
Milliamperes	10.00
Contents of case (silk, bandages, and dressings)	15.00
Contents of desk (hand mirror, 6 sprinklers, medicine case)	8.00
Medicine on desk	25.00
3 McCune chisels	3.75
4 Small chisels	2.00
14 Pairs scissors	2.50
3 Large pairs shears	1.50
2 Pairs retractors	2.00
2 Forceps	2.50
3 Nasal saws	1.50
2 Intestinal clasps	1.00
1 Chain saw	2.00
2 Hayes saws	1.50
1 Small met. saw	.50
7 Needles	1.00
4 Wire twisters	1.00
6 Sponge holders	1.50
1 Clamp	2.00
3 Bullet forceps	2.00
2 Large retractors	2.00
4 Small nasal dilators	1.25
1 Throat forcep	1.50
1 Head reflector	2.50
4 Self retaining female catheters	1.75
2 Tools	.50
5 Bone elevators	2.00
5 Bone forceps	6.00
1 Chain saw guide	.75
1 Bone drill with three tips	.75

Bill of Sale (continued)	
1 Hamilton bone drill with four tips	$3.00
1 Emergency bag No. 2	5.00
1 Emergency bag No. 3	11.00
1 Box — 3 knives and 3 pairs scissors	1.50
1 Stomach pump in box	6.00
1 Stone set in case	8.00
1 Horse shoe turnica	1.00
1 Cloven clutch	4.00
1 Small aspirating set	2.00
1 Kelley pad	.75
1 Syringe	.50
1 Microscope	40.00
2 Syringes	1.50
Total	$1778.10

Cleveland, O., Apr. 10th, 1891

In consideration of seventeen hundred and seventy eight 10/100 dollars I have this day sold to Drs. F.E. Bunts and G.W. Crile all the goods, chattels, instruments and other articles contained in brick house and barn in rear at No. 380 Pearl Street as per inventory marked Exhibit A attached to bill of sale.

C. H. Weed, Administrator of Estate of Frank J. Weed

everything had suddenly come to an end. Our light had gone out. We had no money, no books, no surgical instruments. The only instrument either of us owned, other than my microscope, was a stethoscope. But we agreed to carry on together, to share and share alike both the expenses and the income from the accident practice, each to reserve for himself the income from his private patients."

After talking with Mrs. Weed, Bunts and Crile decided to buy from the estate Dr. Weed's goods, chattels, and instruments. Excerpts from the bill of sale are listed above. This property represented the embryo from which The Cleveland Clinic was born.[3]

The practice of the new partners grew rapidly, and by 1892 they needed an associate. Crile engaged his cousin, Dr. William E. Lower. Both had attended district schools. Lower, too, had been reared on a farm and from an early age had developed a sense of independence as well as the importance of hard work and the necessity of thrift

---

[3] This document is now located in the Archives of The Cleveland Clinic.

Offices of Drs. Bunts, Crile, and Lower at 380 Pearl Street (now West 25th Street),
1890–1897 (artist's drawing)

and frugality. Lower had attended the Medical Department of
Wooster University, from which he was graduated in 1891; he served
as house physician in City Hospital and then set up practice in
Conneaut, Ohio. Bunts and Crile had little difficulty in persuading
him to leave there to share their office practice. By 1895, Bunts, Crile,
and Lower were full partners, equally sharing the expenses and the
income from emergency work but remaining competitors in private
practice. Mutual trust and confidence became a keystone for their
future accomplishments.

With the continued growth of their practices, Bunts, Crile, and
Lower moved their office in 1897 from the west side of Cleveland
downtown to the Osborn Building, at the junction of Huron Road
and Prospect Avenue. A year later, this collaboration was interrupted
by the Spanish-American War; Bunts was surgeon to the First Ohio
Volunteer Cavalry Unit of the Ohio National Guard, and Crile was
surgeon to the Gatling Gun Battery in Cleveland, also a unit of the
Guard. When they volunteered for active duty, Lower was left alone
with the office practice. Not long after the war was over and his part-

Offices of Drs. Bunts, Crile, and Lower, Osborn Building at East 9th Street and
Huron Road, 1897–1920   (artist's drawing)

ners had returned, he retaliated by volunteering to help quell the
Boxer Rebellion in China, entering the Army as a first lieutenant. By
the time he reached China the rebellion was over, so he served as surgeon to the 9th U.S. Cavalry in the Philippines, 1900 - 1901.

By 1901, the various wars were over, and Bunts, Crile, and
Lower were reunited in the Osborn Building office, where they
remained until they were separated again by World War I. The pre-
war period was productive. In addition to their large accident and
private practices, Bunts became professor of principles of surgery at
Wooster University and professor of principles of surgery and clini-
cal surgery at the Western Reserve University School of Medicine.
He was also the first president of the newly formed Academy of
Medicine of Cleveland. Crile was professor of physiology and principles of surgery at Wooster and professor of surgery at Western
Reserve. Lower, whose major interest soon became urology, was
associate professor of genitourinary surgery at Western Reserve.
Both Crile and Lower also served as presidents of the Academy of
Medicine during its first decade.

During these years, Crile maintained his interest in physiology and applied to clinical practice the principles that he discovered in the laboratory in the fields of shock, transfusion, and anesthesia. Lower collaborated in some of Crile's early works, but neither he nor Bunts shared Crile's consuming and lifelong interest in basic laboratory research.

As the practice expanded, Dr. H. G. Sloan, a surgeon, was added to the staff, and Dr. J. D. Osmond was sent to the Mayo Clinic to observe the newly developed techniques of radiology. Osmond returned to establish, in 1913, the group's first X-ray Department. Dr. T. P. Shupe also joined the staff as an associate of Lower in urology.

At that time, Crile was helping to form The American College of Surgeons, whose purposes and functions were to improve the standards of surgical practice in the United States and Canada and provide postgraduate education, improve ethics, raise the standards of care in hospitals, and educate the public about medical and surgical problems.

In 1914, Europe was ablaze with war. In December of that year, Crile, who was then Chief Surgeon at Lakeside Hospital, was asked by Clevelander Myron T. Herrick, then Ambassador to France, to organize a team to work in France. Crile accepted, for even at that time he realized that the United States would be drawn into the war and that experience in military surgery would be valuable.[4] After three months of treating casualties at Neuilly, the group returned, and Crile organized a base-hospital unit.

---

[4] As Crile prepared to leave for France, Lower drafted a report to be presented to the office staff. The report is less interesting than this draft, here reproduced with some minor editing to correct errors. Both drafts are in the Archives of The Cleveland Clinic Foundation.

Partial Report for the Year 1914

In behalf of Drs. Bunts, Crile, and Lower, I want to make a necessarily incomplete report for the year 1914, incomplete because the year is not entirely ended and because the rush of extra work at this time has made it impossible to get all the necessary data ready. It is only by summing up of the year's work that we can get a keen appreciation of what we have accomplished. I wish you to particularly hear this because of the important part you all have taken in the work.

Your loyalty, zeal, enthusiasm, and devotion we have all recognized throughout the year, and we wish to take this occasion to tell you how keenly we appreciate it and also to get your suggestions, if any, for the coming year.

The great European conflict has had its effect upon practically every line of public endeavor in every country of the globe and will continue to do so, more or less, until the war is ended. This means personal sacrifice, more economy and greater efficiency if we wish to hold our place. Our work is particularly trying because it deals solely with others' afflictions. It means great tact, every consideration for the comfort of our patients, the application of the latest and best scientific, and practical means for the alleviation of their ailments; special research and laboratory work, reviewing of the literature, the development of new methods of treatment, and the careful computing of our clinical results, which is a guide as to the value of any method of treatment.

Lt. Col. Frank E. Bunts and Col. George Crile, Sr., at Rouen, France 1918

When the United States entered the war, the Lakeside Unit (U.S. Army Base Hospital No. 4) was the first detachment of the American Expeditionary Forces to arrive in France, taking over a British general hospital near Rouen on May 25, 1917. Crile was the hospital's

---

The following statistics show approximately what we have done.	
Number of cases seen in 1913	8467
Number of cases seen in 1914	9245
Number of examinations for the Railroad Companies in 1913	3185
Number of examinations for the Railroad Companies in 1914	2378
Number of laboratory tests	
Wasserman Reactions	113
Complement Fixation Tests	192
Cystoscopies	105
Ureteral Catheterizations	31
Number of papers read at different meetings	30
Number of articles published in the Medical Journals	30+
Number of reprints sent out	10,000
Number of books published	2

This office has always felt equal to any emergency or occasion that might arise. During the breaking out of the Spanish-American war, when we were just beginning to feel our way, and trying to take our place in the professional world, Drs. Bunts and Crile gave up their work to serve during the war. It was a big office sacrifice. Upon their return I went into our foreign service for a period of nearly one year. Now the opportunity has again arisen to do our part in the great European war and again we are ready. Dr. Crile with his traditional enthusiasm and resources goes to take charge of a division in the American Ambulance Hospital in Paris. With him goes our great aide-de-camp, Miss Rowland, whose ability and capacity for work we all know. With this important division away, the lesser of us must try all the harder to keep the good work going. It means for the rest of us no let down if the coming year is to make anywhere near as good a showing as this one has.

Clinical Director, but later was given a broader assignment as Director of the Division of Research for the American Expeditionary Forces, a post that permitted him to move about and visit the stations wherever the action was.

Lower was with Crile in the Lakeside Unit, and soon Bunts, a reservist, was ordered to Camp Travis, Texas, leaving only Sloan and Osmond to keep the practice going. Both were able to pay the office expenses, but Bunts, concerned about the future, wrote to Lower in France as follows:

"I feel very strongly that we ought to hold the office together at all hazards, not only for ourselves, but for the younger men who have been with us and whose future will depend largely on having a place to come back to. If Sloan and Osmond go, I think we could at least keep Miss Slattery and Miss Van Spyker. It would be quite an outlay for each of us to ante up our share for keeping the office from being occupied by others, but I for one would be glad to do it. We haven't so very many years left for active work after this war is over, and it would seem to be almost too much to undertake to start afresh in new offices, and the stimulus and friendship of our old associations mean much more than money to me."

Bunts succeeded Lower as commanding officer of the hospital near Rouen in August 1918. After the armistice, November 11, 1918, activities at the Base Hospital gradually subsided, tensions eased, and soldiers found time to engage in nonmilitary pursuits and conversations. The long and friendly association of the three Cleveland surgeons is apparent in the following letter written in December 1918 and addressed to Lower in Cleveland from Bunts in France.

"It's getting around Christmas time, and while I know this won't reach you for a month, yet I just want to let you know that we are thinking of you and wishing we could see you. Crile has been here for a couple of weeks, but left again for Paris a few days ago, and evenings he and I have foregathered about the little stove in your old room, leaving G. W.'s door open wide enough to warm his room up too, and there we have sat like two old G.A.R. relics, smoking and laughing, telling stories, dipping back into even our boyhood days and laughing often til the tears rolled down our cheeks. It has been a varied life we three have had and filled with trials and pleasures without number. I have dubbed our little fireside chats the 'Arabian Nights,' and often we have been startled when the coal gave out and the fire died down that it was long past midnight and time for antiques to go to bed."

During those nocturnal chats at Rouen an idea that eventually led to the founding of The Cleveland Clinic took shape. The military hospital experience impressed these men with the efficiency of an organization that included every branch or specialty of medicine and surgery. They recognized the benefits that could be obtained from cooperation by a group of specialists. Before their return to the United States they began to formulate plans for the future.

Bunts and Crile returned to Cleveland early in 1919 and were once more united with Lower in their Osborn Building offices. They began to rebuild their interrupted surgical practices and soon found themselves as busy as they had been before the war.

Although the military hospital was used as a model for their future plan, elements of the pattern were furnished also by the Mayo Clinic, founded by close professional friends. Bunts, Crile, and Lower were surgeons, and in order to develop a broader field of medical service they resolved to add an internist to organize and head a department of medicine. They were fortunate to obtain the enthusiastic cooperation of Dr. John Phillips, who was at that time a member of the faculty of the School of Medicine of Western Reserve University. He, too, had served in military hospitals during the war and held the same broad concept of what might be accomplished by a clinic organization.

John Phillips was born in 1879 on a farm near Welland, Ontario. He was a quiet, serious-minded youth who, nevertheless, had a keen sense of humor. After obtaining his teacher's certificate, he taught for three years in a district school. He then entered the Faculty of Medicine in the University of Toronto, where in 1903 he received the M.B. degree with honors. After graduation he served for three years as intern and resident in medicine at Lakeside Hospital in Cleveland. He then entered practice as an associate in the office of Dr. E. F. Cushing, professor of pediatrics at Western Reserve. During the years before the founding of The Cleveland Clinic, Phillips held assistant professorships in both medicine and therapeutics at the Western Reserve University School of Medicine. Simultaneously he had hospital appointments at Babies' Dispensary and Hospital and Lakeside Hospital. He was also consulting physician to St. John's Hospital. Phillips had a large private and consulting practice and was highly regarded for his ability as a clinician and teacher in internal medicine and the diseases of children. During World War I he served as a captain in the Medical Corps of the United States Army.

In 1920, most private physicians did not like the idea of group practice. Some felt that the large resources available to a group might give them an unfair competitive advantage. Many were openly critical of the concept and might have attempted to block the establishment of The Cleveland Clinic if the founders had not been so highly regarded in the medical community. All were professors in one or more of the Cleveland medical schools. Crile was a major national and international figure in surgery and in national medical organizations; Lower was already well known nationally as a urologic surgeon; Phillips had a solid reputation locally and nationally in internal medicine; and Bunts's professional and personal reputation was of the highest order. As previously noted, Bunts, Crile, and Lower had all been presidents of the Academy of Medicine, and Phillips was the president-elect.

The founders' reputation was not based solely on the medical schools; it also was well established in the community hospitals. They held appointments at Cleveland General, University, City, St. Alexis, St. Vincent's Charity, Lutheran, St. John's, Lakeside, and Mt. Sinai hospitals. Moreover, many of the community's business leaders were their patients and friends. It would have been difficult to stand in the way of any legitimate enterprise that these physicians decided to organize. This point is underscored by a thumbnail sketch of their personalities as Dr. George Crile, Jr., remembered them.

"Crile was the dynamo of the group, imaginative, creative, innovative, and driving. It is possible that some considered him inconsiderate of others in his overriding desire to get things done. For this reason, and because he occasionally was premature in applying to the treatment of patients the principles learned in research, he had enemies as well as supporters. Yet most of his contemporaries would have readily admitted that Crile was one of the first surgeons in the world to apply physiologic research to surgical problems, that he was one of the country's leaders in organizing and promoting medical organizations such as The American College of Surgeons of which he became the president, and that it was largely as a result of Crile's energy, prestige, and practice that The Cleveland Clinic was founded.

"If Crile was the driver, Lower was the brake. He was a born conservative, even to the point of the keyhole size of his surgical incisions. No one but he could operate through them. His assistants could not even see into them. He was a technician of consummate skill and an imaginative pioneer in the then-new field of urology. Lower was also a perfect treasurer. He checked on every expenditure, thus compensating for Crile's tendency to disregard the Clinic's cash position. Later in life, Doctor Lower even went around the buildings, in the evenings, turning out lights that were burning needlessly. He was no miser, but his conservatism afforded a perfect balance to Crile's overenthusiasm. Despite the differences in their personalities, no one ever saw them quarrel.

"I never knew Bunts as well as the others, for he died early, but I do recall that he never, in my presence at least, displayed the exuberant type of humor that Crile and Lower did. I have seen the latter two almost rolling on the floor in laughter as they reminisced on how they dealt with some ancient enemy, but I could not imagine Bunts doing that. He had the presence and dignity that one associates with the image of an old-time senator. 'Bunts was invaluable in our association,' my father once told me. 'He was the one that gave it respectability.'

"Phillips, like Bunts, died early, so that I knew him only as my childhood physician rather than as a personal friend. My impression was of a man who was silent, confident, and imperturbable. I am sure that his patients and colleagues shared this confidence in him and that was why he was able to organize a successful department of internal medicine.

"Although the personalities of the Clinic's founders were so different from one another, there were common bonds that united them. All had served in the military, all had taught in medical schools, all were devoted to the practice of medicine. As a result of these common backgrounds and motivations, there emerged a common ideal — an institution in which medicine and surgery could be practiced, studied, and taught by a group of associated specialists. To create it, the four founders began to plan an institution that would be greater than the sum of its individual parts."

TWO

THE FIRST YEARS
1921-1929

Life is a petty thing unless it is moved by the indomitable urge to extend its boundaries. Only in proportion as we are desirous of living more do we really live.
— *José Ortega y Gasset, 1925*

In October 1919, the founders, with the aid of Bunts's son-in-law Mr. Edward C. Daoust, an able attorney, formed the Association Building Company to finance, erect, and equip an outpatient medical building. Organized as a for-profit corporation, the company issued common and preferred stock, most of which was bought by the founders and their families, and leased a parcel of land on the southwest corner of East 93rd Street and Euclid Avenue.[1] The architectural firm of Ellerbe and Company estimated that a suitable building could be constructed for $400,000. Excavation began in February 1920, and a year later the building was completed. Although the Crowell-Little Company was the contractor, Crile said in his autobiography that " . . . the real builder of the Clinic was Ed Lower, he knew each brick and screw by name and was on hand early enough every morning to check the laborers as they arrived."

The Clinic Building (now known as the "T Building") had four stories, of which the upper three were built around a large central "well" extending from the second floor up to a skylight of tinted glass. The main waiting room, handsome with tiled floors and walls

---

[1] At the time of construction, the corporation acquired the land under the original building from Ralph Fuller through a 99-year lease beginning October 29, 1919.

Clinic Building, 1921   The Cleveland Clinic Foundation

and with arched, tiled doorways and windows, was at the bottom of the well on the second floor. The offices, examining rooms, and treatment rooms opened onto the main second floor waiting area and onto corridors consisting of the balconies that surrounded the central well on the third and fourth floors. On the first floor were the x-ray department, the clinical laboratories, and a pharmacy. On the fourth floor were the art and photography department, editorial offices, a library, a board room in which the founders met, offices for administrators and bookkeepers, and Dr. Crile's biophysics laboratory. Thus, from the beginning there were departments representing not only the cooperative practice of medicine, but also education and research.

From the time of The Cleveland Clinic's formation as a not-for-profit corporation, there were no shareholders and no profits accrued to the founders. All of them received fixed salaries set by the trustees. Likewise, all other members of the Clinic staff received salaries that were not directly dependent on the amount of income they brought into the Clinic.[2]

The founders had donated substantially to the Clinic's capital funds, and in the formative years they had taken the risk of personally underwriting the Clinic's debts in order to establish a nonprofit foundation dedicated to service of the community, medical education, and research. To insure against any future deviation from these aims, the founders empowered the Board of Trustees, at its

---

[2] By Ohio statute, no part of the earnings of a not-for-profit organization can accrue to the benefit of private individuals.

Waiting room, 1921   Clinic Building

discretion, to donate all assets of the organization to any local institution incorporated "for promoting education, science, or art." These assets could, thus, never contribute to anyone's personal enrichment.

At the first meeting of the incorporators on February 21, 1921, the signers were elected Trustees of the new institution, and provision was made for increasing the number of trustees to as many as fifteen if this became desirable. Bunts, Crile, Lower, and Phillips were designated Founders.

The Cleveland Clinic's charter is an extraordinary document for its time because the scope of medical practice it defined was so liberal.[3] The document also raised the issue of the corporate practice of medicine, much criticized at the time.

---

[3] The charter granted by the State on February 5, 1921, reads as follows:
"THESE ARTICLES OF INCORPORATION OF THE CLEVELAND CLINIC FOUNDATION
"WITNESSETH:
"That we, the undersigned, all of whom are citizens of the state of Ohio, desiring to form a corporation not for profit under the general corporation laws of said State, do hereby certify:
"FIRST: The name of said corporation shall be THE CLEVELAND CLINIC FOUNDATION.
"SECOND: Said corporation and its principal office shall be located at Cleveland, Cuyahoga County, Ohio, and its principal business there transacted.
"THIRD: The purpose for which said corporation is formed is to own and conduct hospitals for sick and disabled persons; and in connection therewith, owning, maintaining, developing, and conducting institutions, dispensaries, laboratories, buildings, and equipment for medical, surgical, and hygienic care and treatment of sick and disabled persons, engaging in making scientific diagnoses and clinical studies in, carrying on scientific research in, and conducting public lectures on, the sciences and subjects of medicine, surgery, hygiene, anatomy, and kindred

The practice of medicine in the United States has traditionally been founded on the sanctity of the doctor-patient relationship. A somewhat questionable and clearly self-serving economic corollary is that to preserve this relationship an individual patient must pay a fee for medical service directly to the doctor of his or her choice. Organized medicine has always resisted attempts to change the basis of this relationship, and the legal system has generally been supportive of this view. Similarly, lawyers have sought to preserve the lawyer-client relationship, threatened by large corporations, such as banks, that set out to sell legal services to customers through the offices of their salaried lawyers. If a corporation were allowed to do the same with the services of physicians, *i.e.* engage in corporate medical practice, by analogy a precedent dangerous to the status of lawyers might be established. For this reason, most state legislatures, being dominated by lawyers, passed laws prohibiting the corporate practice of medicine, and most group practices, whether operating for profit or not, were obliged to include within their structure some sort of professional partnership in order to bill patients and to collect fees legally. The properties of the Mayo Clinic, for example, have always been held by a nonprofit foundation. The physicians, however, were organized first as a partnership and then as an association from 1919 to 1969. The doctors received salaries from the fees paid by patients and turned over to the Mayo Foundation the excess of receipts over disbursements.[4] Thus, in most nonprofit clinics devious means have been used to achieve what The Cleveland Clinic accomplishes directly; the organization itself collects fees and pays the salaries of its staff. Today, with the strong trend toward group practice, the right of a nonprofit organi-

---

sciences and subjects; accepting, receiving, and acquiring funds, stocks, securities, and property by donations, bequests, devises or otherwise, and using, holding, investing, reinvesting, conveying, exchanging, selling, transferring, leasing, mortgaging, pledging, and disposing of, any and all funds, stocks, securities, and property so received or acquired, charging and receiving compensation for services, care, treatment, and accommodations, for the purpose of maintaining said hospitals, not for profit, and the doing of all acts, exercising all powers and assuming all obligations necessary or incident thereto.

"IN WITNESS WHEREOF, we have hereunto set our hands this 5th day of February 1921.

Frank E. Bunts
George W. Crile
William E. Lower
John Phillips
Edward C. Daoust"

[4] This "landlord-tenant" relationship between the Mayo Foundation and its medical staff was changed in 1970 when, as a result of corporate restructuring, all interests came under the Mayo Foundation.

zation like the Clinic to "practice medicine" is unlikely to be challenged. The charter of 1921 remains a source of wonder to lawyers.

Thirteen members made up the professional staff of The Cleveland Clinic in its first year. Joining Bunts and Crile were Dr. Thomas E. Jones and Dr. Harry G. Sloan in surgery. Lower was joined by Dr. Thomas P. Shupe in urology. With Phillips in medicine were Dr. Henry J. John, Dr. Oliver P. Kimball, and Dr. John P. Tucker. John was also head of the clinical laboratories. Dr. Justin M. Waugh was the otolaryngologist, Dr. Bernard H. Nichols was the radiologist, and Hugo Fricke, Ph.D., was the biophysicist.

Crile was elected the first president of The Cleveland Clinic Foundation; Bunts, vice president; Lower, treasurer; and Phillips, secretary. Daoust, who had so skillfully handled the Clinic's legal needs, was designated a life member of the Board of Trustees.

At 8:00 P.M. on February 26, 1921, five hundred local members of the medical profession and many physicians from outside the city attended the opening of The Cleveland Clinic.[5] Among those from other cities were Dr. William J. Mayo of Rochester, Minnesota; Dr. Joseph C. Bloodgood of Baltimore, Maryland; and Dr. J. F. Baldwin of Columbus, Ohio. The program included talks by each of the founders and by Charles Howe, president of the Case School of Applied Science. Mayo gave the main address.

Crile described the incorporation of The Cleveland Clinic and outlined its purposes and aims as follows:

"With the rapid advance of medicine to its present-day status in which it evokes the aid of all the natural sciences, an individual is no more able to undertake the more intricate problems alone, without the aid and cooperation of colleagues having special training in each of the various clinical and laboratory branches, than he would be today to make an automobile alone. We have, therefore, created an organization and a building to the end that in making a diagnosis or planning a treatment, the clinician may have at his disposal the advantages of the laboratories of the applied sciences and of colleagues with special training in the various branches of medicine and surgery.

---

[5] This event was modestly noted in the *Bulletin of the Academy of Medicine of Cleveland* as follows:

"CLINIC BUILDING OPENS

"Drs. Frank E. Bunts, George W. Crile and W.E. Lower and their associates, Dr. H.G. Sloan, T.P. Shupe, Bernard H. Nichols, Thomas E. Jones and Justin M. Waugh, announce the removal of their offices from the Osborn Building to the Clinic Building, Euclid Avenue at East 93rd Street, effective March 1st, 1921."

There was no further mention of The Cleveland Clinic in the *Bulletin* until the Clinic disaster of 1929!

"Another reason for establishing this organization is that of making permanent our long-time practice of expending for research a goodly portion of our income. On this occasion we are pleased to state that we and our successors are pledged to give not less than one-fourth of our net income toward building up the property and the endowment of The Cleveland Clinic Foundation. It is through The Cleveland Clinic Foundation under a state charter that a continual policy of active investigation of disease will be assured. That is to say, we are considering not only our duty to the patient of today, but no less our duty to the patient of tomorrow.

"It is, moreover, our purpose, also pursuant to our practice in the past, that by reason of the convenience of the plant, the diminished overhead expense, and the accumulation of funds in the Foundation, the patient with no means and the patient with moderate means may have at a cost he can afford, as complete an investigation as the patient with ample means.

"The fourth reason for the establishment of this Clinic is educational. We shall offer a limited number of fellowships to approved young physicians who have had at least one year of hospital training, thus supplementing the hospital and the medical school. In addition there will be established a schedule of daily conferences and lectures for our group and for others who may be interested.

"This organization makes it possible to pass on to our successors experience and methods and special technical achievements without a break of continuity.

"Since this organization functions as an institution, it has no intention either to compete with, nor to supplant the individual practitioner who is the backbone of the profession and carries on his shoulder the burden of the professional work of the community. We wish only to supplement, to aid, and to cooperate with him.

"Since this institution is not a school of medicine, it cannot, if it would, compete in any way with the University, but what it proposes to do is to offer a hearty cooperation in every way we can with the University.

"Our institution is designed to meet what we believe to be a public need in a more flexible organization than is possible for the University to attain, because the University as a teaching organization must of necessity be departmentalized. As compared with the University, this organization has the advantage of plasticity; as compared with the individual practitioner it has the advantage of equipment.

"The result of such an organization will be that the entire staff — the bacteriologist, the pathologist, the biochemist, the physicist,

Oakdale Street (later East 93rd), looking south from Euclid Avenue, circa 1887
Courtesy: Cleveland Public Library

the physiologist, and radiologist, no less than the internist and the general surgeon, each, we hope and believe, will maintain the spirit of collective work, and each of us will accept as our reward for work done, his respective part in the contribution of the group, however small, to the comfort, and usefulness, and the prolongation of human life.

"Should the successors seek to convert it into an institution solely for profit or personal exploitations, or otherwise materially alter the purpose for which it was organized, the whole property shall be turned over to one of the institutions of learning or science of this city."

Bunts reviewed the concepts underlying the Clinic's unique organizational structure and outlined the founders' aims and hopes for the future. He stated that the founders hoped that, when their associates took the places of their predecessors, they would "... carry on the work to higher and better ends, aiding their fellow practitioners, caring for the sick, educating and training younger men in all the advances in medicine and surgery, and seeking always to attain the highest and noblest aspirations of their profession."

Phillips reemphasized the fact that the founders had no desire for the Clinic to compete with the family physician. Instead they sought to make it a place to which general practitioners might send patients for diagnostic consultations.

Oxley Homes, 1924

Lower explained the design of the building and its plan of construction, which was intended to ensure the greatest efficiency for each department, resulting in the most salutary operation of the Clinic as a whole, for the ultimate welfare of the patients.

Mayo's speech, the main address of the evening, was entitled "The Medical Profession and the Public." Its content was significant, and it contained many truths and ideas which are still worthy of consideration. He spoke in part as follows:

"On every side we see the acceptance of an idea which is generally expressed by the loose term 'group medicine,' a term which fails in many respects to express conditions clearly. In my father's time, success in the professions was more or less dependent on convention, tradition, and impressive surroundings. The top hat and the double-breasted frock coat of the doctor, the wig and gown of the jurist, and the clerical garb of the ecclesiastic supplied the necessary stage scenery. The practitioner of medicine today may wear a business suit. The known facts in medicine are so comprehensive that the standing of the physician in his profession and in his community no longer depends on accessories.

"So tremendous has been the recent advance of medicine that no one man can understand more than a small fraction of it; thus, physicians have become more or less dependent on the skill, ability, and specialized training of other physicians for sufficient knowledge to care for the patient intelligently. An unconscious movement for cooperative medicine is seen in the intimate relation of the private physician to the public health service made possible by the establishment of laboratories by the state board of health and similar organizations. On every hand, even among laymen, we see this growing conception of the futility of the individual effort to encompass the necessary knowledge needed in treating the simplest and most common maladies because of the many complications which experience has shown are inherent possibilities of any disease."

Mayo went on to discuss some of the fundamental political and professional aspects of medical care and ended by stating:

"...[O]f each hundred dollars spent by our government during 1920, only one dollar went to public health, agriculture and education, just one percent for life, living conditions and national progress.... The striking feature of the medicine of the immediate future will be the development of medical cooperation, in which the state, the community and the physician must play a part.

"...[P]roperly considered, group medicine is not a financial arrangement, except for minor details, but a scientific cooperation for the welfare of the sick.

"... Medicine's place is fixed by its services to mankind; if we fail to measure up to our opportunity, it means state medicine, political control, mediocrity, and loss of professional ideals. The members of the medical fraternity must cooperate in this work, and they can do so without interfering with private professional practice. Such a community of interest will raise the general level of professional attainments. The internist, the surgeon, and the specialist may join with the physiologist, the pathologist and the laboratory workers to form the clinical group, which must also include men learned in the abstract sciences, such as biochemistry and physics. Union of all these forces will lengthen by many years the span of human life and as a byproduct will do much to improve professional ethics by overcoming some of the evils of competitive medicine."

With these instructive and challenging remarks, Mayo highlighted the fundamental aims of the founders of The Cleveland Clinic: better care of the sick, investigation of their problems, and further education of those who serve.[6]

---

[6] Although Mayo emphasized that The Cleveland Clinic was organized for "better care of the sick, investigation of their problems, and further education of those who serve," he did not phrase it in such a succinct manner. The earliest documented use of this phrase was in 1941 on a plaque dedicated to the founders that was hung at the entrance to Crile's museum.

On Sunday, February 27, 1921, the Clinic held an open house for some 1,500 visitors. On the following day it opened to the public, and 42 patients registered.

The public accepted the Clinic so enthusiastically that it soon became apparent to the founders that they needed an adjacent hospital, even though the staff continued to have hospital privileges at Lakeside, Charity, and Mt. Sinai hospitals. Crile had agreed with the trustees of Lakeside that he would retire as professor of surgery at Western Reserve in 1924, and Lower had consented to a similar agreement with the trustees of Mt. Sinai. Considering the prevailing attitude toward group practice and the corporate practice of medicine, there was ample cause for concern about whether the hospitals would continue to make available a sufficient number of beds to the staff of the new clinic.

With the prospect of being frozen out of hospital beds a real possibility, the Clinic purchased two old houses on East 93rd Street just north of Carnegie Avenue and converted them into a 53-bed hospital, the Oxley Homes, named for the competent English nurse who was put in charge.[7] Another house was used by Dr. Henry John to treat diabetes, not easy in those days, since insulin had just been discovered and reactions to it were not yet well understood. A fourth house, "Therapy House," was used for radiation therapy, and a fifth for serving luncheons to the medical staff.

At first, Oxley Homes was considered to be essentially a nursing home. Soon, however, an operating room for major operations was installed. This presented some difficulties because there were no elevators in the buildings. Orderlies, nurses, and doctors had to carry patients up and down the stairs of the old houses. In the meantime, plans were made to build a modern 184-bed hospital on East 90th Street. It opened June 14, 1924, and Miss Charlotte E. Dunning was put in charge.[8] The seventh floor contained operating

---

[7] In 1928, Lower wrote, "Dr. Crile suggested one day if we could get two houses near together on 93rd Street, not too far from the Clinic, we could fix them up and use [sic] for a temporary hospital. The suggestion was made at noon. At 2 P.M. a patient of Lower's — a real estate agent — came in to see him professionally. After dispensing with the professional visit, Lower incidentally asked if she knew of any property on 93rd Street which might be bought or leased — preferably the latter as we had no money. She said she would find out. She returned in an hour reporting that two maiden ladies down the street had two houses they would be glad to lease as they wanted to go to California to live. Lower gave the agent $100 to go and close the deal. About 5 P.M. of the same day, Dr. Lower asked Dr. Crile about the property he thought he should have. He replied 'Two houses near together on E. 93rd Street.' Lower said, 'I have them!' Crile said, 'The hell you have!' Thus closed the second land deal on 93rd Street and the first step in the formation of a hospital."

[8] With the successful completion of the Hospital building in 1924, the Association Building Company had fulfilled its useful life. It had provided the founders with the legal and

rooms, living quarters for several residents, and anatomic and clinical pathology laboratories. Although 237 beds were now available, between the Oxley Homes and the new hospital, the demand for beds continued to exceed the supply. Two years later two floors of the Bolton Square Hotel, located one block west on Carnegie Avenue, were equipped for the care of 40 medical patients.

The Cleveland Clinic's experience with hospital beds can be summarized in the phrase, "too few and too late." By 1928, the shortage was again acute, and construction began on an eastward extension of the Hospital to 93rd Street to provide a total of 275 beds excluding Oxley Homes and the hotel rooms. Increasing need for supplementary services necessitated installation of a machine shop in a penthouse atop the Clinic building and construction of a power plant, laundry, and ice plant. Parking of cars became increasingly problematic, and the Clinic bought and razed a number of nearby houses to provide space.[9] By 1928, the biophysics laboratory in the Clinic building had become inadequate because of the expansion of research, and a narrow, eight-story research building was constructed between the Hospital and the Clinic.

In that same year, Bunts, who had appeared to be in good health and had been carrying on his practice as usual, died suddenly of a heart attack. The event saddened all who knew him.[10] During

---

financial means to construct both the Clinic and Hospital buildings. Since 1921, the institution had gradually bought up the stock of the Assocation Building Company. By December 31, 1925, the Clinic owned all common and preferred shares that had at one time represented equity in the old Association Building Company. The founders instructed Daoust to merge all interests into The Cleveland Clinic. The Association Building Company passed out of existence. Its assets formed the nucleus of an endowment fund that was used to help support research and to finance the charitable services of the organization.

[9] Lower writes: "The purchase of these ... houses created a land boom on 93rd Street between Euclid and Carnegie Avenue and no other property was for sale at the prices paid for the parcels already purchased... When we decided to build a hospital unit, we had an agent buy land on East 90th Street, ostensibly for garage purposes. We succeeded in getting enough land on East 90th Street for the first unit of the Cleveland Clinic Hospital. From then on trading in land became an interesting game of chess for the Clinic and the property owners on East 93rd Street between Euclid and Carnegie."

[10] At a special meeting of the Board of Trustees on Wednesday, December 5, 1928, the following resolution was passed: "Resolved: That we, members of the Board of Trustees of The Cleveland Clinic Foundation, wish to place on record our appreciation of our association with Dr. Frank E. Bunts, who died November 28, 1928.

"Dr. Bunts was one of the four members who laid this Foundation, and who helped to carry it forward to its present condition of power and of influence. The relations of its members to each other have been long and intimate. To one that relation covered more that two score years of precious meanings. With the others, either through professional or professional co-working he held closest relations. To another, Dr. Bunts was a father by marriage.

"In Dr. Bunts were united qualities and elements unto a character of the noblest type. Richly endowed in intellect, he was no less rich in the treasures of the heart. Dr. Bunts had an

Cleveland Clinic Hospital, East 90th Street (photographed in the 1930s)

the memorial meeting held in the Clinic auditorium to honor Bunts's memory, Dr. C. F. Thwing, president of Western Reserve University and a member of The Cleveland Clinic's Board of Trustees, remarked that Bunts had always been "... responsive, heart to heart, mind to mind, and added to this responsiveness was a constant sense of restraint; he never overflowed; he never went too far. There was an old set of philosophers called the Peripatetics who

---

outspoken religion which was evident in his daily life. His intellectual and emotional nature gave support to a will which was firm, without being unyielding, forceful yet having full respect for others' rights. He graciously gave happiness to others, as well as gratefully received happiness from them. His smile, like his speech, was a benediction. A sympathetic comrade, he shared others' tears and others' anxieties, and still he was glad and hopeful. Faithful to the immediate duty, his interest was world-wide, covering seas and many lands. Recognized by his professional colleagues as of the highest type of excellence and of service, he was yet humble before his own achievements. Richly blessed in his own home, he helped to construct and reconstruct other homes ravaged by disease. Gratitude for his rare skill, and for the gentleness of his devoted ministries, is felt in thousands of lives restored unto health and usefulness. He loved people and was loved as very few men are by the multitudes.

"His thoughtful judgment and rare kindliness was always evident at Board meetings and his gracious manner will ever be remembered.

"If, however, we would see his monument, we ask ourselves to look about. Seeking for evidence of the beauty of his character, of the happiness which he gave like sunshine, or of the usefulness of his service, we turn instinctively to our own grateful, loving and never-forgetting hearts." (Punctuation in the foregoing quotation has been edited.)

were of this type. He held himself together. He was a being in whom integrity had unbounded rule and control."

Fortunately, the expanding workload of the Clinic had enabled Bunts to appoint a young associate whom he had taught in medical school and residency and who now stood ready to take over his practice. This was Dr. Thomas E. Jones, who was destined to become one of the most brilliant technical surgeons of his time.

In response to continually rising demand for both outpatient and inpatient services, the Clinic increased the professional staff and strengthened the existing departments. Using the remains of the building fund, the Clinic purchased a gram of radium and installed a radium emanation plant. This plant made radon seeds for use in the treatment of cancer in the Therapy House. This was the first such plant in the region. In 1922, the Clinic also added an x-ray therapy unit of the highest available quality and put Dr U. V. Portmann, a highly trained specialist in radiation therapy, in charge. Portmann, in conjunction with Mr. Valentine Seitz, the brilliant engineer who headed the machine shop, and Otto Glasser, Ph.D., of the Biophysics Department made the first dosimeter capable of accurately measuring the amount of radiation administered to a patient. Jones, who was by then on the surgical staff, had received special training in the use of radium and radon seeds and was well prepared to take advantage of the new radiation facilities.

The Clinic also added new departments, including endocrinology, which was still in its infancy but growing fast. At the same time, surgery was becoming more and more specialized, requiring the formation of such departments as orthopedic surgery and neurological surgery. The Clinic took full advantage of the development of the specialties and of the prosperity that characterized the '20s. The future appeared bright, and life was good.

THREE

THE DISASTER
1929

That which does not kill me makes me stronger.
— Nietzsche, 1888

On Wednesday, May 15, 1929, in the course of what began as a normal, busy working day at the Clinic, disaster struck, resulting in great loss of life and threatening the very existence of the institution. Incomplete combustion of nitrocellulose x-ray films, which at that time were stored in a basement room of the Clinic building, generated vast quantities of toxic fumes, including oxides of nitrogen and carbon monoxide. At least two explosions occurred. Toxic gases permeated the building, causing the deaths of 123 persons and temporary illness of about 50.

The first explosion took place about 11:30 A.M. when about 250 patients, visitors, and employees were in the building. Fire did not present a major threat because the building was fireproof. The danger lay in inhalation of toxic gases. The occupants of the nearby research building and hospital experienced no problems. A fire door closed the underground tunnel connecting these buildings, confining gas to the Clinic building.

The room in which old films were stored was located on the west side of the basement next to the rear elevator shaft. There was direct communication between this room and a horizontal pipe tunnel or chase, which made a complete circuit of the basement and from which nineteen vertical pipe ducts extended through partitions to the roof. These provided the principal routes for the passage of gases throughout the building.

The Disaster, May 15, 1929

Old nitrocellulose x-ray films were stored in manila envelopes (averaging three films to the envelope), on wooden shelves and in standard steel file cabinets. No one knew the exact number of films in the room, but it was estimated that there were about 70,000 films of all sizes, equivalent to about 4,200 pounds of nitrocellulose. Some estimates were as high as 10,000 pounds. Water pipes and three insulated steam lines were located below the ceiling of the room. One steam line, pressurized at about 65 pounds per square inch, passed within seven and one-half inches of the nearest film shelf.

The room had no outside ventilation. Electrical wiring was in conduit, and there were several pendant lamps. There were no automatic sprinklers.

Several hours before the disaster, a leak had been discovered in the high-pressure steam line in the film storage room. A steam fitter, who was called to make repairs, arrived about 9:00 A.M. and removed about fourteen inches of insulation, allowing a jet of steam about three feet long to issue from the pipe in the direction of the film rack against the north wall. He went to the power house to close the steam line and then returned to his shop to allow the line to drain and cool. Upon returning to the film room about 11:00 A.M., the workman discovered a cloud of yellow smoke in one upper corner of the room. He emptied a fire extinguisher in the direction of the smoke, but was soon overcome by the fumes and fell to the floor. Revived by a draft of fresh air, he crawled toward the door on hands and knees. A small explosion flung him through the doorway into a maintenance room, where another workman joined him. Together they made their way through a window and out of the building. Another explosion occurred while the men were still at the window. The custodian spread the alarm.

Alarms were telephoned in from several locations. The first was officially recorded at 11:30 A.M., and two others were recorded by 11:44 A.M. A fire company based on East 105th Street just north of Euclid Avenue was the first to respond. When it arrived, most of the building was obscured by a dense, yellowish-brown cloud. Two more alarms brought more fire-fighting equipment and rescue squads. Ladders were raised on each side of the building in an effort to reach and evacuate the people who appeared at the windows. About eight minutes after the arrival of the first fire company, an explosion blew out the skylights and parts of the ceiling of the fourth story, liberating an immense cloud of brown vapor and partially clearing the building of gas. Rescue work then began in earnest. Firemen and volunteers manned stretchers, removed people from inside the building, and helped them down the ladders. A rescue squad wearing gas masks tried to enter the front door on the north side but was forced out of the building by the concentration of gases. Battalion Chief Michael Graham and members of Hook and Ladder Company No. 8 entered the building from the roof. Fire hoses were trained on the flaming gas visible through windows in the rear stair shaft and some of the basement windows.

Many people died trapped in the north elevator and in the north stairway. Descending the stairway in an effort to escape through the Euclid Avenue entrance, they encountered an ascending mass of frantic people who had found the ground-floor entrance blocked by flames. Many died in the ensuing melee. Some reached safety by going down ladders from window ledges. Others, by climbing up through the broken skylight, made it to the roof of the building and then descended by ladder to the ground.

Dr. A. D. Ruedemann, head of the Department of Ophthalmology, perched on the ledge of his office window on the west side of the fourth floor and supported himself by holding a hot pipe inside the room. He managed to grab a ladder when it reached his level and made his way to the ground.[1]

---

[1] Dr. E. Perry McCullagh has left the following account:

"It was customary in those days for one of the Staff or a Fellow to accompany the patient to another department. I had gone to the front of the fourth floor with a lady and had introduced her to Dr. Ruedemann. As I approached the balustrade, I heard a rumbling explosion and saw a high mushroom of dense rust-colored, smoke-like gas arise from the center ventilator. I thought at first of bromine. It was clear to me that the masonry building could not burn and that the staff should help the people out and avoid panic.

"The ventilating system connected the basement with all the rooms individually, so that within a minute or so they were filled with the poisonous smoke. The elevator near the front stair was stopped when someone in the power house turned off the electricity, and those in the crowded elevator died. The front stairway was crowded with frightened, choking people beginning to panic. Those near the bottom were shouting, 'Go back, you can't get out here — there's fire down here.' There were flames across the front doorway where the partially oxidized fumes met the oxygen of the open air. Most and perhaps all of the people who remained in the stairway died there. A few escaped through the skylight to die later, as did the neurosurgeon, Dr. C. E. Locke, Jr.

"I left the stairway and went into the thick gas on the fourth floor. Those who reached an open window on the west were pretty well off because the breeze was from that direction. I stumbled against a door on the east corridor, and Dr. Edward Sherrer, who was then a young staff member, pulled me in and helped me to hang my head out of the window, which did little good as the fumes were mushrooming out the window. With the help of firemen we were able to get down one of the first ladders to be put up.

"After helping with what emergency care could be given in our own hospital, we searched for our friends, some of whom were alive and many dead at Mt. Sinai Hospital. Many were located at the County Morgue; others were visited at their homes. Dr. Sherrer and I were admitted to the Cleveland Clinic Hospital late that evening with shortness of breath, very rapid respirations and cyanosis. After a few days in oxygen tents, we were discharged, only to be readmitted about ten days after the disaster, and were in oxygen tents again for most of six weeks. This relapse was the result of interstitial edema of the lungs which occurred late in all of those who were badly gassed but survived the first few days.

"Among many of us who were most severely ill, courage and calmness seemed to play an important role in recovery. The lack of oxygen caused loss of judgment and encouraged restless activity, so that those who fought against instructions and the use of oxygen died. The courage and complete disregard of fear in the case of my roommate, Dr. Conrad C. Gilkison, was amazing. We both believed we were dying because everyone up to that time who had developed cyanotic nail beds had died, and we could see our blue nails plainly enough. At 1:00 or 2:00 A.M., both of us unable to sleep, Gilk said 'Perry, if you're here in the morning and I'm not, get old Bennett to take me to the ball game.' Mr. Bennett was the undertaker at the corner of East 90th and Euclid Avenue, a block from where we lay.

"Dr. Sherrer, Dr. Gilkison and I were finally able to return to work about November 15. Recovery of pulmonary function was complete."

During the confusion of that tragic morning, those trapped within the building were unaware of the nature of the gas that filled the halls, corridors, and examining rooms. They only knew that it severely irritated the throat and lungs, causing coughing and difficulty breathing. Those who reached the examining rooms at the sides of the building and closed the doors behind them had a chance of survival. They opened the windows widely and leaned into the fresh air. When the ladders reached them, many made their way safely to the ground. A few jumped. Dr. Robert S. Dinsmore of the Department of Surgery broke his ankle leaping from a second floor window on the east side of the building.

A number of non-Clinic physicians came to the hospital and spent many hours assisting members of the Clinic staff with their overwhelming task. Many survivors were cyanotic and short of breath, and it rapidly became evident that the problem was toxic gas inhalation. Respiration became more difficult, cyanosis increased, and severe pulmonary edema developed. Fluid caused by gas-induced irritation of the airways filled the pulmonary alveoli. Many of these persons, including Dr. Locke and Dr. Hunter[2], died in two or three hours. Some died later that afternoon or that night, among them Mr. William Brownlow, artist, and Dr. John Phillips, one of the founders of The Cleveland Clinic and head of the medical department. Phillips had reached the ground by a ladder on the east side of the building. He sat for a while on the steps of the church across 93rd Street and finally was taken by car to his apartment at the Wade Park Manor on East 107th Street. There his condition worsened as the afternoon wore on. About 7:00 P.M. a transfusion team, headed by Dr. Crile, went to his room and performed a transfusion, but to no avail. Phillips died at about 8:30 P.M. He was only fifty years old, and the loss of such a talented physician and leader was a particularly sad event for the Clinic and for Cleveland's medical community.[3]

---

[2] Edgar S. Hunter, M.D., was a neurosurgery resident working with Dr. Locke.

[3] In his book with the grisly title *They Died Crawling and Other Tales of Cleveland Woe* (Gray & Company, Cleveland, 1995), John Stark Bellamy, II, noted "...Dr. Crile himself was at his best throughout the disaster, a veritable battlefield general who tirelessly marshalled [sic] resources to heal the wounded and console the grieving."

Within days after the disaster Crile wrote to all surviving family members that could be identified. For example, in a letter to Mr. A. Lippert of Barberton, Ohio, dated May 23, 1929, he wrote "Because of our sad lack of definite information regarding the family connections of Mr. and Mrs. Carl Long, who lost their lives in the Cleveland Clinic disaster, we are asking you to extend to this family our deepest sympathy in their great sorrow. Only our duty to the surviving has kept us from giving them more promptly this assurance that we sorrow with them."

On the day after the disaster, Dr. Harvey Cushing, a distinguished neurosurgeon in Boston and an old friend of Crile's, arrived in Cleveland to offer his services. His former assistant, Dr. Charles E. Locke, Jr., who was the first neurologic surgeon on the Clinic staff (1924-1929), had died of gas inhalation the previous day. Crile asked his first assistant, Dr. Alexander T. Bunts, to take Cushing around the hospital to see those with any possible neurologic injuries.

Crile and others who had had first-hand experience in treating gassed patients during the war in France commented upon the similarities of the clinical effects of the gas to those observed in soldiers who had inhaled phosgene gas ($COCl_2$) at the front. After the disaster, Major General Gilchrist, Chief of the Chemical Warfare Service, came to Cleveland and initiated a thorough investigation of its possible causes. Decomposition of the nitrocellulose film may have been caused (a) by the rise in temperature produced by the leaking and uncovered steam line, (b) by ignition of the film from an incandescent lamp attached to a portable cord close to the shelves, or (c) by a lighted cigarette on or near the films. None of these theories was ever proved. The investigations conducted by the Chemical Warfare Service did determine the nature of the gases produced by the burning or decomposition of nitrocellulose films: carbon monoxide and "nitrous fumes" (NO, NO_2, and N_2O_4). Carbon monoxide breathed in high concentrations causes almost instant death. "Nitrous fumes," which comprised most of the brownish gases, became nitric acid on contact with moisture in the lungs. This led to acute rupture of the alveolar walls, pulmonary congestion, and edema. The Clinic disaster resulted in worldwide adoption of revised safety codes for storing films and led to the use of safety film that would not explode.

After the disaster many problems confronted the two remaining founders. Miss Litta Perkins, executive secretary to the founders and the Board of Trustees and in whose photographic memory existed most of the records of the Foundation, had died. The Clinic building, although still structurally sound, could not be used. The interior was badly damaged, brownish stains were present everywhere, and there was a rumor that lethal fumes were still escaping. Some advised razing the building, fearing that patients would never again be willing to enter it. Lower and Crile, however, adopted a wise position. "They'll talk for a while," Crile said, "and then, when they forget it, we'll start again to use the building." That is exactly what happened.

A frame house that stood directly across Euclid Avenue from the Clinic had been used as a dormitory for the girls of Laurel

School. This house was made available to the Clinic by Mrs. Lyman, headmistress of the school and a lifelong friend of Crile's. The house was transformed into a temporary clinic. For four days after the disaster the staff and personnel of the Clinic worked unceasingly, aided by carpenters and movers and by a committee of civic leaders headed by Mr. Samuel Mather and Mr. Roger C. Hyatt. Desks, chairs, tables, lamps, x-ray equipment, files, records, and all other necessities were carried across Euclid Avenue and placed on all three floors of the loaned house. Telephone and power lines were installed. On Monday morning, May 20, 1929, just five days after the disaster, the building was opened for the examination of patients.

Liability insurance coverage for such carnage was inadequate, but it did provide eight thousand dollars per person plus funeral or hospital expenses. State industrial insurance gave what Crile termed "cold comfort" to the personnel. The medical staff, however, took on the task of paying the families of the members of the staff who died full salary for the first six months and half salary for the next six. The founders suffered no personal liability because the Foundation, which owned everything, was a nonprofit corporation of which the founders were salaried employees. Expressions of sympathy and offers of financial assistance were received from many Clevelanders as well as from colleagues or patients as far away as India, China, and Australia.[4] More than $30,000 poured in as gifts. Then Crile said, "When Lower and I found we still pos-

---

[4] The sentiment of a Cleveland physician, Dr. Frank A. Rice, who was one of the many local doctors who helped in the efforts to save victims on the day of the disaster, is well expressed in the following letter addressed to Dr. Lower:

"May 18, 1929

"My dear Doctor Lower:

"Our hearts are wrung and we are bowed in sorrow over the loss of your associates, whom we have all learned to love and respect. We feel, too keenly, the pain it has caused you and those of your group who were spared, but we are justly proud of your undaunted spirit to carry on, and out of the ashes of yesterday to erect an institution bound by traditions, to be a worthy monument to lives and ambitions of its sturdy founders.

"I cannot let the opportunity pass without a word of praise and admiration for your nursing staff. I arrived at your hospital as the first of the injured were brought in. Throughout the day, and into the night, I have never seen, not even in 17 consecutive days in the Argonne, such perfect organization. With death increasing horror at every turn, your nursing staff functioned with alacrity, coolness and decision which marked them as masters of their art—truly a remarkable tribute to their institution and your years of instruction.

"Yours most sincerely,

"Frank A. Rice"

Another letter, this one to Dr. Crile, was from Boston's Dr. Ernest A. Codman, the father of quality assessment in medicine, excerpts of which follow:

"I am writing to ask a question.

sessed the confidence of the public, of our own staff, and of the members of our institution, we knew we could finance our own way. So, after holding these gifts for a few months of security, we returned them all with their accumulated interest."[5]

After operating in the Laurel School quarters throughout the summer of 1929, the equipment and functions of the Clinic were transferred in September to the newly completed addition to the hospital, which had just been extended to East 93rd Street. The rooms on several floors were arranged and equipped as examining rooms for outpatients. For the next two years the Clinic's work was carried out here. Although the quarters were cramped, the patients continued to come in increasing numbers.

"I always think of you as an eagle able to look directly into the sun, looking down, perhaps, on the rest of us common birds, who are controlled by our sympathies, petty desires, and emotions.

"You have climbed the ladder of surgical ambition high into the skies of Fame. You have done more good by your introduction of blood pressure measurements, of transfusion, anoci-association, and gas-oxygen anesthesia than could be counteracted by the death of every patient who entered your clinic in a whole year. In the haste of your upward progress you have known that some wings would break and lives be lost.

"Now comes this accident which is not the least your fault, and which will do untold good, as every X-ray laboratory in the world will be safer for it.

"And now, my question: Since you have known both 'Triumph and Disaster' — did you 'treat those two Impostors just the same'?"

To this query Dr. Crile replied:

"Referring to our own terrible blow, the only thing that hurts me, and that will always be, is the loss of life. I saw nothing in France so terrible. It was a crucible. Almost four hundred people were in the building at the time.

"You have always been a close friend. I appreciate you, especially now."

In the June 1929 issue of the *Bulletin of the Academy of Medicine of Cleveland,* the disaster was acknowledged, and the following paragraphs summed up the Academy's sentiments: .

"The Academy of Medicine bows in sorrow with the rest of the city. The suddenness and tremendous import of it all was brought home to us all the more forcibly by the fact that five of our own members lost their lives. They were all men either prominent in their specialties or starting in on careers which promised well for themselves and for the profession.

"The Academy members who died in this disaster are as follows:—

John Phillips, M.D.

C. E. Locke, Jr., M.D.

Harry M. Andison, M.D.

Roy A. Brintnall, M.D.

George W. Belcher, M.D."

A later issue noted two additional deaths, those of Miriam K. Stage, M.D. (one of the leaders of Women's Hospital), and J. H. Swafford, M.D. (radiology).

[5] A commemorative booklet, *In Memoriam,* was issued by the Board of Trustees in June 1929, eulogizing the victims of the disaster. It reads in part: "The integrity of the Cleveland Clinic Foundation could receive no more severe test than that of the recent disaster. Each member of the medical staff, as well as every employee in every department, has faithfully carried on his or her own task, knowing that the Clinic was not destroyed, but rather that from the ruins will arise an even better institution which will be dedicated as a sacred memorial to the dead."

FOUR

THE PHOENIX RISES FROM THE ASHES
1929-1941

Fate loves the fearless;
Fools, when their roof-tree
Falls, think it doomsday;
Firm stands the sky.

— *James Russell Lowell, 1868*

In October 1929, five months after the disaster, the stock market crashed, heralding the Great Depression of the 1930s. It was at this time — with three million dollars of lawsuits filed not only against The Cleveland Clinic but also against Lower, Crile, and the estates of Bunts and Phillips — that the surviving founders decided to build a new three-story Clinic building with foundations to support fourteen stories (eventually known as the "S Building"). They planned to connect this new structure with the original Clinic Building, and to remodel the latter so that it would not remind people of the disaster. At the time of this decision, Crile was 66 years old and Lower was 63. They reasoned that if the court decision went against them and the Foundation, they would all go bankrupt and there would be nothing to lose.[1]

---

[1] Crile and Lower did not think that there would be any liability. Storage of the films had been in accordance with the fire laws, and the fumes from films had not been recognized as potentially fatal. In 1928, however, eight persons had died in a similar fire in Albany, New York. Suffocation was believed to have been the cause of several of those fatalities.

Cleveland Clinic, East 93rd Street (Left to right): Hospital addition, 1929. Research
Building, 1928. Main Clinic (three stories), 1931. Original Clinic Building
(S.E. corner showing), 1921   (photographed in 1935)

The two founders started to raise money for the new building
with trepidation and faced the difficulties posed by this task. "Every
day Ed and I spent the lunch hour in the board room discussing
them," Crile wrote. "I was able to convince Ed that we would
weather our difficulties; but the next day he would appear so
exhausted and excited over a new angle which had occurred to him
while he was fighting out the lawsuits overnight, that I told him if
someone struck a match near him he would explode. But he was
always a joy, appearing one morning with the suggestion that perhaps there would be Christian Scientists on the jury."

From a professional standpoint, 1929 was a good time to start
building. The earnings of both Crile and Lower were at their peak.
Phillips, lost in the disaster, was replaced as head of the medical
department by Dr. Russell L. Haden, a nationally known physician
from the University of Kansas. He began to develop subspecialty
departments in internal medicine and soon accumulated a large
practice in his own specialty, diseases of the blood. There were able
young physicians in all departments, and the reputation and practice of the Clinic were growing rapidly. Indebtedness and the voluntarily assumed burden of paying the salaries of the staff members
who had died in the disaster made it difficult to meet the payroll,
and Lower once sent a telegram to Crile, who was attending a meeting in New York, "Just across without reserve."

The financial success of the Clinic at this time depended mainly on the fact that some of the physicians' earnings were more than four times as great as their salaries, the excess going to the Foundation. But in order to borrow the $850,000 required for the new building, Crile and Lower had to put up their personal life insurance policies to guarantee $150,000 of the loan. Three million dollars in lawsuits resulting from the disaster were settled out of court for about $45,000, for the pragmatic reason that The Cleveland Clinic had no liquid or negotiable assets that would make it worthwhile for the plaintiffs to bring the cases to court.

In September 1932, in order to help repay the debt incurred by the disaster and the cost of the new building, all employees, including the medical staff, took a 10 percent pay cut. This financial curtailment was accepted graciously, if not enthusiastically, because everyone was aware of the Clinic's crisis. At that time no one predicted the severity of the Great Depression that would cloud the years to come. Instead, there was a confident expectation about the future.

"Late in February 1933, while Grace and I were attending a dinner in Cleveland," Crile wrote in his autobiography, "one of the guests, a prominent industrialist and director of one of Cleveland's largest banks, was called to the telephone just as we were seated. He did not return until dinner was nearly over and, when he returned, he seemed deeply perturbed, was without conversation and soon left." The next day the Maryland banks closed; the following day most Cleveland banks announced that only 5 percent withdrawals were allowed. The economic depression deepened. The banks failed while the Clinic was still heavily in debt. A second 10 percent reduction in salaries had been necessary one month before the banks closed. Four months later there was an additional 25 percent cut. Circulating money had almost ceased to exist, but its absence did not impede the incidence of disease. The sick still required treatment, and somehow many of them managed to pay something for it. The staff and employees remained loyal; their choice, in those days of unemployment, lay between a low-paying job and no job at all. The Clinic survived.[2]

In 1934 the Depression was still in its depths. Although Crile was then 70 years old, his surgical practice continued to provide a major part of the Clinic's income. His interest had gradually shifted

---

[2] Crile wrote in 1933, "... the one abiding comfort, as I looked at our beautiful cathedral for service, was that during the years that I had needed least and could give most I had been able to earn in such excess of my salary that we had been able to accomplish that of which we had dreamed."

Aerial view of the Cleveland Clinic (Euclid Avenue at right) in 1931

from thyroid surgery, which had attracted patients from all over the world, to surgery of the adrenal glands, a field that he was exploring to treat such diverse conditions as hypertension, peptic ulcer, epilepsy, hyperthyroidism, and neurocirculatory asthenia. The results of these operations were sometimes promising but rarely spectacular. The field was so controversial that Crile's personal practice began to shrink. During that time he underwent surgery on his eyes for glaucoma, and soon thereafter, he began to develop cataracts.

Fortunately, Crile had able young associates in the Department of Surgery, including Dr. Robert S. Dinsmore, who continued his interest in surgery of the thyroid and breast, and Dr. Thomas E. Jones who had already become nationally famous for abdominal surgery, particularly for cancer of the rectum and colon. The surgical specialties were headed by capable surgeons, and under Haden's leadership, the Department of Medicine was expanding rapidly. Therefore, Crile began to disengage himself from conventional surgery and to spend more of his time researching the energy systems of man and animals, traveling twice to Africa to collect and study the brains, thyroids, and adrenals of various species of African wildlife .[3]

---

[3] Crile's research into the energy systems of animals was supported in part by an endowment received from Sarah Todd McBride. In 1941, the Museum of Intelligence, Power, and Personality was built adjacent to the old Clinic Building, to exhibit the specimens that Crile had collected. Dr. Alexander T. Bunts wrote in 1965, "Many parties of school children visited the museum and

On the way home from Florida in 1941, Dr. and Mrs. Crile and the Clinic's anatomist, Dr. Daniel Quiring, were injured when their airplane hit a tornado and crashed in a swamp near Vero Beach.

"It had been a great day, a manatee was dissected and cast," Dr. Crile wrote, "and we had also stored away in jars the energy organs of a marlin, a sailfish and a barracuda, so we decided to take the early morning plane to Daytona Beach, visit Marineland and catch our train at midnight. This was Quiring's first flight.

"When the steward told us that there were a few thunderheads beyond, Grace remarked that Quiring was going to see a little of every kind of weather. We had left the usual beach route and were flying over marshland that looked like the waterhole country in Africa. The mist became thicker. Suddenly I was conscious of an abrupt vertical upsurge; we had entered the thunderheads and were shrouded in darkness and a violent hail storm, pierced by zigzag lightning that flashed from every bit of metal in the plane. We must have resembled a Christmas tree hurling through space.

"A deafening roar as of a high pressure wind under a powerful drive beat on our ear drums. Blankets, hats, pillows, trays were sucked to the ceiling, then flew in all directions about the cabin. I did not suspect it at the time but we were in an active tornado and were actually observing its mechanism at work. The plane seemed to be whirling. Blackness spun before my eyes. Everything was tipping — I recall how difficult it was to pull my tilting body to the left.

---

were fascinated by the mounted specimens of lion, alligator, elephant, gazelle, giraffe, shark, porpoise, manatee, zebra, and many other interesting creatures. Models of the hearts of race horses and whales, fashioned of paraffin or plaster, and wax models of the sympathetic nervous systems, brains, thyroids, and adrenal glands attracted the interest of the curious and challenged the logical thinking of visiting scientists and physicians.... Those of us who were working at the clinic in those days were never surprised to encounter a dead lion or alligator in the freight elevator of the Research building or occasionally even a live one, as well as a battery of vats filled with viscera of various animals. In the study of this material, emphasis was placed on the relative weight of thyroid, adrenals, liver, and brain, and the complexity of the autonomic nervous systems."

Mr. Walter Halle, later to become one of the Clinic's trustees, recalled the following episode:

"I got a call from Doctor Crile one day asking if I would come down to the Clinic and serve in some sort of protective capacity, armed with my Mauser 3006, while they were attempting to uncrate a lion sent to him from the Toledo Zoo. The lion was brought up on an elevator in a cage, in a very irritable condition, and moved into the room where he was supposed to be dispatched in some fashion that had not been too thoroughly worked out. After much thrashing around the lion was quieted and someone gave him a shot to put him away peacefully. I hesitate to think what would have happened had the lion broken out of the cage, which he was attempting to do. Fortunately for everyone we did not have to use our firearms because firing a high-powered rifle in a room 14 x 18, with Doctor Crile and three other doctors, would have made it problematical just who would get drilled.

"I can't tell you what an interesting session I had afterwards watching him dissect the lion and listening to his marvelous running-fire commentary about the glands and various parts of the anatomy."

Henry S. Sherman, President, The Cleveland Clinic Foundation, 1941–42

"A lurch! A feeling of gratitude that Grace got off our manuscript to the publisher. Then oblivion!"

Quiring's shoulder was dislocated; Grace Crile suffered two broken ribs, a broken sternum, and a cracked vertebra; and Crile, the most seriously injured of any of the passengers (his seat was at the point where the plane buckled), had three fractures of the pelvis, three broken ribs, and fractures of the transverse processes of two vertebrae as well as severe contusions. Despite these injuries, he was the first to break the silence after the crash. As the chill marsh mire began to rise in the cabin he imagined himself at home in a bathtub. "Grace," he called to his wife, "Grace, would you mind turning on the hot water please?"[4]

---

[4] Miraculously no one in that accident died. Crile then made the following observation:

"After the experience of everyone in the plane it seems clear to me that the cause of the blackout in aviation must be the failure of the blood to return to the brain and the heart because of the rapid ascent of the plane. Had I been standing on my head or lying flat with feet elevated and head down — the position used in surgical shock when the blood pressure fails, probably I would not have lost consciousness.... Were an aviator encased in a rubber suit and the pneumatic pressure established, the suit in itself would prevent the pooling of the blood in the large vessels in the abdomen and extremities and would maintain the conscious state. I believe that an aviator thus equipped would be protected against the failure of the blood to return to the heart and hence would have protection against blackout."

Edward C. Daoust, LL.B., President, The Cleveland Clinic Foundation, 1943–1947

Although Crile had remained president of The Cleveland Clinic until 1940, more and more of the executive duties had been turned over to an Administrative Board composed of four staff physicians. They were responsible for the professional aspects of administration. The Board of Trustees, then composed exclusively of laymen, was responsible for properties and finance. Prosperity had returned to the country, and it seemed that the Clinic was out of its financial straits. But there were still other troubles ahead, many of them arising from conflicts of personalities.

For the Clinic, governed as it had been by the founders for many years with no thought of succession planning, the transfer of authority was bound to be difficult. As the old leaders faltered or stepped down, there ensued a struggle for power among the next generation of leaders. As Dr. Joseph Hahn put it many years later under similar circumstances, "Let the games begin!" It was at this point that the Board of Trustees, which had previously acted main-

Crile thought of the pneumatic suit that he had developed years before to treat shock. Why not use such a suit to prevent blackouts that occurred when pilots "pulled out" after dive bombing? The suggestion was passed on to appropriate officers in the Army, Navy, and Air Force. Crile at the age of 77 was made an honorary Consultant to the Navy, and in cooperation with engineers of the Goodyear Tire and Rubber Company produced the first G-suit for military use.

ly in support of the founders' decisions, showed their value. Without them it is doubtful that the institution could have survived. Much of that part of the history of the Clinic is recounted in a later chapter. It is sufficient to say here that able physicians and surgeons are not necessarily the best administrators.

By 1940, Crile's eyesight was failing badly, and he retired from the position of president of the Clinic. His brother-in-law, Mr. Henry S. Sherman, a former industrialist who at the time was president of the Society for Savings (a Cleveland financial institution) and one of the Foundation's trustees, succeeded him as president. Although Lower was still active in an advisory capacity, he, too, was now in his seventies and was equally anxious to turn over the administrative responsibilities to the next generation.

Three years later Mr. Edward C. Daoust, who had participated so effectively in the founding of the Clinic, was elected to the full-time presidency of the Foundation. Sherman became Chairman of the Board of Trustees.[5]

The Foundation had been growing steadily ever since the financial depression began to lift, and the number of employees had increased from 216 in 1930 to 739 in 1941. In September 1941 the Foundation was able to repay the last $180,000 of its indebtedness. The founders then relinquished the last of their administrative duties with the comment, "The child has learned to walk." But the road still led uphill.

---

[5] Henry Sherman married Crile's sister-in-law, Edith McBride. He was a trustee of The Cleveland Clinic Foundation from 1936 to 1956. He is remembered not only for his wise counsel in the affairs of the Foundation but also for his friendly concern for the professional staff, many of whom he knew personally. Sherman's son-in-law is James A. Hughes, who was chairman of the Board of Trustees from 1969 to 1984, with the exception of a two-year interruption (1973-1974).

FIVE

TURBULENT SUCCESS
1941-1955

The dogs bark, but the caravan moves on.
— *Arabic Proverb*

Although the "child" was walking, the problems of adolescence still had to be met. No firm leadership, either autocratic or democratic, capable of replacing that of the founders had as yet developed. The dominant personalities on the staff were men like Dr. William V. Mullin, head of the Department of Otolaryngology; Dr. A. D. Ruedemann, head of the Department of Ophthalmology; Dr. Russell L. Haden, head of the Department of Medicine; and Dr. Thomas E. Jones, who replaced Crile as head of the Department of Surgery in 1940. Problems arose as a result of the conflicts among these brilliant and competitive personalities. Sadly, some of their arguments were settled by Dr. Mullin's untimely death in 1935 and by Dr. Ruedemann's resignation from the Clinic in 1947.

One factor that helped to tide over the difficult years of the early 1940s was the sheer weight of work. The military draft had reduced the staff by more than 20 percent and the number of residents by one third. Since most of the young physicians in the area had been drafted, many of their patients came to the Clinic. Surgical schedules and new patient registrations rose to an all-time high. In 1942 there were 21,500 new patients, and by 1944 the number had increased to 27,900. Everyone was too busy to spend much time discussing administrative affairs. Daoust was an effective and respected chief executive, and Sherman, chairman of the Board of Trustees, had a unique insight into the problems of the Clinic in which he had been interested since its inception.

43

The Clinic's Naval Reserve Unit was called to active duty in the spring of 1942. Two months of training were spent on Pier No. 14 of the Brooklyn Naval Yard, a bleak, barn-like structure in which, as Crile, Jr., recalled, there was very little to do but read *The New York Times*. The Unit then sailed for New Zealand to establish Mobile Hospital No. 4, the first of its kind in the South Pacific.[1] In the Unit were Drs. George Crile, Jr., William J. Engel, A. Carlton Ernstene, W. James Gardner, Roscoe J. Kennedy, Joseph C. Root, William A. Nosik, and Edward J. Ryan, as well as Guy H. Williams, Jr. (a neuropsychiatrist from City Hospital, Cleveland) and Don H. Nichols (a Cleveland dentist).

Mobile Hospital No. 4 was based in New Zealand for 18 months and dealt more with tropical diseases and rehabilitation of the sick than with wounds. Thereafter its officers were dispersed to other stations. As soon as the war was over, the Clinic physicians returned home.[2]

Crile was 77 years old when the United States entered World War II. In 1940, after a cataract operation made difficult by a previous operation for glaucoma, he lost an eye. Remaining vision had failed to the point where he could no longer easily recognize people by sight, and he had become subject to occasional spells of unconsciousness. Crile then contracted bacterial endocarditis, and, after an illness of several months, he died in January 1943.[3]

---

[1] Construction of the portable hospital, all of which was shipped from the United States, was a race against time, for the landing on Guadalcanal was being planned and there would have to be a hospital ready to receive the casualties. For three weeks the physicians and corpsmen labored in the mud of a cricket field on the outskirts of Auckland to put the hospital together. Marie Kennedy, widow of Dr. Roscoe "Ken" Kennedy, recalls that "Someone accidentally walked across what was to be the ceiling of a large ward, from one corner to another. The footprints dried, and they wouldn't come off. That turned out to be the ceiling of a psychiatric ward! Apparently the admiral said, 'if you weren't nuts when you were brought in, you would be nuts when you came out!' "

Miraculously they succeeded and were ready when the hospital ship Solace brought its first load of wounded. Most of them had had excellent attention, and there was little left to do except give them convalescent care. But there was a lot to be learned about tropical diseases. A young Marine, strong and apparently well, fell sick one day and the next day was dead with convulsions and the meningeal manifestations of malaria. In his journal Kennedy noted "What Sherman said about war ('War is hell') still holds."

[2] After their tours of active duty, the Clinic paid the returning men their full salaries less the amount paid them by the Navy.

[3] Lower expressed the feelings of many when he wrote on the occasion of Crile's death, "George Crile had a quest and a vision that he pursued throughout his entire adult life with a devotion amounting almost to mystic fervor. This is the striking thing that distinguished him from other surgeons and that gave special meaning to his life. He was not content to make use of known truths, but was forever searching for the answer to 'What is Life?' This was the stream into which his tremendous energies flowed, and all his activities and observations were purposeful and tributary to this."

Crile died with his major quest unfulfilled: he had failed to divine the unfathomable mystery of life. Nonetheless, he left The Cleveland Clinic, complete with its own hospital, research, and educational facilities, to stand as a memorial to its founders. The institution's prosperity in the early 1940s made possible many improvements in its facilities. There were troubles ahead, however, and tumultuous times were to characterize the late 1940s.

On January 1, 1943, Daoust retired from his law practice and became the full-time president of The Cleveland Clinic and its chief administrative officer, responsible to the trustees. He had been associated with the founders and the Clinic for more than twenty years. On that date, Sherman became chairman of the Board, and Mr. John Sherwin, whose activities as a trustee were to be so important to the Foundation through the years, joined Daoust and Sherman as the third member of a new executive committee of the Board of Trustees. In Sherwin's words, "While formal meetings were infrequent, luncheon meetings and telephone conversations took place often, and a closer rapport was established with the Administrative Board then composed of Daoust and Drs. Thomas Jones, Russell Haden, A. D. Ruedemann, W. James Gardner, and E. P. McCullagh."

The Administrative Board referred to by Sherwin was established to represent the professional staff at the same time the new Executive Committee was established. The new Administrative Board had its first meeting in January 1943. The meetings of that body in earlier years have been described as always interesting and frequently almost frightening. Lower would sometimes leave the meeting trembling visibly. Impressions of the meetings of the Administrative Board were recalled by McCullagh, the youngest member of the Board. "The original Medical Administrative Board was formed in February 1937, and was composed of Dr. Crile, Dr. Lower, Dr. Russell Haden, Dr. Thomas E. Jones, Dr. A. D. Ruedemann, and Dr. Bernard H. Nichols with Mr. Edward Daoust attending. These were exciting meetings, for Dr. Ruedemann, Dr. Jones, and Dr. Haden often reacted suddenly. Sometimes this, added to a hot temper, would threaten physical violence. Drs. Haden and Jones, it seemed to me, always disagreed, apparently on general principles. Dr. Ruedemann had no favorites, disagreeing with everyone in turn. This concerned Dr. Crile and Dr. Lower very much, and I'm sure caused them anxiety for fear that no plans for satisfactory Clinic administration were evolving."[4]

---

[4] The two most powerful figures on the Administrative Board in the 1940s were Jones, Chief of Surgery, and Haden, Chief of Medicine. According to Mrs. Janet Winters Getz, who attended

John Sherwin, President, The Cleveland Clinic Foundation, 1948–1957

During the war and immediately thereafter, the Clinic enjoyed prosperity and reached professional maturity. Specialization was increasing in both medical and surgical divisions. New patient registrations continued to increase, by 1947 rising to 31,504, nearly three times the number served a decade earlier. This growth necessitated further building, and seven stories were added to the new Clinic building in 1945. One year later a wing was added to the hospital, connecting it to the research building.[5] The turbulence of the post-war years required the steady hand of Daoust in administering the growing organization, and his accidental death in June 1947 was a serious blow to the Foundation. The airliner on which Daoust was a passenger crashed into a mountain top. All on board were killed.

---

some of the meetings of the Administrative Board in a secretarial capacity, it seemed that these two brilliant and attractive men had agreed to disagree. Sometimes their shouting could be heard over the entire floor. Often the fiery Ruedemann would add his bit. He was a particularly colorful and outspoken man, as exemplified by a story that is told about him when he was in medical school. When asked about the blood count of a patient with leukemia, he reported that the white cell count was 500,000. "Did you count them?" his professor asked. "Hell no, I weighed them," said Ruedemann.

[5] Few beds were added by the new wing, however, as much of the space was taken up by elevator shafts designed to serve future additions.

Clarence M. Taylor, Executive Director, 1948–1955

The trustees promptly confronted the administrative crisis pre-cipitated by Daoust's death. Sherwin's own account states that on the morning following the airplane crash, Lower, Sherman, and Sherwin met to determine how to best assume Daoust's responsi-bilities. There had already been many discussions about how to administer the Foundation after its founders retired. Conversations had taken place with the management consulting firm of Booz, Allen, and Hamilton with an idea of engaging that firm to study the Clinic and its operations and to make recommendations.

Sherman, Sherwin, and Lower agreed to recommend to the Board of Trustees that:

- the position of president would be left vacant for the time being;
- the responsibilities of the president would be assumed by the Executive Committee;
- Sherwin would become chairman of the Executive Committee;
- recently elected trustees John R. Chandler, Benjamin F. Fiery, Walter M. Halle, and John C. Virden would join Sherman and Sherwin on the Executive Committee;

- the Executive Committee in conjunction with the Administrative Board would employ Booz, Allen, and Hamilton to make a study and recommend (a) how the Foundation should be administered and (b) how the compensation of the professional staff should be determined.

These recommendations were adopted by the Board of Trustees on June 26, 1947, and a new Administrative Board composed of Drs. Dickson, Ernstene, Gardner, Jones, and Netherton was appointed. That same day the staff assembled to learn of these actions.

During the ensuing four months the Executive Committee and Administrative Board met almost weekly, usually from five o'clock in the afternoon through dinner and on to ten o'clock or later. Representatives of Booz, Allen, and Hamilton attended most of these meetings. They reviewed the entire operation of the institution and developed a plan for the organization and operation of the Foundation. The plan of August 14, 1947, had the unanimous support of the trustees and the Administrative Board. It was during the last year of Lower's life that Booz, Allen, and Hamilton gathered data for their report to the trustees. The idea of spending money for this sort of thing annoyed him, and Lower, the ever frugal and conservative founder, finally refused to talk with the management consultants.[6]

During these sessions everyone realized the need for an administrative head. A search started for such a person, and in October, Mr. Clarence M. Taylor, recently retired as executive vice president of Lincoln Electric Company, was invited to become executive director. He assumed the office on January 1, 1948, but spent the balance of 1948 acquainting himself with the Booz, Allen, and Hamilton report and the Clinic's operations. Sherwin continued to handle the duties and responsibilities of executive director until Taylor's arrival.

The new plan of organization and operation and the appointment of Taylor were announced at a special meeting of the staff on September 19, 1947.[7] Jones described the plan as the staff's "Magna

---

[6] Mrs. Janet Winters Getz, who at that time served as Dr. Lower's secretary, stated that he refused to allow their representatives on his floor or to permit any of the personnel on his corridor to talk with them. Yet the firm's report, when it finally came, was constructive. Although it was not accepted in full (the staff was opposed to the suggestion that there be a medical director), it paved the way for the development of a committee system. The death of Lower in June 1948 at the age of 80 years severed the last of the personal ties to the origins of the Clinic. The era of the founders had passed, and the Clinic was on its own.

[7] On September 19, 1947, the Executive Committee, in cooperation with the Administrative Board, made appointments of professional administrative officers: (1) Thomas E. Jones, chief of

Charta" and the new executive director as a "welder — formerly of metals, now of people." Both statements proved to be accurate. Although some staff members had misgivings, the plan was, on the whole, enthusiastically accepted. The plan provided that administration and policy were the responsibility of lay trustees and that the entire professional operation was the responsibility of a professional staff organization. It was then that Sherwin was elected president of the Clinic.

A member of the professional staff observed many years later that one of the most extraordinary events in the Clinic's history took place at that time.[8] Without salary or remuneration of any kind, the Executive Committee of the Board of Trustees, and Sherwin in particular, devoted many hours a week to meeting with representatives of the professional staff and with the management consultants. The issue was how to manage the Clinic. All of the board members were busy executives with full-time careers of their own. At that critical time they were not figurehead trustees. They shouldered the full responsibility of their office, bringing to it the organizational skills, the patience, and the understanding that characterize top-flight executives. To these men the Clinic owes an enormous debt of gratitude.[9]

At the time of Daoust's death in 1947, there was little harmony among the members of the staff and no organization in which the democratic process could function. The president had been empowered to conduct the Foundation's business affairs; each department head was an autocrat in charge of the professional policies of his own department, and the sometimes tumultuous sessions of the Administrative Board have already been described. The composition of the board was altered in 1947, when Ruedemann resigned from the staff, and in 1949, when Haden retired and Jones died. Jones fell dead in the surgeons' locker room of a ruptured aneurysm of the heart. Through these events, traumatic at the time, the climate

---

staff, surgery; (2) Russell L. Haden, chief of staff, medicine; (3) Irvine H. Page, director of research; and (4) Edwin P. Jordan, director of education. A professional policy committee was organized to "consult with, advise and make recommendations to the Board of Trustees or the Executive Committee on major professional policies regarding the operation and activities of the hospital and the clinical, research, and allied departments of the Foundation." The first membership of that committee consisted of Jones, Haden, Ernstene, Gardner, Page, and Jordan.

[8] Crile, Jr., recalled the trustee involvement in the reorganization of the Clinic in the late 1940s.

[9] The trustees became more active than they had been in Clinic affairs with a view to establishing rapport between themselves and the staff. The Executive Committee of the trustees and the Professional Policy Committee held frequent joint meetings. Subcommittees of trustees and staff members considered many of the problems involving property, facilities, research budgets, and the hospital. A fundamental feature of the new plan of organization was that policies were established by committees. For nine years this form of administration continued.

was improving for the development of a more democratic organization of the professional staff.

Sometimes aging renders leaders too rigid in outlook. Several persons remaining in key positions were in their sixties. In the early 1950s there was hardening of the lines of authority. One department chairman noted that it was impossible to run a department and, at the same time, win a popularity contest. Some of the younger members of the staff began to feel that there was no democratic process allowing them to register either protests or preferences. In those days, one of the ethical principles of the American Medical Association stated that "a physician should not dispose of his professional attainment or services to a hospital, body, or organization, group or individual by whatever name called or however organized under terms or conditions which permit exploitation of the physician for financial profit of the agency concerned." This historic principle made it unethical for any physician to permit a third party to intervene in the relationship between the doctor and his patient. Members of the staff were also members of the A.M.A., and some began to feel insecure under a plan of organization that seemed sometimes to infringe upon this ethical principle.[10]

With the purpose of investigating this and related problems, the trustees of the Clinic and the Professional Policy Committee met on October 13, 1954, at which time they appointed a Medical Survey Committee.[11] After several months of careful deliberation and consultation with every member of the staff, the Medical Survey Committee issued a report recommending changes in both administrative and professional affairs of the Foundation.[12]

---

[10] The complex relationships among the consumer, provider, and payer that now characterize American health care were only foreshadowed in the 1950s. In earlier times the ethics of the doctor-patient relationship were often cited in sharp criticism of the Clinic by competing or outside doctors, and amazingly (and anachronistically) this topic occasionally still emerges at meetings of the Board of Directors of the Academy of Medicine of Cleveland.

[11] The members of this committee were: Mr. Richard A. Gottron (Chairman), Drs. Robin Anderson, Victor G. deWolfe, C. Robert Hughes, Alfred W. Humphries, Fay A. LeFevre, Ausey H. Robnett, John F. Whitman, Walter J. Zeiter, and Mr. Clarence M. Taylor (ex officio).

[12] A quotation from the preamble of the report states that "The Cleveland Clinic Foundation is celebrating its 34th Anniversary this year (1954). Under the leadership of its four dynamic founders it pioneered in the practice of group medicine and laid the ground work which has brought it world renown. Many changes have taken place since the Clinic's founding days. Its physical plant has expanded immeasurably and is in the process of further expansion. From the original four men has grown a medical staff approaching 100. Instead of four successful rugged individualists, the staff now consists of 25 times that number, perhaps less successful, perhaps less rugged, but nonetheless individualist. In many organizations faced with the loss of the leaders who were their creators, a time for appraisal comes somewhere around the 30th year of their history. It is desirable to pause then for some serious thought as to whether the institution

The Medical Survey Committee suggested that many of the Clinic's problems could be solved if the trustees delegated certain responsibilities to an elected Board of Governors composed of members of the professional staff.[13] They recommended that a Planning Committee of trustees and staff be charged to study the administrative structure of the Clinic. The Board of Trustees accepted the recommendation.[14]

The Planning Committee met frequently during the summer of 1955, and as a result of its deliberations a new plan of organization was adopted by the Board of Trustees. The new organization provided that all professional matters pertaining to the practice of medicine be under the jurisdiction of a Board of Governors. Provision was made also to form elected committees within the divisions of medicine, surgery, and pathology.[15] These divisional committees

---

continues to carry on the ideals which made it great, and if so, whether it is doing only that or is actually continuing to aggressively meet the challenge of the future."

[13] The Medical Survey Committee identified administrative and medical practice issues they felt were critical to the continued success of the Clinic's development. The report recommended that:

- the government of The Cleveland Clinic Foundation must become more democratic, so that every member of the staff will feel a greater responsibility for the welfare of the institution and have a more definite stake in its future
- the legal status of the Clinic must be clarified
- the Clinic's research and educational programs must be reevaluated and strengthened where possible, since the professional eminence of the institution depends in large measure upon their accomplishments
- the financial well-being of the professional staff must be evaluated to determine whether or not it is adequate
- the Clinic should evaluate the medical needs of the area served, and modify its services to fit these needs
- the Clinic must make a vigorous effort to improve its relations with patients and with physicians both in local and outlying areas
- the Clinic must increase its efforts to keep the public informed about its services, facilities, and achievements
- patient care in the Cleveland Clinic Hospital must be improved.

[14] The Board of Trustees in consultation with the Professional Policy Committee recommended that the staff elect members of a Planning Committee, with three members from the Division of Medicine, three from the Division of Surgery, and one from the Division of Research. It was suggested also that members represent varied groups in terms of years of service and include some of the younger men. Those elected were Drs. A. Carlton Ernstene, Fay A. LeFevre, Robert D. Mercer, Robin Anderson, John B. Hazard, W. James Gardner and A. C. Corcoran, with five alternates, namely: Drs. Harold R. Rossmiller, Arthur L. Scherbel, William J. Engel, Stanley O. Hoerr, and Irvine H. Page. The trustee membership consisted of the Executive Committee of the Board of Trustees. Donald H. McLean, Jr., an advisor of John D. Rockefeller, III, was appointed to the Board of Trustees and made chairman of the Planning Committee. Richard A. Gottron served as secretary.

[15] The plan also proposed formation of committees for research, the hospital, properties, education and planning. The committees would be composed of trustees and members of the professional staff.

were to manage the professional affairs within their respective domains under the authority of a Board of Governors.[16] The proposed plan delegated responsibility for medical practice to a Board of Governors to be composed of seven members of the professional staff.[17] These were to be elected by the staff for staggered terms of five years. To prevent self-perpetuation, no member would be eligible for re-election for one year after expiration of the term. To prevent election of members of the board by cliques, an indirect method would be employed. Each year a Nominating Committee would be elected by the staff. After deliberation this committee would nominate a member of the staff to fill each vacancy. The entire staff would then vote on the nominees, and if 60 percent approved each candidate, he or she would be elected.[18] Only twice in the years since this system was introduced has the staff failed to support the nominating committee's candidates.

Since the Division of Research was supported by endowment funds, earnings of the Clinic, and outside grants, its administrative problems were to be the responsibility of the Board of Trustees. For this purpose the Committee on Research Policy and Administration

---

[16] During the early deliberations of the Planning Committee, it became quite clear that there were certain ancillary professional services that could not be separated from professional responsibility. These areas included the following: central appointment desk, routing desk (including information and patient registration), professional service personnel (including clinic nurses, medical secretaries, and desk receptionists), records and statistics, telephone operators, and patient relations.

The work of the Planning Committee was greatly facilitated by a study of the structure and operation of the Mayo Clinic, in which a board of governors had been the responsible body of government since 1919. From this study, with due regard for the differences that existed between the two clinics, a plan of organization was developed and adapted to the corporate structure of the Cleveland Clinic.

[17] The Board of Governors was given authority to select and appoint new members of the staff, but the setting of the salaries of these and all other members of the staff remained a function of the Compensation Committee of the Board of Trustees. To aid this committee in evaluating the performance of each member of the staff, the Board of Governors was authorized to discuss each member and rate his or her performance, not in respect to the number of patients seen or money earned, but in respect to his scientific and other achievements, so that, in effect, the performance of each staff member would be judged by peers.

[18] In the professional area an effort was made to diminish the authority of the chiefs and to encourage individual initiative. Thus, the Chiefs of Medicine and Surgery, who previously had absolute authority in their divisions, became chairman respectively of the Medical and the Surgical Committees that were elected annually by the members of their respective divisions. These chairmen were appointed by the Board of Governors for a period of a year, but almost without exception the appointments were renewed annually. Short of illness or mismanagement, the divisional chairmen had what amounted to tenure in their offices. Yet they did not have total control, for they had no authority to act completely independently of their committees. They could be out-voted. Moreover, the actions of the committees were subject to review by the Board of Governors. This afforded protection to the individual staff member from capricious or unfair treatment by the chiefs.

was established. A Research Projects Committee, appointed by the Board of Governors from the members of the Division of Research and from members of the clinical divisions who had special knowledge or interest in research problems, was put in control of all research projects undertaken by members of the clinical divisions. The long-range program of research, devoted largely to the study of hypertension and arteriosclerosis, remained under the control of the Director of Research, Dr. Irvine H. Page, who reported only to the Board of Trustees.[19]

As a memorial to Bunts, an educational foundation was established and named for him some years after his death.[20] The same Board of Trustees that directed The Cleveland Clinic Foundation also directed the Cleveland Clinic Educational Foundation. The original endowments and also the profits of the Cleveland Clinic Pharmacy (incorporated as a taxable, profit-making company) supported the Educational Foundation.

The report of the Planning Committee was a significant document that addressed many issues and had far-reaching consequences. The months of effort in 1955 were rewarded by a truly new system of governance for the Foundation. At a meeting of the professional staff it was unanimously recommended that the professional members of the Planning Committee nominate the first Board of Governors.[21]

---

[19] In 1969 the Division of Research was brought under the control of the Board of Governors.

[20] The Bunts Fund, established shortly after Bunts's death in 1928, was changed to an education fund in 1935 at the time the Educational Foundation was created.

[21] The names of the nominees were sent to the staff for approval and, thus was created the first Board of Governors, composed of Drs. Fay A. LeFevre (chairman), William J. Engel (vice chairman), George Crile, Jr., A. Carlton Ernstene, W. James Gardner, E. Perry McCullagh, and Irvine H. Page. Dr. Walter J. Zeiter was elected executive secretary, and Mrs. Janet Winters Getz was elected recording secretary. The first meeting was held on Thursday, December 8, 1955, at 12:15 p.m. in the Board Room of the Main Clinic Building. In attendance by invitation were Richard A. Gottron, business manager of the Foundation, and James G. Harding, director of the Hospital. Thus began a new era.

Section II

The Board of Governors Era

SIX

THE LEFEVRE YEARS
1955-1968

*The physician must have at his command a certain
ready wit, as dourness is repulsive both to the
healthy and the sick.*

— Hippocrates, about 400 B.C.

Little did the group of physicians who first met as governors in December 1955 realize the magnitude of the responsibilities they would come to assume and the importance of the decisions they and future Boards of Governors would make. Nor, obviously, did LeFevre know that he would serve as chairman for the next 13 exciting and formative years. Following months of discussion and deliberation the Planning Committee had recommended, and the Board of Trustees had approved, the policy that delegates responsibility for all professional matters to the Board of Governors.

Fay A. LeFevre, M.D., became the first chairman of the Board of Governors on December 7, 1955, just four months before his 51st birthday. A lifelong Clevelander and son of a physician, LeFevre was a graduate of Cleveland Heights High School, the University of Michigan, and the Western Reserve University School of Medicine. His postgraduate training included an internship at St. Luke's Hospital and further training in cardiovascular disease at The Cleveland Clinic. After a few years of private practice, he joined the Clinic's staff in 1942, and in 1947 he founded the Department of Peripheral Vascular Disease, now the Department of Vascular Medicine. In addition to chairing that department for eight years, he served a four-year stint as the Clinic's Director of Education begin-

Fay A. LeFevre, M.D., Chairman, Board of Governors, 1955–1968

ning in 1952. LeFevre's gentlemanly demeanor, impeccable integrity, and reputation as an outstanding physician made him the ideal
choice for the chairmanship of the new board.

Besides LeFevre, the first Board of Governors consisted of W.
James Gardner, M.D. (neurosurgeon), William J. Engel, M.D. (urologist), George Crile, Jr., M.D. (general surgeon), E. Perry McCullagh,
M.D. (endocrinologist), A. Carlton Ernstene, M.D. (cardiologist),
and Irvine H. Page, M.D. (research). It was their responsibility to
plan and coordinate all professional activities. Among their most
important duties were the appointment, promotion, and termina-
tion of members of the professional staff. With the growth of the
institution this became increasingly crucial and difficult. Members
of the Board also reviewed criticisms and complaints concerning
relationships with patients and initiated corrective measures. In
addition it was their responsibility to review and establish fees for
professional services and to review at regular intervals the financial
results of professional activities. As the Clinic expanded, planning
and policy-making were tasks that took increasing amounts of time.
The success of these efforts required the cooperation and collaboration of trustees and governors.

LeFevre had for many years served as a director of the
Chesapeake and Ohio Railroad and was knowledgeable in business

Board of Governors, 1956, Left to right: Drs. W. James Gardner, E. Perry McCullagh, Walter J. Zeiter (Executive Secretary), Irvine H. Page, Fay A. LeFevre (Chairman), George Crile, Jr., A. Carlton Ernstene, William J. Engel

and finance. Although he was chairman of the Board of Governors he wished to continue the part-time practice of medicine. He believed that by keeping in touch with his medical practice roots he would be in a better position to understand issues and problems associated with them. For some time LeFevre was able to do this, and he found it both satisfying and stimulating. "It was also a great protective mechanism for me," he said. "When things got 'too hot' in the first floor administrative offices, Janet Getz would call me and say that my patients were ready on the third floor. This gave me an ideal opportunity to excuse myself. Likewise, when some patients became too longwinded, I could politely say that an urgent problem had occurred in the administrative office that would require my immediate attention. This best of two worlds did not last long, however, for it was necessary to spend more and more time in the administrative office."

In the early years some of the trustees thought that the administration of medical affairs by the Board of Governors would not succeed. The responsibility for professional affairs had been delegated to a professional group, and business affairs were under the direction of a business manager. The weakness in this arrangement was that no one person or group had the final authority to make a major decision when professional and business issues were both involved.

Throughout this era the trustees kept a tight rein on the management of the Clinic by placing their representatives in key author-

Aerial view of The Cleveland Clinic Foundation, 1968

itative roles — those of business manager and hospital administrator. Nonetheless, the Board of Governors had plenty to do. There were pressures to provide new facilities, to expand existing services, and to subspecialize clinical practice to meet both the demands of patients and the opportunities of practice. These pressures led to the growth of the professional staff and ultimately to the need to acquire property and build new facilities. The impetus for these changes (growth and increasing numbers of patients) lay with the professional staff, but it was for the Board of Governors to interpret and present the needs of patients and staff so that the trustees could understand and respond.

Between 1956 and 1968, the trustees were ably led first by John Sherwin and then by George Karch. James A. Hughes became chairman in 1969 and, except for the period when Arthur S. Holden, Jr., served in that post (1973 - 1974), continued his leadership through 1984. The first members of the professional staff to serve on the Board of Trustees were Drs. W. James Gardner, Fay A. LeFevre, and Irvine H. Page, and since 1956, members of the staff have always been included in that body. This representation quickened the tempo of decision making and the rudimentary planning process of that time, but decision making was still not easy. Investment in new property, buildings, and equipment led to increased amounts of work and therefore to increases in revenues, staff, and the total number of employees. The Board of Governors looked to the trustees for authorization of its plans and allocation of the money necessary to fund them. The money for all these expansion projects was in hand. There was no debt financing, and funds set aside from operational revenues were adequate for payment in full. Long-term financial obligations would not be incurred until a later era.

Several construction projects undertaken during LeFevre's administration laid to rest a nagging issue for the Clinic, *i.e.*, whether or not to abandon the inner city location of the Clinic and move the entire operation into or even beyond the eastern suburbs of Cleveland. A bequest from Martha Holden Jennings financed the Education Building, and that was followed by additions to the Clinic and Hospital buildings and by the construction of a hotel (now called the P Building) to lodge out-of-town patients and their families. Parking garages were built, and the trustees authorized the acquisition of real estate adjoining the Clinic to allow for future expansion. The die was cast: the Clinic would remain in the city.

The Board of Governors made a decision in December 1965 that was to have an impact far beyond what they imagined. This was the decision to close the obstetrical service, which then occupied the south wing of the hospital's sixth floor. Behind this move was a steadily mounting pressure for space and facilities for cardiac surgery. Something had to give, and a declining national birth rate and low obstetrics unit occupancy eased the decision. The winner of the institutional support sweepstakes was the heart disease program.

Obstetrical services in American hospitals, as decreed by the Joint Commission on Accreditation of Hospitals, must be isolated from the rest of the hospital. Therefore, delivery rooms, newborn nurseries, and the rooms for mothers were separated from rooms for medical and surgical patients and the general operating rooms of The Cleveland Clinic. The Department of Thoracic and Cardiovascular Surgery moved their inpatient functions into this area, thereby consolidating the operating rooms, recovery room, intensive care unit, and convalescent wards into what would become the most productive and renowned department in the Division of Surgery.

During the LeFevre era, two sets of issues generated conflict in matters of governance and authority. Conflict was inevitable because Mr. Richard A. Gottron, the business manager of the Clinic, and Mr. James G. Harding, the administrator of the Hospital, reported to the Board of Trustees and not to the Board of Governors or its chairman. Sitting *ex officio* with the Board of Governors was helpful to Gottron and Harding in the exercise of their duties and provided them the opportunity to be sympathetic with the wishes and the ideas of the governors, but their sympathy could not have been expected to endure, and it didn't.

The main issue was institutional growth and its capital cost. The trustees were anxious that the ambitions of the staff might launch the institution on a breakneck pace of development in which the prudence of businesslike standards could easily be cast aside. Gottron nourished that fear, and his pessimism respecting the growth of the Foundation irreconcilably alienated him from the governors by the summer of 1968.[1]

The second and more subtle issue had to do with management, authority, and control in what by then had become a large enterprise. By 1968 it had been nearly thirteen years since the first meeting of the Board of Governors, and that body had successfully faced matters of policy, planning, and professional practice. Under LeFevre's leadership, the governors had worked together and had discovered that they represented the strength of the professional staff. Governance of the organization was beginning to take on a new meaning. The governors could not take the next step, however, without the willingness of the trustees to recognize them as a responsible body and to delegate the operations of the Clinic and the Hospital to them. Dialogue between trustees and governors in the summer of 1968 led to that next step. Mr. James H. Nichols replaced Gottron as business manager, and both he and Harding were directed to report to the chairman of the Board of Governors.[2] LeFevre, who was ready to retire, would be succeeded by a chairman who was destined to function like a chief executive officer of a large corporation.

---

[1] Gottron was ill at this time, seriously suffering from an unrecognized depression.

[2] Gottron, when replaced by Nichols, was given the job of president of the Bolton Square Hotel Company, a subsidiary operation of the Clinic. Not long thereafter he took his own life.

SEVEN

The Wasmuth Years
1969-1976

More history's made by secret handshakes than by battles, bills, and proclamations.

—John Barth, 1960

Carl E. Wasmuth, Jr., M.D., LL.B., became the second chairman of the Board of Governors on January 2, 1969, about six weeks before his 50th birthday. A native of Pennsylvania, he had received his undergraduate and medical degrees from the University of Pittsburgh and interned at Western Pennsylvania Hospital (Pittsburgh), followed by nine years of private practice. He then completed a fellowship in anesthesiology at The Cleveland Clinic and joined the staff in 1951. Wasmuth obtained his LL.B. degree, on his own initiative and at his own expense, from the Cleveland-Marshall Law School in 1959 and taught there until 1974. He became chairman of the Department of Anesthesiology in 1967, a post he held until he was appointed chairman of the Board of Governors. He was elected president of the American Society of Anesthesiologists in 1968.

Wasmuth's chairmanship was the outgrowth of a struggle between the non-physician administration (led by Gottron), who wanted to constrain the organization's growth, and the medical staff, who wanted the Clinic to grow. Although he was never elected to the Board of Governors, Wasmuth was chosen to lead the staff because he was viewed as the toughest proponent of the staff's viewpoint. His law degree lent credibility to this perception. In a secret meeting at Cleveland's Union Club, from which LeFevre was excluded, a small

Carl E. Wasmuth, M.D.,LL.B., Chairman, Board of Governors, 1969–1976

group of Clinic leaders made the decision to put the administrative functions of the organization, which had previously reported to the trustees, under the Board of Governors. Subsequently, the Board of Governors selected Wasmuth to replace LeFevre and put the Clinic on a new, centrally directed course with true physician leadership.[1]

The Cleveland Clinic's modern era began with Wasmuth's chairmanship of the Board of Governors. He was the Clinic's first genuine physician manager, and the tasks he addressed in this role were similar to those faced by executives in industry, government, or education. In his first year as chairman he was confronted by a formidable workload, compounded by the fact that there was no one else in the organization to whom he felt comfortable delegating authority.[2] Early in his administration both Nichols and Harding,

---

[1] According to the recollections of Dr. Ralph Straffon and Dr. Thomas Meaney, those present at the meeting were Mr. James Hughes, Mr. John Sherwin, Mr. George E. Enos, Dr. Meaney, and Dr. Straffon. Gottron was removed as business manager and placed in charge of subsidiaries, as noted in the previous chapter. Nichols remained as secretary, taking over Gottron's managerial functions. Harding, Gottron, and Nichols were to report to the Board of Governors.

[2] There was no other physician administrator. Wasmuth recalled that he relied heavily on Messrs. James E. Lees, Robert J. Fischer, and Paul E. Widman when he became chairman. However, Wasmuth reserved ultimate administrative control for himself. Lees functioned as an executive assistant, Widman as director of operations, and Fischer as treasurer.

the most seasoned professional managers in the administration, resigned. The governors were clinicians with little managerial experience. Wasmuth, therefore, assumed a degree of personal authority unknown since the early days, when the founders themselves had provided day-to-day direction. He considered it essential that he devote full time to his office; therefore, he gave up clinical practice as well as his post as head of the Department of Anesthesiology.

As early as 1968 it was clear that the scope of the chairman's responsibility had become too broad. The Board of Governors was in charge not only of all professional matters but also of operations and could not be conversant with all the necessary details.[3] Moreover, the Board of Trustees required increasing amounts of time and attention, as did a vast array of public interests. Wasmuth assumed this burden with energy and enthusiasm, but he, the trustees, and the governors realized the need for an "understudy." A search committee identified Dr. William S. Kiser, a urologist who was serving on the Board of Governors, to fill the role of Wasmuth's assistant. Like Wasmuth, Kiser gave up his clinical practice, a decision that was difficult for many staff members to understand. However, the professional staff was determined to have a strong voice in the direction of the institution, and this sacrifice was seen as necessary. Kiser enrolled in the Advanced Management Program at Harvard University, where he became the second physician to complete that course. In due time he was named vice chairman of the Board of Governors and placed in charge of operations.

During the LeFevre years, the west wing of the hospital had been added. Soon after it opened, however, it became clear that escalating patient demand would require more beds before long. Plans for the south hospital addition and a new research building were developed. It was also necessary to build a hotel and two parking garages. Financing the new development was one of Wasmuth's most important priorities.

The Clinic's traditional "cash on the barrelhead" method of financing capital projects was no longer tenable. The costs were too high, and the Clinic's ongoing operations and routine capital needs required most of the available cash. Therefore, Wasmuth proposed the use of long-term borrowing from local banks to pay the construction costs that could not be supported by current operations. This was the first use of debt financing by The Cleveland Clinic.

---

[3] The key administrative team that kept the Clinic running smoothly and tended to the details in those early years of the Wasmuth era consisted of John A. Auble, general counsel, and Gerald E. Wolf, controller, as well as Fischer, Lees, and Widman. Neither Wasmuth nor any other chairman could have functioned without them.

Nonetheless, significant commitments of operating funds for these projects in the early 1970s severely restricted cash flow, and money for routine needs was limited. To make matters worse, the federal government imposed price and wage controls at that time. The staff began to grumble. General paranoia was exacerbated by the fact that cost containment methods were carried to ridiculous lengths, for example, eliminating pens and removing sanitary napkin dispensers from the women's rest rooms. The bitter aftertaste of these ineffective, petty measures dissipated slowly. Yet, throughout the 1970s the Clinic thrived, largely because of the expansion that had increased the capacity to provide patient care. Although the cash squeeze produced by those projects was stressful, the organization's leadership learned important lessons that they would eventually apply to the more grandiose building programs of the 1980s. Few would now deny that Wasmuth deserves plaudits for launching the expansion of the 1970s and for persuading the governors and trustees that all available real estate adjacent to the Clinic should be acquired. He clearly foresaw the Clinic's position as the national and international health resource that it eventually became.

As the Clinic purchased land and razed the deteriorated buildings on its new property, its presence became increasingly conspicuous. These activities began to be viewed by some detractors not as neighborhood improvements but rather as evidence of the Clinic's voracious appetite for growth. To put it bluntly, the Clinic was developing a predatory image. As the Clinic became more dependent on public goodwill to permit new projects and methods of financing growth, the days when it could remain aloof and ignore the public's perceptions and feelings about its actions were over. During the Wasmuth years there was more adverse public feeling against the Clinic than at any previous time.

During Wasmuth's administration the Clinic became involved in two public arenas: (a) social responsibility and (b) city politics. The organization had little or no experience shaping opinions held by such diverse groups as the neighborhood, underserved minorities,[4] the professional community, health care planning agencies,

---

[4] The Cleveland Clinic Foundation gave one million dollars in aid and assistance to the Forest City Hospital, a hospital struggling to remain operational as a provider of care to many of the urban poor. This hospital later closed its doors. The Collinwood Eldercare Center was partly supported and staffed by the Clinic, and in cooperation with the Cuyahoga County Hospital System the Clinic helped to establish and maintain the Kenneth Clement Family Care Center. A neighborhood revitalization effort, the Fairfax Foundation (now the Fairfax Renaissance Development Corporation), received both financial aid and operational assistance from the Clinic.

payers, and local politicians. And yet the resolution of issues such as zoning changes and neighborhood use variances, the building of viaducts over city streets, street closures, and the addition of costly technology and hospital beds[5] were all increasingly dependent upon the attitudes and opinions held by these constituencies.

To complicate matters further, Clinic leaders approached community issues naively, with no public relations policies or expertise, and in some cases with careless disregard of legal nuances. In 1976 a committee of governors and trustees chaired by Hughes conducted a confidential inquiry into these matters. The courts eventually had to address some particularly blatant improprieties. The most visible outcome of this inquiry was a change in the Clinic's leadership. The trustees, general counsel's office, and governors worked well together in this effort to preserve the integrity of the Clinic.

By 1974 the staff was becoming restless. They felt the Board of Governors had become increasingly estranged from their concerns. This apparent alienation was symbolized by the removal of Wasmuth's office and the board room from the first floor of the Main Clinic Building to the new south wing of the hospital. Nearly all the staff had walked by his office door many times a day for several years, and the remoteness of the new, well-furnished location seemed to represent an aloofness.[6]

The staff was far larger than it had been in the 1950s and early 1960s, and the issues that faced the governing boards did indeed eclipse some of the professional and personal matters that the staff felt should be addressed by the governors. The governors met only once a week, and Wasmuth did not have time for these concerns. Therefore, the Board of Governors appointed Dr. Leonard L. Lovshin, chairman of the Department of Internal Medicine and a former governor, to function as mediator and liaison to the professional staff. He was given the title of Director of Professional Affairs. Lovshin's amiability, popularity, and seniority were assets, but the job was not designed to allow the director to influence policymaking and decisions at the highest level. Recognizing this, the governors eventually took another step to augment the administrative

---

[5] A conflict with the local health planning agency, then called the Metropolitan Health Planning Corporation, took place over the issue of the Clinic's need to add 173 hospital beds in the new South Hospital. Although the Clinic prevailed, it was an unpleasant experience and attracted unfavorable public notice.

[6] Perhaps a more appropriate symbolism for this move was the shift in emphasis from the outpatient clinic to the hospital, which was assuming the financially dominant role in the Clinic's operations.

staff that Wasmuth sorely needed by appointing one of their own to be Vice Chairman for Professional Affairs.

The person they selected to fill this role was Dr. Shattuck W. Hartwell, Jr., a plastic surgeon, member of the Board of Governors, and member of the Board of Trustees. Hartwell and Lovshin worked together through the Wasmuth years and into the Kiser era, when Lovshin retired. By that time the Office of Professional Affairs had evolved into a full-time extension of the Board of Governors, assisting the professional divisions in matters of staffing, recruitment, benefits, policy, and dispute resolution. In time, the title of Vice Chairman of the Board of Governors would be reserved for the chief operating officer, and the title of Vice Chairman for Professional Affairs would become Director, Professional Staff Affairs. Nonetheless, the physician manager emerged as a specialist and an essential player in the governance of the Clinic during the Wasmuth years. We shall see how in the Kiser era the position of physician manager became even more important.

Wasmuth and his board recognized the need for specialists in management. The legal and financial offices were ably staffed, but personnel matters were not administered in ways that were up-to-date for an organization that by then numbered 3,500 employees. The institution had grown too rapidly for existing systems to keep pace, and the modern practice of personnel management required an experienced expert. Mr. Douglas A. Saarel was such a person, and he served as director of Human Resources from 1974 to 1977. Saarel had a great influence on personnel practices at the Clinic, and his imprint persisted long after his departure.

EIGHT

THE KISER YEARS
1977-1989

*A decision is an action an executive must take when
he has information so incomplete that the answer
does not suggest itself.*
— *Arthur William Radford, 1957*

William S. Kiser, M.D., officially became the third chairman of
The Cleveland Clinic's Board of Governors in January 1977, just
before his 49th birthday. A native of West Virginia, Kiser had
received his undergraduate and medical degrees and postgraduate
training as a urologist from the University of Maryland. He had
served in the United States Air Force from 1954 to 1957 with tours
of duty in Texas, Morocco, and Germany, receiving Commendation
Medals in 1956 and 1957. After completing his residency in 1961, he
had joined the Surgery Branch of the National Cancer Institute in
Bethesda, Maryland, where he had held the positions of senior
investigator and staff urologist. He had remained at the National
Institutes of Health until he was recruited to join The Cleveland
Clinic's Department of Urology in 1964 by chairman Ralph Straffon,
who wished to add a research dimension to the department.

Kiser's unique (for the time) background, his bright, enthusiastic personality and personal warmth, and his clinical skill made him
a popular addition to the staff. His election to the Board of
Governors in 1972 set him on a course that led to his selection by
Wasmuth for ultimate succession to the chairmanship, through a
search process concluded in 1974 (see chapter 7). Although he was
thrust into this role somewhat prematurely and unexpectedly, he

William S. Kiser, M.D., Chairman of the Board of Governors, 1977–1989

rose to the occasion and eventually left his own indelible mark on the Clinic's developmental history.

The Cleveland Clinic's modern period of physician governance had begun with Wasmuth. When Kiser succeeded Wasmuth as chairman, the Board of Governors had been in existence for 20 years. Governance of the Clinic had been evolving over that period of time, and the purview of the board now included a number of new responsibilities, such as policy development, fiscal responsibility, long-range planning, and day-to-day operations. Under Kiser's leadership these management functions would be increasingly systematized in line with his belief that a corporate model of management should replace the traditional scientific model with which physicians were comfortable.

By 1982, the day-to-day operation of the institution required the cooperative input of the division chairmen, whose managerial role was now better defined. This cooperation was formalized by the creation of a committee of the division chairmen called the Management Group. The Management Group reported to the Board of Governors through its chairman, Dr. John J. Eversman. Eversman, an endocrinologist, became the first chief operating officer of the Clinic and a vice chairman of the Board of Governors. He was well

John J. Eversman, M.D., Chief Operating Officer, 1982–1989

suited to these tasks by virtue of his intelligence and additional education, having been the first member of the staff sent by the Clinic to complete an executive M.B.A. program. Kiser, Eversman, and Hartwell were members of the Board of Trustees and its Executive Committee by virtue of their positions.

Differences between Wasmuth and Kiser may be partly due to the way each perceived himself as a chief executive: where Wasmuth had concentrated authority centrally, Kiser encouraged decentralization of operating responsibility among a group of physician managers (the division chairmen) and lay administrators. These managers were accountable, through the chief operating officer, to the Board of Governors (the policy makers).[1] The Board of Trustees

---

[1]The distinction between policymaking and the implementation of policy has been an important development. It has happened because there has been a conscious effort by institutional leaders to define carefully what the responsibilities are for all groups and individuals and to place accountability appropriately. This has not been easy to do. Doctors are trained in their formative years not only to decide for themselves what is the right thing to do (policy) but to involve themselves in doing it (operations). Training programs have been established for the Clinic doctors, not to undo their dynamic approach to patient care but rather to add to their abilities in managerial skills. These programs have been very popular.

held the chairman of the Board of Governors responsible for the operational management of the Clinic.

With the delegation of operational responsibility to the divisions and the departments, decentralization meant that preparation of the annual budget would require input from the department and division chairmen. Inexperience made this problematic at first, but by 1979 budgeting had become a more manageable process for the chairmen, many of whom by then had dedicated administrators. The divisions and departments became responsible for other managerial functions, although there was still a strong egalitarian culture within the staff that made it difficult for the chairmen to be true managers. It seems almost quaint today to review the language of the previous edition of this book, which stated, "Large organizations tend naturally to be hierarchical. The titles of department chairman and division chairman indicate responsibilities and influence, but they are not autocratic; this would not be tolerated by the staff."

Beginning in 1975 the relationship of the staff to the Board of Governors was formalized in a process known as the Annual Professional Review. This relationship was linked to an annual appraisal of the professional departments and of each member within the departments.[2] The reviews, organized by the Office of Professional Staff Affairs, are conducted throughout the year and provide the doctors an opportunity to discuss their accomplishments, plans, career goals, and departmental issues with representatives of the Board of Governors and divisional leaders. More than anything else the Annual Professional Review keeps the division chairmen and the Board of Governors in touch with the staff and is a potent check on the performance of departmental leadership. The Compensation Committee of the Board of Trustees is apprised of the annual reviews. The reviews, begun in a rudimentary form during Wasmuth's tenure, matured under Kiser and Hartwell and have become a well-established and accepted part of professional life at the Clinic.

Hartwell, always curious and innovative, left the Office of Professional Staff Affairs in 1986 to form the Page Center for Creative Thinking in Medicine. After an exhaustive search process he was succeeded as chief in 1987 by Dr. Ralph Straffon, who also

---

[2] The Compensation Committee of the Board of Trustees is regularly informed about the Annual Professional Review of the staff. Since 1975 trustees have been advised by the consulting firm of Towers, Perrin, Forster and Crosby, specialists in executive compensation programs. The reviews and the consultants' reports have been key elements in the salary program for the staff and key administrative personnel. Better organized and administered than in the past, the review of salaries and benefits is one of the most important activities of the trustees.

received the new title of Chief of Staff. Straffon had been chairman of the Department of Urology and later of the Division of Surgery. He was one of the most highly respected and well known members of the professional staff. He further strengthened the Annual Professional Review process and computerized the Office of Professional Staff Affairs. In addition, he modernized the staff recruiting process and developed new policies governing the professional staff. Notable among these were redefinition of the category of assistant staff and adoption of the requirement that all members of the full staff be board-certified in their (sub)specialties.

One of the important new features of the Clinic's management under Kiser was an attempt to begin an organized long-range planning process in 1979. This was to be a cooperative effort of the Board of Trustees and the Board of Governors. It was necessitated by increasing demand for services, proliferating technology, and staff growth, all leading to crowding of the facilities. The Minneapolis consulting firm Hamilton and Associates worked with the staff and governing groups for two years to develop the Clinic's Master Plan. Although this plan was flawed and many details were never implemented, it spawned the most ambitious facilities expansion program the Clinic had ever seen — the Century Project — described below.

Concurrent with the planning effort, studies were carried out to determine the best way to finance the growth of the Clinic. Robert Fischer, treasurer of the Foundation, and Gerald E. Wolf, controller, were responsible for financial forecasting, a risky business at best. They correctly predicted that an enormous amount of money would be needed over the next ten years to expand the Clinic. The unfortunate experiences of the mid-1970s, when major capital expansion had been funded from operating revenues, suggested that alternative financing methods should be sought. It was eventually concluded that long-term bonds issued by the county would be the method of choice. The Board of Trustees authorized a bond sale to raise $228,000,000, and in June 1982, all the bonds were quickly sold. This was the largest private financing project in the history of American health care to date.

Kiser also established offices of public affairs, development, archives, staff benefits, and long-range planning. Wasmuth had been farsighted enough to see the value of a full-time architect, planner, and an internal auditor, and he had filled these positions. Kiser advanced the idea that a support staff of administrative specialists was essential to the continuing development of the Clinic.

Kiser recognized early on that times were changing for health care and, hence, for medical practice. Although he initially clung to

The Crile Building viewed from the mall; in the foreground, Dennis Jones's sculpture "Three for One", a gift from the family of Thomas Vail, trustee

his modified idea of the Clinic's mission, *i.e.* "...better care of the sick *through specialty care*, research, and education,..." he knew that an ongoing planning process would be critical and that the institution would have to be prepared to change to meet the new environment. In 1980, Frank J. Weaver became the Clinic's first director of Public Affairs and Corporate Development, now known as the Divisions of Marketing and Managed Care and of Health Affairs. After Weaver's arrival, the rhetoric changed as well.

Weaver was a professional health care marketer from Texas. Everything about him was big, including his physical size, intellect, capacity for work, and appetites. He cut a natty figure with his boisterous (usually jovial) demeanor, flamboyant clothes, and boutonniere. Weaver had a clearer vision of what lay in store for health care than anyone else at the Clinic, and during his nine-year tenure with the organization, he imprinted many innovative concepts and ideas which have only recently begun to be appreciated and, in some cases, implemented. He had Kiser's confidence, and for his first years at the Clinic, much of what Kiser said reflected Weaver's thinking.[3]

During the early 1980s Kiser made some prophetic pronouncements about health care in his "State of the Clinic" addresses, which

---

[3] Weaver left the Clinic in 1989 to join Dallas Medical Resource, where he assembled a nine-hospital network to work with self-insured companies in north Texas to provide medical care for their employees. Tragically, he died unexpectedly at the age of 49 on June 16, 1995, in Boston, where he was to have addressed a medical conference.

were traditionally delivered at the second or third staff meeting of each year. In his 1982 speech, for example, he said:

"... [N]o single institution can remain an 'island unto itself' in these times. We must seriously consider a departure from the past by developing a strategy for alliance with other groups of physicians and with other health care institutions. We can no longer stand in splendid isolation hoping that patients will come for our attention.

"In the last month Dr. James Krieger *(chairman, Division of Surgery)*, Mr. Dick Taylor *(public relations)*, and Mr. Bill Frazier *(head of planning)* visited the 15 major group practices in Ohio and Indiana. The observations which they made on location at the various clinics in our region were sobering:

- Referrals of patients more frequently go to other local hospitals because of comparable care and easier access.
- Cleveland Clinic postgraduate courses are no longer a strong attraction to referring physicians due to excessive numbers of CME courses throughout the country — more than 15,000 in 1980!
- Local and university hospitals are actively 'courting' each group for referrals, using incentives the Clinic has used for many years (CME, circuit riding consultants, timely reporting, etc.)
- Larger groups are developing their own specialty staff.
- Increasing difficulty communicating with individual Clinic staff members and . . . problems with patient access to our system.

"The conclusions from this survey are that The Cleveland Clinic can no longer count on the reputation of the institution or of its staff to ensure flow of patients in the future. We must formalize relationships with referring doctors or with multi-institutional systems to insure access to patient populations of sufficient size to maintain the economic viability of the Foundation in the future."

During Kiser's tenure as chairman of the Board of Governors and executive vice president of the Foundation, three major projects which were to change the shape of the organization radically were undertaken. These were (a) the Century Project, (b) the establishment of Cleveland Clinic Florida, and (c) the Economic Improvement Program. Each of these projects warrants some additional discussion.

The Century Project was a building program that grew out of the long-range planning activities referred to previously. Although the Century Project was designed to accommodate the projected growth of the organization through the turn of the century, it was so

Main entrance, showing 1985 Hospital addition, the "G Wing"

named because an important feature of it was the construction of a spectacular new outpatient facility on East 100th Street. The major components of the Century Project as outlined in the Master Plan of 1980 were (a) the East 100th Street outpatient facility (initially called the A Building, but later dedicated as the Crile Building), (b) the enclosed pedestrian walkway from the hospital to the A Building, now known as the Skyway, (c) the southeast wings of the hospital (F and G wings), and (d) the Carnegie Avenue parking garage.

The A Building, designed by award-winning architect Cesar Pelli, opened in September 1985 with an outdoor extravaganza choreographed by Weaver, including speeches by Clinic officials, Speaker of the Ohio State House of Representatives Vernal Riffe, and a congeries of local dignitaries. Members of the Cleveland Orchestra provided ruffles and flourishes, and they had, fortunately, left by the time a gust of wind blew down their platform. A high point of the program was the introduction of the newly appointed chairwoman of the Division of Research, Bernadine P. Healy, M.D. Dr. Healy was the first woman appointed to a Cleveland Clinic division chair. The new building had more than 520,000 square feet of space designed for efficiency by the projected occupants.

The formidable task of moving the outpatient practices of 70 percent of the staff to the A Building was carried out in just four weekends with no interruption of service. The move included the Departments of Allergy, Otolaryngology, Dermatology, Plastic Surgery, Endocrino-logy, Hypertension and Nephrology, Urology, Internal Medicine, Pediatrics, Pulmonary Disease, Rheumatic Disease, Orthopedics, Colorectal Surgery, General Surgery, Gynecology, and Ophthalmology. The "stay-behind" departments included Neurology, Neurosurgery, Cardiology, Thoracic and Cardiovascular Surgery, Vascular Medicine, Vascular Surgery, Primary Care, Gastroenterology, and Infectious Disease. An attempt was made to keep sister services together. Although some shifting of locations has occurred, most departments have remained in their 1985 locations, and the whole design has functioned quite efficiently.

The Skyway opened at the same time as the A Building. Originally envisioned merely as an environmentally protected, quarter-mile connecting link between the hospital, the new outpatient facilities, and the new garage, it has turned into a meeting ground for all who work at the Clinic. Nearly everyone at the Clinic traverses the Skyway at least once a day, and it is nearly impossible to get from one end to the other without encountering someone with whom some item of business needs to be transacted. Many "curbstone consultations" are conducted on the Skyway, and patient care is the beneficiary.[4] The Skyway has also become the preferred site for numerous events, including the poster sessions for Research Day, the Senior Health Day, and many of the events of the annual Martin Luther King, Jr., Celebration of Diversity. It is truly one of the major focal points for life at the Clinic.

About three months after the opening of the A Building, with its associated 1,500-car Carnegie Avenue garage and Skyway, a state-of-the-art 400-bed addition to the hospital was dedicated. This modern facility included new medical, surgical, and neurological intensive care units, several telemetry units for cardiology patients, a number of regular nursing units and classrooms, and a VIP ward. This allowed closure of some of the oldest areas of the hospital and, thus, represented a net addition of only about 200 beds, bringing the maximum bed count to almost 1,200. Given the changes in the health care environment which were beginning about that time, including

---

[4] The comparability of this meeting-place function of the Skyway with that of the "pike" in Boston's old Peter Bent Brigham Hospital was described by Clinic staff member James K. Stoller, M.D., in an article entitled "A Physician's View of Hospital Design" in the December 1988 issue of *Architecture*.

a trend to delivering more care in the ambulatory setting, the maximum number of staffed beds peaked at 1,018 during the Kiser era.

While the Century Project was being implemented, work was beginning on an even more significant undertaking, the establishment of a remote satellite. In 1984, Kiser was approached by physician groups in Florida regarding a possible joint venture with the Clinic. A two-man task force consisting of Robert Fischer, the chief financial officer, and Frank Weaver, the head of public affairs and corporate development, was dispatched to Florida to investigate the possibilities there. At the same time another task force, pursuant to a 1983 invitation from the Singapore Ministry of Health, was looking into the feasibility of establishing a Cleveland Clinic-like institution in that country. Teams were also created to look at opportunities in Turkey, Sweden, the United Kingdom, Ireland, and Morocco. But eventually attention focused on Florida. Several sites in Florida were evaluated, and, with the help of a 1986 study by the Peat Marwick Mitchell Company, Broward County eventually was selected as the most favorable.

The preliminary work needed to establish a Cleveland Clinic-style group practice in Florida was formidable indeed. In addition to finding the appropriate site, identifying the appropriate physicians, and setting up the necessary hospital affiliations, state legislation allowing the Cleveland Clinic to practice "corporate" medicine had to be passed. All of this was done with some difficulty, but due to the astute work of John Auble, the Clinic's general counsel, James Cuthbertson, Cleveland Clinic Florida's first chief operating officer, and William Hawk, M.D., Cleveland Clinic Florida's first chief executive officer, it was achieved. On February 29, 1988, Cleveland Clinic Florida opened its doors on Cypress Creek Road in Fort Lauderdale with 28 staff physicians and a total of about 100 employees. A month later, Hawk retired, and Carl Gill, M.D., a pediatric cardiac surgeon and medical director of Cleveland Clinic Florida, became chief executive officer.

The Florida physicians had privileges at North Beach Hospital (a for-profit hospital owned and operated by Health Trust, Inc.) located about 10 miles away on the beach. The Cleveland Clinic had leased 50 beds at North Beach and was responsible for filling them or paying for them. Since that 153-bed hospital did not have a certificate of need allowing the performance of cardiac surgery, and because the Clinic was not able to secure one, an arrangement was eventually worked out with Broward General Hospital for the cardiac surgeons to work there. The medical staff of the hospital balked, however, at allowing Cleveland Clinic physicians to have hospital privileges there, or even to provide support for the Clinic's cardiac surgeons. This led to a bitter battle and finally to an investigation by the Federal Trade Commission, which found against the Broward General Hospital staff, who were all forced to sign a consent decree to avoid prosecution.

During the months before Cleveland Clinic Florida opened, a 320-acre property in Weston was acquired. This was to be the ultimate site for the envisioned hospital-clinic-research complex that was to comprise the fully developed Cleveland Clinic Florida, with initial occupancy of a 200,000-square-foot clinic and a 150-bed hospital at the Weston location by 1992. Although the projected size of the facilities was out of proportion with Peat Marwick Mitchell's estimate that 63 physicians would be needed by 1994, Kiser felt strongly that this institution could grow as large or larger than the Cleveland campus because of (a) the rapid growth of the population in south Florida as compared with the shrinking population in northeast Ohio and (b) the greater accessibility to travelers from Europe, the Middle East, and Latin America, all growing markets for The Cleveland Clinic. This dream sustained the new group through the tough early going. The going remained tough longer than expected, however.

Just as the fledgling clinic was enduring its perinatal angst, the health care environment was changing dramatically. Costs were rising rapidly. Hospital and specialty care, both traditional mainstays of the Cleveland Clinic, were giving way to ambulatory and primary care. Managed care was on the rise. Competition among providers was getting more vicious. All these factors, together with some misreading of the unfamiliar south Florida market by the Clinic's leaders and consultants, led to poor initial financial performance. This was to be one of the major factors necessitating the third big project, the Economic Improvement Program.

Because of reimbursement and practice changes, hospital management was getting more difficult. It was no longer possible to pass cost increases on to the third party payers; the golden era of cost-based reimbursement had become a thing of the past. In the case of The Cleveland Clinic, both in Cleveland and Florida, this problem was compounded by the relative complexity of the organization, inexperience and lack of training of physician managers to whom authority had been decentralized, and a false sense of permanence created by a period of prosperity that had spanned the entire careers of the majority of the relatively young professional staff.

But the storm clouds were gathering. Although the size of the organization continued to grow unabatedly, growth in new patient

activity was slowing, and there were some unexpected cash hemor-
rhages that began to make the trustees nervous. The Florida project
was losing over $1 million per month. A major computer project on
the Cleveland campus, which was to have resulted in an electronic
medical record and billing system, was floundering, finally failed,
and eventually was estimated to have cost the organization at least
$95 million. For good measure it was disclosed that the Florida land
had somehow escaped appraisal and was worth less than half of the
$55,000 per acre that had been paid for it.[5]

The trustees requested Kiser and the Board of Governors to
retain McKinsey & Company, a consulting firm with offices in
Cleveland noted for masterminding turnarounds for failing companies. Although McKinsey had little health care experience at the
time, they took on the project with gusto, and the resulting plan
became known within the organization as the Economic
Improvement Program. Their initial assessment of the institution's
financial status was that if nothing were done, within 18 months the
Clinic would have a negative cash flow of $75 million and would
begin an economic death spiral from which it could not recover.

On a hot July afternoon in 1989, the Board of Governors held an
executive session to consider the situation. During that meeting,
Kiser announced his intention to step down as the Clinic's chief
executive officer. He agreed to stay on until plans for a smooth tran-
sition could be made. The Board of Governors and the Board of
Trustees decided to run the institution with a transition team con-
sisting of three of the senior governors, Fawzy G. Estafanous, M.D.
(chairman of the Division of Anesthesiology), D. Roy Ferguson,
M.D. (a member of the Department of Gastroenterology), and Carlos
Ferrario, Ph.D. (chairman of the Department of Brain and Vascular
Biology in the Research Institute), along with trustees William
MacDonald (chairman of the Board of Trustees), E. Bradley Jones
(who became chairman of the Board of Trustees in 1991), and Arthur
B. Modell (who became president of The Cleveland Clinic
Foundation in 1991). This dedicated team took over the functions of
the chief executive officer on July 20, 1989.

The Board of Trustees accepted Kiser's resignation with regret.
They approved the hiring of McKinsey in August 1989, and they
approved the Economic Improvement Plan the following month.

---

[5] Much of this loss was eventually recovered by obtaining a land-use change and selling the
bulk of the property for residential development. A great deal of the credit for this goes to Mr.
Samuel H. Miller, chairman of the board of Forest City Enterprises, Inc., who became one of the
Clinic's most active trustees.

The Economic Improvement Plan called for implementation of ten projects in two waves. The first five projects included (a) development and implementation of a plan to bring Cleveland Clinic Florida to a cash flow break-even status by the end of 1991; (b) restriction of capital expenditures to $50 million, freeing $25 million in cash; (c) reduction of costs in Cleveland by $35 million through a combination of difficult measures, including careful control of the employee "head count"; (d) improvement of the budgeting process; and (e) contingency planning. These projects were to start immediately. The second wave of projects, slated to begin during the first quarter of 1990, included (a) the notorious AVA (Activity Value Analysis) project[6]; (b) a "level scheduling" project to improve access; (c) an incentive pay project, euphemistically referred to as "professional staff motivation and rewards;" (d) development of a marketing program that would lead to a 10 percent increase in patient activity by 1993; and (e) a demonstration project to examine the feasibility of reorganizing into patient-focused activity units rather than traditional specialty departments.

On October 9, 1989, the transition team decreed that the actual first-wave projects would be (a) the Cleveland Clinic Florida project; (b) revenue recapture; (c) AVA; (d) resource utilization; and (e) market strategy. The second-wave activities were to be (a) planning and budgeting; and (b) head count and remuneration. The transition team took on for themselves the tasks of communication and evaluation of information services.

As these projects were getting under way, a search committee composed of the elected members of the Board of Governors and several members of the Trustees' Executive Committee was going about the work of identifying Kiser's successor. Unlike Wasmuth, Kiser had done no succession planning, and there was no one in line to step into the position.[7] The committee reaffirmed the concept that the chief executive should be a physician and interviewed several inside and outside candidates. After deliberating for nearly four months, they chose Floyd D. Loop, M.D., then chairman of the Department of Thoracic and Cardiovascular Surgery and a member of the Board of Governors.

---

[6] Activity Value Analysis is a management engineering term that refers to the setting of stretch goals for cost savings followed by the development of ideas for achieving the savings. The ideas are then written up and presented to a leadership team for decisions on which ideas are to be implemented. Many of the ideas involve reductions in personnel.

[7] Kiser did, however, identify certain promising staff members who were encouraged to obtain further education in management, organizational behavior, or law, who would be candidates for managerial roles in the future. Some have moved into such roles.

NINE

THE LOOP YEARS
1989-

It is the bright, the bold, the transparent who are cleverest among those who are silent: their ground is down so deep that even the brightest water does not betray it.

— *Nietzsche, 1892*

Floyd D. Loop, M.D., became The Cleveland Clinic's fourth physician chief executive on November 8, 1989, a month before his 53rd birthday. A native of Indiana and son of a country doctor, he was educated in science at Purdue University. He received his medical training at the George Washington University. After he graduated in 1962, he completed a residency in general surgery at George Washington, interrupted by two years in the Air Force. During this residency his mentor was Brian Blades, M.D.,[1] who influenced him to become a thoracic surgeon. Blades arranged for him to receive cardiac surgery training at The Cleveland Clinic with the understanding that he would subsequently return to the university to practice cardiovascular surgery. His cardiothoracic surgery training was supervised by Donald B. Effler, M.D., who had been Blades's first chief resident after World War II. Loop's training in Cleveland coincided with the beginning of coronary artery surgery. Effler and his colleagues, René Favaloro, M.D., and F. Mason Sones, Jr., M.D.,

---

[1] Blades was at that time the chief of surgery at George Washington; he was a noted thoracic surgeon, a pioneer in the field of lung cancer surgery, and a friend of the Criles.

Floyd D. Loop, M.D., Chairman of the Board of Governors and Chief Executive
Officer, The Cleveland Clinic Foundation, 1989–

taught him well. When George Washington University was unable
to comply with Loop's lofty plans for cardiac surgery there, he
joined the Clinic staff in 1970 and, upon Effler's retirement, was
appointed department chairman in 1975. Under his leadership the
department doubled the volume of cases and became one of the
world's great heart centers. In 1988 he was elected to fill the unex-
pired term of Dr. Carl Gill on the Board of Governors when Gill
became a permanent member of the Board by virtue of his executive
position with Cleveland Clinic Florida. Loop's unrelenting pursuit
of quality led to his appointment with Richard G. Farmer, M.D., then
chairman of the Division of Medicine, to chair the Quality Assurance
Task Force.

At the time Loop succeeded Kiser, shortly after the initiation of
the previously mentioned McKinsey "turnaround" projects, the
Clinic's future was uncertain. Cash flows had begun a downward
spiral in early 1989. Cleveland Clinic Florida had become a symbol
of the cash hemorrhage, and there was talk of shutting it down.
Loop gave his first Health of the Clinic address on February 12, 1990,

which he began by citing DaCosta's comment that "[i]t won't help a man much to be a hundred years ahead of his time if he is a month behind in his rent." [2] Though not formally trained in business, Loop became the most visionary and, at the same time, the most fiscally prudent and conservative of the Board of Governors' chairmen. He recognized the opportunity represented by the Florida project, and he knew that the Clinic's future, both in Cleveland and Fort Lauderdale, would depend on controlling costs and building market share. The latter could only be accomplished by acknowledging that "[f]or the first time we need to think strategically. We must adapt or we will go the way of the dinosaurs ourselves. We can't rest on our laurels. For a competitive advantage, the choices are clear — we must provide exemplary service of highest quality, increase our patient activity, manage internal systems better, and individually manage our practices better. In other words, if we want to stay the same, things will have to change."

With Loop, the pendulum of leadership had swung back to a more centralized, hierarchical approach, although decentralization of marketing clinical "product lines" was an important feature as well. He reorganized his management team to decrease the number of individuals reporting directly to him. The "professional" divisions (including Medicine, Surgery, Anesthesiology, Pathology and Laboratory Medicine, Radiology, Education, Research, and the "Centers of Excellence") all reported to the Chief of Staff, Ralph Straffon, but the chairpersons of these divisions and centers had direct access to Loop in the Medical Executive Committee, which he also chaired.

Perhaps more than any other individual Clinic staff member, Ralph Straffon, whose name appears many times in this book, personifies all that is excellent about The Cleveland Clinic's system of medical group practice. A native of Michigan and a graduate of the University of Michigan, he came to the Clinic's Department of Urology in 1959. Just four years later he assumed the department chairmanship, and in 1978, he became chairman of the Division of Surgery. In 1987, he was appointed Chief of Staff, the position he continues to hold. He has served on the Board of Governors, both as an elected member (1967-1971, 1973-1976) and as a permanent member by virtue of his office (since 1987). He also serves on the Medical Executive Committee and the Administrative Council. His profes-

---

[2] Other Loop quotes include "Money isn't everything, but you need it to buy things," (Joe Louis) and "Every tub must stand on its own bottom" (anonymous).

Ralph A. Straffon, M.D., Chief of Staff, The Cleveland Clinic Foundation, 1987–

sional achievements are too numerous to list here,[3] and through all of this he has continued to set an enviable example of the group practice ideal of leadership combined with collegiality.

On the administrative side Robert Ivancic was recruited from the Meridia Health System to head the Division of Human Resources. John Clough, M.D., relinquished his chairmanship of the Department of Rheumatic and Immunologic Disease to head a new Division of Health Affairs, which encompassed many of the Clinic's external relationships. Daniel J. Harrington, who had been Director of Finance and an officer of the Foundation since 1986, became the Chief Financial Officer. Frank L. Lordeman, formerly the president and chief executive officer of Meridia Hillcrest Hospital, was recruited to the position of Chief Operating Officer to head the Clinic's vast Division of Operations; he became Loop's closest partner in engi-

---

[3] A few examples of Straffon's national leadership positions include trustee (1973-1979) and president (1979) of the American Board of Urology, member (1974-1980) and chairman (1978) of the Residency Review Committee for Urology, president of the Council of Medical Specialties (1983-1984), president of the American Association of Genitourinary Surgeons (1986-1987). His crowning achievement was his election as regent (1980-1989) and later to the presidency (1991-1992) of the American College of Surgeons. He has also received the Distinguished Alumnus Award of the University of Michigan (1980), the American Urological Association's Hugh Hampton Young Award (1983), and the National Health Professional Award of the VNA (1989).

neering the changes that needed to be made in the organization. After the retirement of John Auble, who had founded the Clinic's legal office two and a half decades before, the office of general counsel was outsourced to Squire, Sanders and Dempsey, a Cleveland firm that showed excellent judgment in selecting David W. Rowan to oversee the Clinic's legal activities. This team, together with Loop's administrator Gene Altus, who was also the administrator of the Department of Plastic and Reconstructive Surgery and who had played a vital role in the restructuring of Cleveland Clinic Florida, became the Administrative Council chaired by Loop.

In order to strengthen the marketing program in managed care, Peter S. Brumleve was recruited from Group Health Association of Puget Sound in 1994 to become Chief Marketing Officer. Marketing and managed care became a separate division under his leadership, and he joined the Administrative Council. Two more members were added to the Administrative Council in 1995. Robert Kay, M.D., a pediatric urologist who also held the position of Chief of Medical Operations, and Alan E. London, M.D., Executive Director of Managed Care, formerly medical director of National Medical Enterprises, a California-based corporation that owned a chain of hospitals and managed care organizations, rounded out the Council.

The heart of the Board of Governors continued to be nine elected staff members serving staggered five-year terms. In addition, the Chief of Staff, Chief Financial Officer, Chief Operating Officer, and Chief Executive Officer of Cleveland Clinic Florida, as well as the Chairman, were permanent appointed members. Thus, Loop, Lordeman, and Straffon were members of all three of the major governing bodies.

These administrative changes coincided with appointment of approximately thirty physician-managers to assume new roles in heading most of the clinical functions. Included among these were Norman S. Abramson, M.D. (emergency medicine), Muzaffar Ahmad, M.D. (Division of Medicine), Jerome L. Belinson, M.D. (gynecology), David Bronson, M.D. (general internal medicine, later Division of Regional Medical Practices), Delos M.Cosgrove, III, M.D. (cardiothoracic surgery), Vincent Dennis, M.D. (nephrology/hypertension), Cynthia Deyling, M.D. (Cleveland Clinic Independence), Charles Faiman, M.D. (endocrinology), William R. Hart, M.D. (pathology and laboratory medicine), J. Michael Henderson, M.B., Ch.B. (general surgery, Transplant Center), Gary S. Hoffman, M.D. (rheumatic and immunologic disease), Hilel Lewis, M.D. (ophthalmology, Eye Institute), David Longworth, M.D. (infectious disease), Hans Lüders, M.D., Ph.D. (neurology), Roger Macklis, M.D. (radiation oncology), Maurie Markman, M.D. (hematology/oncology, Cancer Center), Kenneth E. Marks, M.D. (orthopedics), Daniel J. Mazanec, M.D. (Center for the Spine), Harry K. Moon, M.D. (chief of staff, Cleveland Clinic Florida), Thomas J. Morledge, M.D. (Cleveland Clinic Willoughby Hills), Robert Palmer, M.D. (geriatrics), Robert Petras, M.D. (anatomic pathology), Elliot Philipson, M.D. (obstetrics), Joel Richter, M.D. (gastroenterology), Vinod Sahgal, M.D. (physical medicine and rehabilitation, Rehabilitation Institute), Marshall Strome, M.D. (otolaryngology), George Tesar, M.D. (psychiatry), Eric J. Topol, M.D. (cardiology), A. Mary Walborn, M.D. (Cleveland Clinic Westlake), John A. Washington, M.D. (clinical pathology), Herbert P. Wiedemann, M.D. (pulmonary disease), and James Zins, M.D. (plastic and reconstructive surgery).

In the midst of all these changes, George "Barney" Crile, Jr., M.D., the last direct link with the Founders of The Cleveland Clinic, became terminally ill. In a moving ceremony on May 30, 1992, shortly before his death at age 84, the A Building was rechristened the Crile Building in honor of Barney and his father, both of whom had given so much to the Cleveland Clinic throughout its history. More than 40 members of the Crile family attended this Founders' Celebration. The building is a living monument to the Criles as well as to the Clinic itself. But 10 years after its grand opening and five years before the turn of the century, it is filled to capacity, and space is once again an issue for the organization.

With his team in place, Loop set out to move the Clinic forward into the era of managed care. Implementation of the Economic Improvement Plan was the highest priority during the early part of his administration. This included reducing costs through Activity Value Analysis (AVA), revenue recapture, stepping up the marketing effort, making Cleveland Clinic Florida cost effective, and reorganizing the Clinic's management structure. About 135 jobs were eventually eliminated through the AVA process, generating some savings. Among other things, the revenue recapture project led to the first of several revisions of the inpatient and outpatient billing processes, which, according to some, still have plenty of room for improvement. Marketing was initially placed in the Division of Health Affairs, and a new marketing strategy that emphasized building the Clinic's traditional business while developing managed care capability was formulated. In Fort Lauderdale, the Clinic purchased North Beach Hospital from Health Trust, Inc., and started down the difficult path toward converting red ink to black. By early 1990 these measures had produced a $60 million turnaround in cash flow (from -$30 million to +$30 million), and the future seemed brighter.

David L. Bronson, M.D., Chairman, Division of Regional Medical Practice, 1995–

The Clinic was now poised to tackle several major projects, which would keep the news media, the Ohio Department of Health, and the competition in an unprecedented state of agitation for the next few years. Among these projects were (a) affiliation with The Ohio State University; (b) affiliation with Kaiser Permanente; (c) establishment of an inpatient rehabilitation unit; (d) management of the William O. Walker Center for Vocational Rehabilitation; (e) construction of a new state-of-the-art Access Center and emergency facility; (f) formation of the Cleveland Health Network; (g) creation of the Division of Regional Medical Practice, (h) development of the Cleveland Clinic Eye Institute and an eye care network; (i) creation of a Division of Pediatrics and a Cleveland Clinic Children's Hospital; (j) reestablishment of obstetrics; and (k) initiation of a major fund-raising campaign to build the Cleveland Clinic Research and Education Institute.

Bernadine Healy, M.D., chairperson of the Research Institute since 1985, had long recognized the need for the Clinic to develop a strong academic affiliation with a medical school. She and her associates tried hard to work out a satisfactory arrangement with Case Western Reserve University, but for a variety of reasons (mostly related to competition with University Hospitals of Cleveland), this was not possible. So she turned to The Ohio State University, where

The Cleveland Clinic received a cordial welcome. An affiliation with The Ohio State University was consummated and announced in 1991.[4]

The Clinic's entry into managed care was greatly accelerated by the completion of a contract with Kaiser Permanente in 1992 under which Cleveland Clinic Hospital became the major inpatient care site for Kaiser members in northern Ohio. This dramatic and, in the eyes of some, unlikely linkage was made possible through the strong leadership and vision of Loop along with Ronald Potts, M.D., Medical Director of the Ohio Permanente Medical Group, and Kathryn Paul, Regional Manager of the Kaiser Health Plan. Hospitals which had previously provided inpatient facilities for Kaiser Permanente (St. Luke's on the east side and MetroHealth[5] on the west side, which had recently merged) waged media campaigns and filed lawsuits in an attempt to derail the affiliation, but to no avail. As a result of this agreement, many physicians in the Ohio Permanente Medical Group were granted staff privileges to admit and care for their patients in Cleveland Clinic Hospital, and Kaiser, which had at one time operated three hospitals in the Cleveland area, closed its last remaining hospital. This was the first time that physicians other than those employed by The Cleveland Clinic had been admitted to the Clinic's medical staff, an arrangement that was problematic for some Clinic physicians in their quest to continue to act as a unit. However, the affiliation has greatly benefited both organizations since full consolidation occurred in January 1994, and the Clinic doctors have had an enlightening first-hand look at HMO-style primary care as delivered by the experts.[6]

---

[4] This led to an incredible series of events locally, culminating in the appointment of a blue-ribbon panel by the Cleveland Foundation to explore the area's opportunities in medical research and to make recommendations about the advisability of having two separate academic medical centers in the city. After protracted deliberations, the panel finally recognized The Cleveland Clinic as a separate "emerging" academic medical center. Shortly thereafter officials at Case Western Reserve University arranged an affiliation with Henry Ford Hospital in Detroit. Despite all this, the Clinic's relationship with Ohio State has prospered, and one of the most visible results is the establishment of a joint Department of Biomedical Engineering chaired by J. Fredrick Cornhill, D. Phil. Many medical students from Ohio State have core rotations at the Clinic.

[5] MetroHealth is the reincarnation of the old Cleveland Metropolitan General Hospital. It was set up to provide an umbrella organization for the merger of that hospital and St. Luke's into a "system." Shortly after the completion of the agreement between The Cleveland Clinic and Kaiser Permanente, the merger was dissolved, and the name MetroHealth subsequently referred only to the county hospital.

[6] The earliest discussions about possible affiliation took place in the late 1980s between the Clinic's Dr. Shattuck W. Hartwell, Jr., and the Ohio Permanente Medical Group's Dr. Ronald Potts. The concept was resurrected by Loop after he assumed the role of chairman of the Board of Governors. Dr. Robert Kay played a key role in bringing about the affiliation and has the responsibility of maintaining liaison with Kaiser Permanente; he sits on the Board of Directors of the Ohio Permanente Medical Group.

Clinic leaders saw the necessity to develop satellites to deliver geographically distributed primary care services. This became the responsibility of the new Division of Regional Medical Practice under the direction of David L. Bronson, M.D. Five satellite family health centers were planned, each to be 30-45 minutes' driving time from the main campus. The first to open was in Independence, located in the Crown Centre Building at Interstate 77 and Rockside Road. The second was in Willoughby Hills on Ohio Route 91 (S.O.M. Center Road) at Interstate 90. The third was in Westlake at Interstate 90 and Crocker-Bassett Road. At this writing, another property is under development in Solon, and the fifth site is being sought. Although some specialty services are in the satellites (orthopedics at Independence and ophthalmology at Willoughby Hills), the emphasis is on primary care (internal medicine, pediatrics, and obstetrics.)

Vinod Sahgal, M.D., an internationally known physiatrist from the Chicago Institute of Rehabilitation, joined the staff in 1992 to build a Rehabilitation Institute. As a necessary first step in this process, the Clinic applied for a certificate of need to operate a 34-bed rehabilitation unit. The Cleveland Clinic had never had a problem obtaining state approval for new programs or technology, but times had changed. Nonetheless, despite opposition from the competition, Loop negotiated a settlement with the Director of the Ohio Department of Health which allowed the Clinic to open a 20-bed unit. Legal appeals went on for another two years before finally being laid to rest.

Kaiser Permanente's move to the Clinic, continued pressure from the Clinic's own patients for an improved emergency medicine facility, and the need to provide better access to The Cleveland Clinic for residents of the inner city, led to the decision to build a new Emergency Medicine and Access Center. It was located on the south side of Carnegie Avenue between East 93rd and East 90th Streets and was designed to house four separate units on its first floor: (a) The Cleveland Clinic's Emergency Medicine Department, which was about six times the size of the old facility, (b) Kaiser Permanente's Emergency Department, which enabled them to close their old East Side emergency room, (c) a shared Clinical Decision Unit with 20 observation beds, and (d) The Cleveland Clinic's Access Department, intended to provide same-day service for outpatients. These departments opened in the spring of 1994 and were formally dedicated in October of that year. The second floor of the Access Center Building, which opened in 1996, houses 24 new operating rooms, replacing the same number of outmoded operating rooms that have served the Clinic's needs for some four decades.

Foundation House (8615 Euclid Avenue)

After many months of intricate negotiations led by Frank Lordeman, Loop hosted a press conference on May 13, 1994, to announce the formation of the Cleveland Health Network. Flanked by Robert Shakno, chief executive officer of Mt. Sinai Hospital, and Thomas LaMotte, chief executive officer of Fairview General Hospital, representing the charter members of the network, Loop announced the association of ten hospital systems [Cleveland Clinic, Mt. Sinai/Laurelwood, Fairview Health System (Fairview/ Lutheran), Parma, MetroHealth, Elyria Memorial, Summa (St. Thomas/Akron City), Akron Children's, and Aultman (Canton); Marymount joined later] and their affiliated physician-hospital organizations (PHOs) for the purpose of contracting to provide managed care. The Cleveland Health Network was unlike the other local hospital systems (Meridia and University Hospitals Health System) in that it did not involve single ownership of all the participating hospitals. It was also considerably bigger and geographical-ly more far flung, with participating hospitals in five counties, and it encompassed three pre-existing two-hospital networks: Summa (Akron City and St. Thomas hospitals), Fairview Health System (for-merly Health Cleveland, including Fairview and Lutheran hospi-tals), and the Mt. Sinai Health System (Mt. Sinai and Laurelwood hospitals).[7] The Cleveland Health Network is still evolving as of this

---

[7] To outsiders the most surprising member of the network was MetroHealth, the Cuyahoga County hospital, which had recently been at odds with the Clinic over the Clinic's reestablish-ment of rehabilitation services and had a long history of close affiliation with Case Western

writing.[8] Marymount Hospital has merged with The Cleveland Clinic and joined the network, and ties with MetroHealth have been strengthened. Development of a Cleveland Health Network managed care organization, comprised of the above-named hospitals and hundreds of their affiliated physicians, is the major focus of the network, and the development of this will be crucial to the overall success of the network.[9]

In preparation for the formation of The Cleveland Clinic Eye Institute, Hilel Lewis, M.D., was recruited from the Jules Stein Eye Institute of Los Angeles to head it. The Division of Ophthalmology was removed from the Division of Surgery and accorded divisional status. Plans for a new building to house both clinical and research activities related to the eye were developed. Lewis expanded the already excellent ophthalmologic services available at the Clinic by adding new talent to the group, and set about forming a network of community ophthalmologists and optometrists to offer eye services on a contractual basis.

Pediatrics, which existed as a department since the early 1950s, was also granted divisional status and removed from the Division of Medicine. Under the chairmanship of Douglas Moodie, M.D., the new Division of Pediatrics, together with The Cleveland Clinic Children's Hospital[10], newly remodeled and containing a state-of-the-art pediatric intensive care unit, as well as new pediatric cardiac surgery suites, has assumed a leadership role in the care of diseases of children, which will persist for years to come.

In Chapter 6 we noted that the Clinic's obstetrical program had closed down in 1966 to make room for the growing cardiac surgery

---

Reserve University, the parent organization of University Hospitals. MetroHealth and The Cleveland Clinic have complementary strengths, however, and the association has been beneficial for both.

[8] In December 1995, Primary Health System, a for-profit organization that previously bought Deaconess and St. Alexis Hospitals, announced the purchase of Mt. Sinai, which then left the Cleveland Health Network. Aultman had quietly withdrawn from the network some months before.

[9] Dr. Alan London has the responsibility of organizing this important component of the Cleveland Health Network.

[10] The Cleveland Clinic Children's Hospital was accepted as an associate member of the National Association of Children's Hospitals and Related Institutions (NACHRI) in 1987. In 1989 the Ohio Children's Hospitals Association, at the instigation of University Hospitals, successfully lobbied the state to add a definition of the term "children's hospital" to the certificate of need law which specifically excludes The Cleveland Clinic Children's Hospital on the grounds that it does not have 150 beds! No other state has such a law, and NACHRI does not have this requirement. Nor is it necessary to have a certificate of need for the designation as a children's hospital. Such are the arcane political twists that Rainbow Babies' and Children's Hospital officials have used to justify calling their hospital the only children's hospital in Cleveland.

program. On June 1, 1995, the program was reopened under the direction of Elliot Philipson, M.D. Its location on the sixth floor of the hospital is just around the corner from its original site, and the delivery suites, which have in the interim sequentially served cardiac surgery, orthopedic surgery, and ambulatory surgery, have been returned to their original function. Outpatient obstetrical services are provided both on the main campus and in the satellites.

After several fits and starts at fund raising, and one successful campaign which raised $30 million for Phase 1 of the Research and Education Institute (the Sherwin Research Building), the Board of Trustees approved a full-scale campaign, the "Campaign for the Twenty-first Century," to build the remainder of the Research and Education Institute. William Grimberg was recruited from Cleveland Tomorrow to head the Department of Institutional Advancement, which has the responsibility for organizing the campaign. Grimberg had cut his teeth on the campaign that revitalized Cleveland's Playhouse Square a few years earlier, and he had become interested in health research and technology through his association with the Technology Leadership Council of Cleveland Tomorrow. He was no stranger to The Cleveland Clinic, having labored mightily to develop collaborative arrangements between the Clinic and Case Western Reserve University to attract state money to support research at both institutions. As of this writing, the campaign is just beginning and its goal is $225 million.

The Cleveland Clinic's prospects have never been brighter. National and international recognition of the Clinic as a provider of extremely high quality medical care is at an all-time high.[11] Although the health care scene is undergoing fundamental change characterized by a shift to managed care and increasing emphasis on primary care and prevention, the Clinic's new initiatives will allow the organization to continue as a major player in the health care of the future while maintaining the underlying values of the institution. The basic needs of patients remain the same, and the Clinic is here to serve them.

---

[11] In the *U.S. News & World Report*'s annual evaluation of hospitals, The Cleveland Clinic has been recognized among the top 10 hospitals in the country for each of the six years the survey has been done. Singled out for special recognition were cardiology (tops in the nation in 1995), urology, gastroenterology, neurology, otolaryngology, rheumatology, gynecology, and orthopedics. No other hospital in the state or the region has been so recognized. Moreover, many of the staff have received similar recognition in lists of "best doctors" assembled by various organizations.

Section III

The Divisions and Centers

TEN

DIVISION OF MEDICINE

Every physician almost
hath his favourite disease.

— Henry Fielding, 1749

The Division of Medicine has played an important role in the development of medical practice at the Clinic since its opening in 1921. Dr. John Phillips, the only internist among the four founders, was the first chief of the Division of Medicine, then called the Medical Department. He was a true family physician who saw medicine begin to move away from house calls and toward an office-based practice during the eight years between 1921 and his untimely death at age 50. Nevertheless, he continued to treat patients with diverse disorders and make house calls, often spending his entire weekend visiting patients in their homes.

Despite his own inclination and experience, Phillips recognized the value of specialization. In 1921, he assigned Henry J. John, M.D., the field of diabetes and supervision of the clinical laboratories. In 1923, he appointed Earl W. Netherton, M.D., head of the Department of Dermatology, and in 1929, E. Perry McCullagh, M.D., head of the Department of Endocrinology. The rest of the staff, like Phillips, practiced general medicine.

In September 1930, one and a half years after Phillips's death (see Chapter 3), the Board of Governors appointed Russell L. Haden, M.D., chief of the Division of Medicine. Formerly a professor of experimental medicine at the University of Kansas School of Medicine, he approached medicine in a significantly different way: While Phillips had been interested primarily in the clinical aspects of disease, Haden was a modern, laboratory-oriented medical scientist.[1] Although his interests spanned the entire field of internal medicine, he was a hematologist, and he made many important contributions to the field of blood diseases, most notably the discovery of spherohemolytic anemia. However, his enthusiasm for physical therapy combined with the reluctance of most physicians to tackle the problems of arthritic patients resulted in a large referral practice in rheumatic diseases. Dynamic, brilliant and possessing impeccable manners, Haden treated everyone with equal respect. Renowned as a superb clinician, he impressed patients and physicians alike by the speed at which he arrived at correct conclusions.[2]

Haden's first appointment to the Clinic staff was A. Carlton Ernstene, M.D., as head of the Department of Cardiorespiratory Disease in 1932. Ernstene had been trained in internal medicine and cardiology on the Harvard services of Boston City Hospital and served on the Harvard faculty. His interest in laboratory and clinical research made him an excellent choice to direct the new department. In 1939, Ernstene was joined by H.S. Van Ordstrand, M.D., who had been appointed head of the Section of Pulmonary Disease.

Gastroenterology, allergy, and physical medicine were added between 1932 and 1937. Then economic restrictions imposed by the Great Depression required the staff to devote most of their energy to providing the highest volume of patient care at the lowest cost. The Clinic experienced almost no further growth until World War II.

A gradually improving economy brought visions of expansion that were dimmed by the war. Young physician candidates for the staff were drafted into military service, along with several members of the Division of Medicine and many residents. The entire Cardiorespiratory Department was depleted when Ernstene and Van Ordstrand departed for military service. Fortunately, Fay A. LeFevre, M.D., a former fellow, was able to return to the Clinic to replace them.

Immediately after the war, the Clinic experienced a rapid increase in staff as well as further specialization. As a result of mili-

---

[1] During his eight years at the Clinic, Phillips published 26 papers, 23 of which were concerned with unusual cases or the diagnosis or treatment of diseases. On the other hand, in Haden's first five years at the Clinic he published 26 papers, 23 of which were descriptions of laboratory innovations or attempts to define the causes or interrelations of various diseases.

[2] Residents coming to Haden's service did so with apprehension because "the chief" demanded high performance. This challenge usually brought out the best in the young physicians. Haden never seemed to forget small mistakes and frequently reminded the offender much later. However, he rarely mentioned major errors again because he knew how miserable the trainee felt and that the lesson had been learned. Although he never complimented residents for a job well done, they knew when Haden was pleased by the twinkle in his eye and slight smile.

Muzaffar Ahmad, M.D., Chairman, Division of Medicine, 1991–

tary training, many young physicians recognized the value of group practice and applied to the Clinic for training. Haden preferred to accept those who had served their country, and actually took more than his residency program needed.

When Haden retired in 1949, the chairmanship fell on Ernstene. Aside from his love of work and clinical abilities, he had little in common with Haden. Meticulous order was his hallmark. He started his hospital rounds at 8 a.m. and finished in one hour. He would rapidly complete any brief, unscheduled activities before he returned to his office, by which time he expected his first patient of the day to have been examined by his resident. He would question the patient closely, recheck much of the physical examination, and make careful and concise notes in a tight, angular, small script.[3] Although he had a good background in internal medicine, cardiology was his field and he had all the attributes of an outstanding clinical cardiologist.[4]

---

[3] Residents were occasionally heard to comment that Ernstene's handwriting was reminiscent of 60-cycle interference commonly seen on the electrocardiograms of the time.

[4] Ernstene was a model of uncluttered, perfectly logical judgment, although he was not a good teacher in the traditional sense. His lectures were excellent because of their superb organization and precise delivery.

Seven new departments were established during Ernstene's tenure as division chairman,[5] and the Department of Cardiorespiratory Disease was divided into Clinical Cardiology and Pulmonary Disease. However, Ernstene discovered that as a physician with a large practice who also served as an officer of several national medical societies, Clinic administrative duties were burdensome. A committee was formed to advise and assist him, and this was the beginning of democratic governance in the Division of Medicine.

At the time of Ernstene's retirement in 1965, there were 28 physicians on the division's staff. Expansion continued under the successive chairmanships of Van Ordstrand, Ray A. Van Ommen, M.D., and Richard G. Farmer, M.D. They were respectively specialists in pulmonary disease, infectious disease, and gastroenterology, but each sought a balanced development in the division, and each brought a unique character and style to the job.

In 1991 Farmer retired, and Muzaffar Ahmad, M.D., a pulmonary specialist, was appointed chairman. The division continued to grow, adding Emergency Medicine and Rehabilitation Medicine as new departments. By 1995, there were 240 staff members in the division, excluding the pediatricians who had become part of a separate Division of Pediatrics in 1994.

NEPHROLOGY AND HYPERTENSION

The senior Crile was interested in blood pressure his whole life, and early in his career made notable contributions to the understanding of blood pressure maintenance under certain conditions. Through a considerable amount of experimental and clinical work, he became convinced that hypertension was mediated through the sympathetic nervous system, and that denervation of the celiac ganglion would be beneficial to the hypertensive patient. Although the therapeutic results of his surgical endeavors did not meet his expectations, he remained interested in hypertension and tried, with mixed success, to interest others on staff.

For many years, hypertensive patients at the Clinic were treated by general internists and cardiologists. After 1945, those with severe problems were studied in the hospital and then followed in

---

[5] These departments were Internal Medicine (1949), Pediatrics (1951), Peripheral Vascular Disease (1952), Rheumatic Disease (1952), Hematology (1953), Hypertension (1959) and Pediatric Cardiology (1960).

Russell L. Haden, M.D., Chief of Medicine, 1930–1949

the clinic by Robert D. Taylor, M.D., from the Division of Research. It was natural that with the large number of patients referred for the treatment of hypertension, drugs for its treatment were often tested at the Clinic. Soon, the need for specialized services to supplement those provided by Taylor became evident. In 1959, the Clinic formed a new Department of Hypertension and appointed David C. Humphrey, M.D., to head it.

In 1967, Ray W. Gifford, Jr., M.D., succeeded Humphrey. Gifford forged a strong alliance between the clinical and research programs in hypertension. Innovative and accomplished investigators, such as Irvine Page, Merlin Bumpus, Robert Tarazi, and Harriet Dustan, and their successors, Fetnat Fouad and Emmanuel Bravo, pioneered research programs in the humoral, hemodynamic and neurologic aspects of hypertension. These activities were linked to clinical programs that focused on treatment options and their benefits as well as the education of physicians and their patients, leading to a national standard of excellence for departments of hypertension.

The Division of Research also focused on the development and application of dialysis. Willem J. Kolff, M.D., Ph.D., head of the Department of Artificial Organs, had developed an artificial kidney in Holland during World War II and demonstrated its value in the treatment of reversible kidney disease.[6] At the Clinic, it was discovered that regular dialysis could prolong life and relative comfort even when kidney function was seriously impaired. This activity was officially merged with hypertension in 1967 to form the Department of Hypertension and Nephrology. Members of the department led the development of standard hemodialysis techniques and newer approaches to prolong life in end-stage renal disease, including slow continuous ultrafiltration, continuous ambulatory peritoneal dialysis, and special interventions for critically ill patients in intensive care units.

Donald G. Vidt, M.D., an investigator and practitioner of pharmacologic approaches to hypertension, became chairman of the combined department in 1985. He consolidated programs in hypertension and expanded those in nephrology to include all aspects of dialysis. Gifford remained on Vidt's staff until his retirement in 1994, at which time the department established the Ray W. Gifford, Jr., Chair in Hypertension and Nephrology, and honored him as Distinguished Alumnus.

The succession of department chairmen with roots in The Cleveland Clinic changed in 1992 with the appointment of Vincent W. Dennis, M.D., from Duke University. By this time the department was heavily engaged in research and patient care in kidney diseases, and so it was renamed Nephrology and Hypertension. In 1995, the department was composed of 14 members with research and practice specialties in renovascular hypertension, immunologic aspects of transplantation, endocrine causes of hypertension, treatment for acute renal failure, and metabolic disturbances in kidney disease and stone disease. They were also closely involved in the selection

---

[6] Kolff was one of a trio of physicians who profoundly influenced the development of cardiology at the Clinic. The other two were cardiologist F. Mason Sones, Jr., M.D., and Donald B. Effler, M.D., a cardiovascular surgeon. Their contributions were monumental and received international acclaim. There were times, however, when these men did not get along. Their effect upon one another became so stressful to them and others around them that the Board of Governors decided that something had to be done and formed a committee to address the issue in 1956. It was headed by William L. Proudfit, M.D., a cardiologist on speaking terms with each of the dissident colleagues. The four men met daily at 8 a.m. and often would talk to each other only through the chairman. Much of the dissension surrounded the death of several high risk patients who were operated on and had been expected to live. At one point, Effler decided to stop operating. However, Dr. John W. Kirklin, then at the Mayo Clinic, said he felt there was nothing wrong with the approach or selection of patients and that the operations should be resumed. His judgment proved correct, and with improved results, bad tempers eased. Nevertheless, Kolff left the Clinic in 1967 to continue his work with artificial organs at the University of Utah.

and treatment of patients in the kidney and kidney-pancreas transplant program.[7]

CARDIOLOGY

The Department of Cardiology has its roots in the Department of Cardiorespiratory Disease, which was established in 1932. In the late 1950s when image-amplifying radiographic equipment first became available, Sones became interested in photographing the coronary arteries. Some incidental photographs showing portions of the coronary arteries already had been made in Sweden, but Sones attempted to photograph the vessels by injecting contrast material near their openings. One day he accidentally injected a large amount of dye directly into a coronary artery. When no dire consequences were noted, he deliberately injected small doses directly into the coronary arteries. The result was a clear x-ray picture of the coronary arteries. Thus selective coronary arteriography began, and Sones was soon able use his technique to verify the location of blockages in the arteries as well as the effectiveness of a coronary bypass operation.

In 1960, an offshoot of the department (now called Clinical Cardiology) was formed to reflect the diagnostic laboratory studies developed under Sones. Named the Department of Pediatric Cardiology, it was renamed the Department of Cardiovascular Disease and Cardiac Laboratory in 1967, and Sones was appointed chairman. Two years earlier, Ernstene had retired as chairman of Clinical Cardiology, and had been replaced by William L. Proudfit, M.D. Although the two cardiology departments overlapped in many areas, their relationship remained harmonious.

Upon Proudfit's retirement in 1974, the two departments were merged into one Department of Cardiology and William C. Sheldon, M.D., was named chairman. After 16 years of excellent leadership, Sheldon was replaced by Eric J. Topol, M.D., a pioneer researcher in the field of ischemic heart disease and leader in interventional cardiology.

Over the next few years, the department grew from 33 to more than 55 physicians. Beyond its primary mission of delivering outstanding patient care, the department has gained a reputation for international leadership in education and research through its exceptional contributions to the specialty. These include the orches-

---

[7] Although the first cadaver kidney transplant was done elsewhere, the Clinic was one of the first institutions to apply this technique in 1963.

tration and successful completion of a 41,000-patient heart attack trial in 15 countries (entitled GUSTO); the first large-scale, randomized medical device trial in history to evaluate atherectomy and balloon angioplasty; and the establishment of the Joseph J. Jacobs Center for Thrombosis and Vascular Biology.

VASCULAR MEDICINE

Like the Department of Cardiology, the roots of Vascular Medicine were formed in the Department of Cardiorespiratory Disease under LeFevre. LeFevre had spent two years as a fellow in medicine at the Clinic, followed by a year of postgraduate study in London and several years in practice before joining the Clinic staff in 1942. Upon the departure of Ernstene and Van Ordstrand for World War II, LeFevre singlehandedly manned the Department of Cardiorespiratory Disease. After Ernstene returned and new staff members were added, LeFevre was able to concentrate on his main interest, diseases of the blood vessels. The lower limbs especially fascinated him. In 1952, the Clinic formed a new Section of Peripheral Vascular Disease and appointed him head. He was joined by Victor G. deWolfe, M.D., who had trained in this field in New York and had been a member of the Clinic staff for three years.

In 1955 the section was given department status and LeFevre was named chairman. However, his duties as chairman of the Board of Governors soon encroached excessively on his practice, and deWolfe was appointed to succeed him as chairman of Peripheral Vascular Disease. Upon deWolfe's retirement in 1976, Jess R. Young, M.D., was named chairman.

Under Young, a busy non-invasive vascular laboratory for the study of patients with peripheral vascular disease was established and fully accredited. A non-surgical vascular intervention lab was organized in conjunction with the Departments of Cardiology, Vascular Surgery, and the Department of Radiology's Section of Vascular and Interventional Radiology. The physicians work closely with the peripheral vascular surgeons in the care of patients needing surgery. The department is now recognized as a national leader in vascular medicine.

PULMONARY AND CRITICAL CARE MEDICINE

The Department of Pulmonary Disease separated from the Department of Cardiorespiratory Disease in 1958. Howard S. Van Ordstrand, M.D., who subsequently became chairman of the

Division of Medicine, was appointed its first head. Van Ordstrand also served a one-year term as president of the American College of Chest Physicians. He was known for his original description of acute berylliosis, a potentially lethal inflammatory disorder of the lungs that occurred in workers exposed to high concentrations of beryllium.[8]

In 1973 Joseph F. Tomashefski, M.D., succeeded Van Ordstrand as department chairman. Under Tomashefski, the department successfully navigated the changes that were rapidly transforming the specialty of pulmonary medicine. During this time, fiberoptic bronchoscopy and the activities of the Pulmonary Function Laboratory were formally organized. The department also was given responsibility for the medical intensive care unit.

Following "Dr. Tom's" retirement in 1983, Muzaffar Ahmad M.D., was appointed chairman. During his eight years of leadership, effective recruiting practices doubled the number of staff members to 10 and established a productive blend of individuals who contributed to the department's growing national reputation for clinical expertise and research. In 1985 the department became the first in the Division of Medicine to appoint a full-time laboratory scientist, Mary Jane Thomassen, Ph.D., to its primary staff, thus providing an important model for collaborative research. The addition of a Section of Respiratory Therapy laid the groundwork for subsequent growth in clinical activity and academic accomplishment.

Following Ahmad's appointment as chairman of the Division of Medicine in 1991, Herbert P. Wiedemann, M.D., was named chairman of the department and its name was changed to Pulmonary and Critical Care Medicine. Under Wiedemann's direction, clinical and research activity continued to increase. In conjunction with the Department of Thoracic and Cardiovascular Surgery, the department developed one of the leading programs of lung transplantation in the country which is, at this time, the only one in Ohio (see Chapter 14). There are currently 15 physicians on staff, including two adult allergists.

The National Institutes of Health supports five separate research projects in the department: a clinical center for research in adult respiratory distress syndrome (ARDS) ; a data coordinating center for the registry of patients with severe deficiency of alpha-1

---

[8] Van Ordstrand worked on this problem with Sharad D. Deodhar, M.D., Ph.D., of the Department of Immunopathology. Deodhar demonstrated the immunological nature of berylliosis, an outstanding example of the interdivisional collaboration that typifies the Clinic's approach to clinical investigation.

antitrypsin; a study of alveolar macrophage function in lung disorders; the development of inducible vectors for gene therapy; and the assessment of pulmonary function in pediatric AIDS patients. Other research projects, such as the investigation of innovative therapies for sepsis, ARDS, and asthma, and new bronchoscopy techniques for detecting or palliating lung cancer, are supported by private donations. As a link to the past, the department recently rekindled its research into beryllium-induced lung disease.

In 1991, the Department of Pulmonary and Critical Care Medicine absorbed the Department of Allergy, which became the Section of Adult Allergy and Immunology. It had been created in 1934 with I. M. Hinnant, M.D., as head. He was succeeded by J. Warrick Thomas, M.D. (1939-44) ; C. R. K. Johnston, M.D. (1944-66); Richard R. Evans, M.D. (1966-76), co-discoverer of the enzymatic defect responsible for hereditary angioneurotic edema; Joseph F. Kelley, M.D. (1976-86) ; and Sami Bahna, M.D. (1987-90). Today, the department concentrates on rhinitis and sinusitis, asthma and latex allergy.

ENDOCRINOLOGY

Although the treatment of hypertension and coronary artery disease greatly influenced the Clinic's growth and development, significant advances were made in many other specialties. The first medical specialty at the Clinic was endocrinology, which was established in 1921 as a "diabetic service" under Henry J. John, M.D. Dr. John founded Camp Ho Mita Koda, the oldest summer camp in the world for diabetic children, with the assistance of other Clinic staff, including E. Perry McCullagh, M.D. A formal Department of Endocrinology was formed in 1928 with McCullagh as chairman. McCullagh had started his training in surgery, but gradually shifted his interests to endocrinology, which was a new specialty at that time. Like John, he started with diabetes, but soon expanded to encompass the entire field of endocrinology. He was a walking encyclopedia, a colorful and friendly person with an inexhaustible supply of poems, jokes, and stories.[9]

---

[9] Sometimes McCullagh gave orders that were clear only to himself. Once his resident misinterpreted an order and requested that a radiological examination of the colon be done on a woman with no gastrointestinal symptoms. The patient was undergoing the study when McCullagh was making rounds, and he became visibly annoyed. However, the x-ray film showed a large cancer of the colon, so McCullagh accepted the report in good grace and complimented the resident.

In the early days, McCullagh was engaged in laboratory and clinical research on a wide variety of endocrinologic topics. His work with testosterone and intermedin received wide recognition. His belief in rigid control of blood glucose levels for diabetics was later discounted, but is now being revived

Diabetes has remained a driving interest of the department, which, following McCullagh, was headed successively by Penn G. Skillern, M.D., O. Peter Schumacher, M.D., Byron J. Hoogwerf, M.D., and, since 1992, Charles Faiman, M.D. Over the years, department interests have included lipid disorders, bone and mineral metabolism, and general endocrinology. The areas of reproductive medicine and pituitary disorders, which fascinated McCullagh, have recently again become centers of attention. The Clinic's research and education in endocrinology and metabolism have grown to become premier programs in the country.

DERMATOLOGY

The second specialist appointed to the Clinic staff was Earl Netherton, M.D., who served as chairman of the Department of Dermatology from 1923 to 1958. Although dermatology was generally disliked and even omitted from most training programs at that time, it was a treasured rotation among the Clinic's internal medicine residents. Netherton was a kindly teacher, respectful of students' opinions, who sharpened their observational skills. His charts vividly describe patients' skin lesions along with their diagnoses and treatments, and include prescriptions and directions for use. A true "hands-on" physician, Netherton could tell whether or not an ointment had been prepared properly by merely rubbing it between his fingers. He was a pioneer in dermatopathology and safe radiation therapy for skin diseases, and was an expert in the tedious investigation of patients with contact dermatitis.

John R. Haserick, M.D., succeeded Netherton as chairman of dermatology in 1958. He is best known for his contributions to the diagnosis and treatment of disseminated lupus erythematosus, a disease sometimes only affecting the skin but that often affects other organs and leads to death if untreated.[10] The current chairman is

---

[10] Haserick discovered the L. E. cell phenomenon, which for years was the mainstay diagnostic test for this disease. He never really got credit for this, however, because his publication was a few months behind that of Hargreaves at Mayo Clinic, who had simultaneously observed the same phenomenon. Haserick was the first to describe the fact that the phenomenon was due to a circulating "factor," which later turned out to be one of the anti-nuclear antibodies.

Philip L. Bailin, M.D., who assumed the position in 1977. Under Bailin's guidance, the department has grown from four to nine, making it one of the largest dermatology programs in the country. Bailin also expanded the residency program and developed post-residency fellowships in dermatologic surgery and dermatopathology.

The department has achieved international recognition in the areas of cutaneous oncology (MOHS); pediatric dermatology; oral medicine and cutaneous immunology; contact dermatitis; psoriasis and related diseases. One of the best-known members of the department, Wilma F. Bergfeld, M.D., holds the distinction of having been the first woman president of the Academy of Medicine of Cleveland. She was also elected to the presidency of the American Academy of Dermatology and has held other offices in local and national organizations.

GASTROENTEROLOGY

E. N. Collins, M.D., came to the Clinic in 1931 as a radiologist with a special interest in disorders of the digestive tract. By 1934, his reputation as a "stomach specialist" was firmly established, and he was asked to set up a Department of Gastroenterology. Thus, he became a practicing internist. His background in radiology, extensive knowledge, and aptitude for teaching made him popular with residents.

Upon Collins' death in 1959, Charles H. Brown, M.D., was named head of the department. During his tenure, he added two important physicians to the staff: Benjamin H. Sullivan, Jr., M.D., and Richard G. Farmer, M.D. Sullivan was a pioneer in the development and popularization of fiberoptic endoscopy, whose influence greatly affected the practice of that specialty worldwide. Farmer, who was destined to succeed Brown as chairman of the department, shared his interest in inflammatory bowel disease. By working with his colleagues in pediatrics, surgery, and pathology, Farmer led the Clinic to international prominence in the management of this affliction.

When Farmer became chairman of the Division of Medicine, Bertram Fleshler, M.D., was named his successor in the Department of Gastroenterology. Fleshler continued to strengthen the department, particularly in the areas of motility and diseases of the esophagus.

The next chairman was Michael Sivak, M.D., who established an outstanding training program in innovative endoscopic technology and procedures, including endoscopic ultrasound and sclerosis of bleeding varices.

The Department of Gastroenterology has been chaired by Joel Richter, M.D., since 1994. Richter divided the 17-member group into six academic centers of excellence: colon cancer, endoscopy, hepatology, gastrointestinal motility (with swallowing center), inflammatory bowel disease, and nutrition. Their goal is to expand clinical and research activities while working with colleagues in Colorectal Surgery, General Surgery, Liver Transplant Surgery, Thoracic Surgery, Radiology, and Pathology to make the Clinic's Digestive Disease Center one of the best in the country.

NEUROLOGY, PSYCHIATRY, AND PSYCHOLOGY

The need for a Department of Neuropsychiatry brought Professor Louis J. Karnosh from City Hospital (now called MetroHealth) to the Clinic in 1946. His stature lent immediate prestige to the new department. According to his colleagues, what Karnosh did not know about neuropsychiatry was either unimportant or false.

Karnosh was a master neuropsychologist who inspired the confidence of patients, residents, and colleagues. His clinical approach was characterized by insightful questioning and therapeutic recommendations. His clinical notes were so complete and exquisitely phrased and executed that he never dictated reports to physicians; his secretaries merely copied his notes. Underneath his sharp features and stern countenance lay a good sense of humor, which was intensified by his deadpan delivery.[11]

When Karnosh retired in 1957, Guy H. "Red" Williams, M.D., succeeded him. He was a gentle, good-natured man and an accomplished physician who was popular with his staff. He gradually expanded the department and developed an outstanding Section of Electroencephalography. Due to increasing specialization in both areas, Williams advised that Neuropsychiatry be divided into two departments. This was accomplished in 1960. Williams became chairman of the new Department of Neurology, and A. Dixon Weatherhead, M.D., was appointed chairman of the Department of Psychiatry.

In 1976, John P. Conomy, M.D., became chairman of the Department of Neurology, succeeding the brief and tumultuous but productive chairmanship of Arnold H. Greenhouse, M.D. Green-

---

[11] Karnosh found time to write books and illustrate them with superb woodcuts of his own making. He also built a model railroad system and cultivated an encyclopedic knowledge of railroading.

house had recruited several young, highly talented neurologists who eventually came to occupy leadership positions within the department, including Conomy. As chairman, Conomy expanded the department by adding experts in all major neurological subspecialties. Today, the effort continues under Hans O. Lüders, M.D., who joined the Clinic in 1978 as head of the Section of Electroencephalography and was appointed department chairman in 1991.

Since Lüders' appointment, Asa Wilbourn, M.D., has established an electromyography laboratory of national repute, and Hiroshi Mitsumoto, M.D., has developed a Section of Neuromuscular Disease and a laboratory for amyotrophic lateral sclerosis (ALS) research. Conomy was instrumental in establishing the Mellen Center for Multiple Sclerosis, which has become a model of integrated clinical and research efforts (see Chapter 14).

Under Lüders's direction, the Section of Epilepsy and Sleep Disorders has become an international leader, with a four-bed adult monitoring unit and specialized four-bed pediatric unit. Computer software to monitor epilepsy — a paperless EEG system called *Vanguard* — was developed by Richard Burgess, M.D., and his team of engineers. It is now considered the most advanced software of its kind in the world . When Harold "Holly" Morris, M.D., was named head of the Section of Epilepsy and Sleep Disorders in 1991, he expanded the capabilities of *Vanguard* to include monitoring during epilepsy surgery.

Subspecialty programs of national visibility and successful clinical research efforts were established in the fields of pediatric neurology, neuro-oncology and movement disorders. The creation of the Department of Neuroscience within the Research Institute under the direction of Bruce Trapp, Ph.D., provided the necessary infrastructure to help the Neurology Department make essential contributions in the quest to conquer neurologic diseases.

The Department of Psychiatry developed more gradually during Weatherhead's tenure as chairman. The department's first clinical psychologist, David A. Rodgers, Ph.D., was hired in 1966.[12]

When Richard M. Steinhilber, M.D., was named chairman in 1977, a five-year growth spurt brought the number of staff members to a

---

[12] Clare Robinson, M.S., had been hired as a child psychologist by the Department of Pediatrics in 1953. However, lack of a Ph.D. degree prevented her from being promoted to full membership of the professional staff. When the "Associate Staff" category was created in 1968, she was immediately promoted to that position.

total of 13 psychiatrists and three psychologists.[13] He added special Sections of Child and Adolescent Psychiatry, Consultation-Liaison Psychiatry, Alcohol and Drug Recovery, Chronic Pain Management, and Psychology. Neal Krupp, M.D., who succeeded him in 1982, recognized the broader membership by changing the name to the Department of Psychiatry and Psychology. During Krupp's decade of leadership, a Section of Neuropsychology was established, the psychiatry residency expanded and post-doctoral training in psychology and neuropsychology added. George E. Tesar, M.D., assumed the chairmanship of this respected department in 1993.

RHEUMATIC AND IMMUNOLOGIC DISEASE

Despite Russell Haden's interests in arthritis in the 1930s and '40s, the Department of Rheumatology was not established until 1953. Arthur L. Scherbel, M.D., was named the first chairman and held the post for 27 years.

In Scherbel's time, most practitioners were discouraged by the problems of joint disease. Yet his optimistic attitude helped to create a great demand for this service. During his tenure, the department conducted important studies in cytotoxic drugs, especially mechlorethamine and methotrexate, for rheumatoid arthritis, systemic lupus erythematosus, vasculitis and allied disorders. Scherbel also had a strong interest in scleroderma and was one of the first to recognize the importance of vascular lability and ischemia in this disease.

In 1981, John D. Clough, M.D., succeeded Scherbel as department chairman. Within a few years, he increased the department to 11 physicians in order to handle the growing patient load as well as increased interest in the specialty by young physicians. He also changed the name to the Department of Rheumatic and Immunologic Disease to recognize the staff's involvement in the care of patients with immunologic abnormalities and immunological research. Sections of Adult and Pediatric Rheumatology, Clinical Immunology, Special Clinics, and Physical Medicine and Rehabilitation were formed.[14] Leonard H. Calabrese, D.O., the first

---

[13] Steinhilber was dynamic and energetic in a way that belies the stereotype of the quiet, thoughtful, contemplative psychiatrist. Farmer used to say that "within his chest beats the heart of an orthopedic surgeon."

[14] Beginning in 1974 the department also operated the Special Immunology Laboratory in the Department of Immunopathology, where modern testing for autoantibodies and immune complexes was developed and research projects on immunocyte interaction were conducted. This laboratory was another model of interdivisional collaboration, but it fell victim to the reorganization of the Division of Laboratory Medicine that occurred subsequent to Deodhar's retirement.

osteopath appointed to the staff, became the head of Clinical Immunology. Calabrese has achieved national prominence for his work with rheumatological manifestations of AIDS, central nervous system vasculitis, and inclusion body myopathy. William S. Wilke, M.D., has played a prominent role in the popularization of methotrexate for the treatment of severe rheumatoid arthritis and some forms of systemic lupus erythematosus. Daniel J. Mazanec, M.D., led the department's efforts in metabolic bone disease, and Anna P. Koo, M.D., ran the therapeutic apheresis program.

In 1992, Gary S. Hoffman, M.D., became the third chairman of the department, filling the vacancy created when Clough was named Director of Health Affairs for The Cleveland Clinic. During his years at the National Institutes of Health, Hoffman had founded the International Network for the Study of Systemic Vasculitides, of which he is chairman. The organization is now based at the Clinic and serves to coordinate large multicenter studies for a variety of rare disorders. Hoffman himself is an internationally known expert on Wegener's granulomatosis, a rare form of vasculitis.

The department continues to advance clinical studies, develop new publications and books, and has formed an outstanding Section of Pediatric Rheumatology. Department members conduct a variety of research activities aimed at enhancing the understanding and quality of care in rheumatoid arthritis, fibromyalgia, chronic fatigue syndrome, systemic lupus erythematosus, and vasculitis.

HEMATOLOGY AND MEDICAL ONCOLOGY

Although Haden was primarily a hematologist, the Department of Hematology was not established until 1953. John D. Battle, M.D., was its first chairman. Over time, the medical treatment of cancer was recognized as a separate specialty, and the name was changed to the Department of Hematology and Medical Oncology.

James S. Hewlett, M.D., succeeded Battle in 1971. One of Hewlett's most important contributions to the field was his use of exchange transfusion for the effective treatment of thrombotic thrombocytopenic purpura, which previously had almost always been fatal. This treatment became the standard therapy until it was replaced by the much simpler technique of plasmapheresis, which was also pioneered at the Clinic.

When Hewlett retired, Robert B. Livingston, M.D., led the department until 1982. Livingston established the Predictive Assay Laboratory, where tumor cells from patients are grown and their reactions to various chemotherapeutic agents is determined.

James K. Weick, M.D., succeeded Livingston as chairman in 1983, and held the post until he left to become chairman of the Department of Hematology and Medical Oncology as well as chairman of the Division of Medicine at Cleveland Clinic Florida in 1991 (see Chapter 20).

Maurie Markman, M.D., who was recruited from Memorial Sloan-Kettering Cancer Center in 1992, is the current department chairman as well as director of the Cleveland Clinic Cancer Center (see Chapter 14). Under Markman, the staff has been active in testing the effectiveness of experimental drugs and drug combinations in the treatment of malignant disease. This commitment requires a great deal of time, accurate record keeping, careful analysis and persistent optimism, despite frequently discouraging responses. The staff treats benign hematological conditions as well.

Since the mid-1980s, the Department of Hematology and Medical Oncology has demonstrated significant growth in patient numbers as well as the size and scope of clinical research programs. Bone marrow transplantation, chemotherapy, and immunotherapy are among the treatments widely used by the staff. The bone marrow transplant program, which performs 50 percent of all transplants in Ohio, is nationally recognized. The department's palliative care and hospice program has been designated a pilot program of the World Health Organization, and the Horvitz Center, which opened in 1994, provides a unique focus on symptom management of patients hospitalized with cancer.

The Hematology/Medical Oncology staff has played a major role in the Clinic's multidisciplinary cancer efforts, including its highly regarded program in experimental therapeutics, which examines innovative treatments for malignant disease. The search for effective treatments continues, often drawing upon the cooperation of other medical and surgical departments at the Clinic.

GENERAL INTERNAL MEDICINE

Amid the rapid growth of specialty medicine at the Clinic, the value of general internal medicine was finally recognized by the establishment of the formal department in 1949. John Tucker, M.D., the first chairman, had been a member of the Division of Medicine since 1921. He was succeeded in 1960 by Leonard L. Lovshin, M.D., who founded the Section of Headache Medicine. The growth of this subspecialty continued under the stewardship of Robert Kunkel, M.D., an internationally recognized headache specialist. He was joined in 1986 by Glen Solomon, M.D., who became section head in

1994. All three physicians have held national leadership roles in the study of headache, bringing the Clinic wide recognition in experimental therapeutics and medical outcomes.

Ray A. Van Ommen, M.D., became the third chairman of the Department of Internal Medicine in 1970, and he also served as chairman of the Division of Medicine as well as founder of the Department of Infectious Disease. William H. Shafer, M.D., served ably as department chairman from 1972 until 1989.

In 1971, the Clinic responded to corporations seeking periodic health evaluations for their executives by establishing a Section of Preventive Health Services under the direction of Alfred Taylor, M.D. He was succeeded by Richard Matzen, M.D., and the section spun off into its own department.

In 1986, a Section of Geriatric Medicine was formed and headed by Dennis Jahnigen, M.D., who was recruited from the University of Colorado. Under his direction, the program became one of the top 10 geriatric medicine programs in the United States. After Jahnigen left the Clinic in 1994, Robert Palmer, M.D., was appointed as section head.

In 1989, the Department of Internal Medicine underwent a restructuring by chairman Stephen Ockner, M.D. The Department of Preventive Medicine was reabsorbed, and Richard Lang, M.D., was named section head. At the same time, the Department of Primary Health Care, which had been established in 1974 for employees and their families and was headed by Gilbert Lowenthal, M.D., was also brought under General Internal Medicine. Geoffrey Lefferts, M.D., was appointed head of the new Section of Primary Care. To reflect the wider scope of activities encompassed by the internists, the department was renamed General Internal Medicine.

After the consolidation, David L. Bronson, M.D., was recruited from the University of Vermont to serve as department chairman. Tremendous growth in the number of new staff members, patient visits, and residents occurred between 1992 and 1995. By the end of 1994, the department was serving more than 97,000 patient visits annually, making it the busiest in the Clinic. The residency program had grown to include 110 internal medicine residents, most of whom were receiving the majority of their experience in the Department of General Internal Medicine.

In the early 1990s, Clinic leaders recognized that the organization could provide more convenient service to patients in the surrounding communities through satellite facilities. The first satellite opened in Independence, Ohio, in 1993, with a group of orthopedists and one internist, Cynthia Deyling, M.D. A graduate of the

Clinic's internal medicine residency program, Deyling had already established an active practice in the Independence area. Over the next 18 months, Cleveland Clinic Independence grew to include four internists, two pediatricians, and a large sports medicine/orthopedic practice. In January 1995, a second satellite was opened in Willoughby Hills, headed by internist Thomas J. Morledge, M.D., and in September, 1995, a third was opened in Westlake, headed by internist A. Mary Walborn, M.D. A fourth satellite is scheduled to open in Solon in early 1996.

The rapid, planned growth of regional practice facilities pointed up the need for an organizational structure to provide coordination and leadership. In 1995, the Clinic established a new Division of Regional Medical Practice and asked Bronson to serve as chairman. The group is providing visibility and guidance to the development of new multispecialty services offered in the satellite facilities, regional group practices, and other off-campus programs.

INFECTIOUS DISEASE

Infectious Disease originated as a section of the Department of Internal Medicine under Van Ommen. In 1972, a separate department was created, and Martin C. McHenry, M.D., was named chairman.

The department flourished under McHenry's guidance, and was soon recognized for excellence in both clinical medicine and education. McHenry epitomized the consummate scholar, combining excellence at the bedside with compassionate care, superlative teaching, and active clinical research. For these reasons, he was the first recipient of the Bruce Hubbard Stewart Award for humanism in the practice of medicine.

During McHenry's chairmanship, the department grew to five physicians and conducted clinical trials and outcomes research in many areas, including new antimicrobials, heart and bloodstream infections, and osteomyelitis.

McHenry stepped down in 1991, and David L. Longworth, M.D., was appointed chairman in 1992. Three new staff physicians were recruited, and the department intensified its commitment to research. Programs in transplantation, infectious disease, outcomes research related to hospital epidemiology, and laboratory-based investigation regarding antiviral susceptibility testing were initiated. Numerous clinical trials of newer antimicrobial agents were begun, along with studies to determine the optimal therapy for difficult infectious diseases.

The department's close relationship with the Section of Microbiology in the Department of Clinical Pathology has proven to be fruitful. Many collaborative studies have resulted from this, as well as a combined fellowship program leading to certification in both disciplines. Clinical activity has grown steadily, with routine evaluations performed on difficult infectious disease problems in the areas of nosocomial and postoperative infections, endocarditis, bone and joint infections, HIV disease, fever of unknown origin, tropical disease, and community-acquired infections. Under Longworth's leadership, research productivity has increased, and the department has begun to achieve national stature commensurate with its recognized excellence in clinical medicine and education.

EMERGENCY MEDICINE

In May 1994, the Cleveland Clinic entered the arena of emergency medicine with the opening of an 18,000-square foot, state-of-the-art facility on the southwest corner of E. 93rd St. and Carnegie Avenue, the E Building. In stark contrast to the old 2,000-square foot "emergency room," which had functioned basically as a transfer center for ambulance patients, the Clinic's new facility signaled the organization's commitment to serving patients and the general public in times of crisis.

The new facility, which is a far cry from a standard emergency room, includes an 18-bed emergency treatment area, a four-bed minor illness area and is adjacent to a 20-bed "Clinical Decision Unit" — a new concept in emergency medicine shared with Kaiser Permanente. In this unit, patients who do not require immediate hospitalization can be observed and treated for up to 24 hours after their initial evaluation. Kaiser Permanente of Ohio, a branch of the giant HMO which formed a partnership with the Clinic in 1992, shares space in the Clinical Decision Unit, and has a separate emergency department within the same building. Patients of both organizations benefit from on-site radiology facilities, operating rooms directly overhead, and efficient access to the clinical laboratories and rooftop helipad.

Responsibility for providing care in this new facility belongs to the Department of Emergency Medicine, which the Board of Governors created in 1993 in anticipation of the new enterprise. Norman S. Abramson, M.D., became its first chairman. In the first year, he assembled a board-certified emergency medicine staff and, working with Sharon Coulter, M.S.N., M.B.A., R.N., (director of nursing), expanded the nursing staff to accommodate the patient volume. The department instituted education and training programs for The Ohio State University medical students and Cleveland Clinic internal medicine residents and laid plans for an emergency medicine residency program. The Department of Emergency Medicine became the linchpin for establishing centers for the evaluation and treatment of patients with chest pain, stroke, and asthma, as well as pediatric emergencies.

REHABILITATION MEDICINE

Recognizing the necessity of rehabilitation for continuity of care, the Clinic established an Institute of Rehabilitation Medicine in 1990. Vinod Sahgal, M.D., a respected neurologist and rehabilitation specialist, was recruited from Northwestern University Medical School to head the new program. The department now employs 150 and collaborates with nearly every department in the Clinic.

In its first two years, the department obtained funding for rehabilitation projects from the National Academy of Sciences, Project ACTION, and local donors. The department is part of the teaching program at Ohio State's medical school, and faculty members have presented or published a number of papers. Plans are under way to expand the staff to six physicians and six engineers.

CONCLUSION

Although practice methods have become more scientific since 1921, the Clinic's approach to patient care has remained unchanged: one physician is responsible for each patient's care and orders any consultations with other physicians that may be required. With drastic changes in health care under way, the Clinic agrees that the role of the primary physician is more important than ever to ensure appropriate care and the timely, judicious use of resources.

ELEVEN

DIVISION OF PEDIATRICS

Children are poor men's riches.

— *English Proverb*

Children with rare and complicated diseases have been cared for at The Cleveland Clinic since its inception. In the early days the care was disease-oriented rather than child-centered. That changed in 1951 when Robert D. Mercer, M.D., arrived from Western Reserve University to start a Department of Pediatrics.

The Clinic's first pediatric outpatient department was located in two rooms "loaned" by the Department of Urology. They were just around the corner from Sones' cardiac catheterization laboratory. A pediatric cardiologist, Sones was using his new angiography technique to help Clinic surgeons perform heart operations on children and obtain excellent results.[1] The Clinic reserved 30 of its 357 hospital beds for a pediatric ward.

The first pediatrician Mercer recruited was Viola Startzman, M.D., a superb clinician admired and respected throughout the community. Startzman had been trained as a laboratory technician before going to medical school, and her understanding of blood chemistry proved invaluable.

1953 was a landmark year in which the Department of Pediatrics started a residency program and gave its first postgraduate education course.[2] It was also the year Clare Robinson, M.S., became the department's third staff member.[3]

---

[1] At that time there was no pediatric cardiologist or pediatric cardiac surgeon at Western Reserve University, and patients from that institution were sent to the Mayo Clinic.

[2] In 1953, first-year pediatric residents were paid $150 a month.

[3] Considered to be one of the best pediatric and adolescent psychologists in the profession, she nevertheless lacked the doctoral degree necessary for full staff status. When the "Associate

In 1954, the department initiated a program with St. John School of Nursing for training student nurses in pediatrics. This was the first student nurse program at The Cleveland Clinic. A few years later, the department developed a program for training third-year medical students, and this became the first medical school program at the Clinic.

During those years, the Clinic had an excellent Department of Obstetrics under the supervision of Howard P. Taylor, M.D. It was among the first in the country to use amniocentesis, invite fathers into the delivery room, and permit newborns to stay in their mothers' hospital rooms. Clinic obstetricians even attempted intra-uterine transfusions. Their newborn nursery was open to all pediatricians in the community. Yet despite its artistic success, the Department of Obstetrics was closed in 1966 to make room for expansion of cardiac surgery. This was a severe blow to the pediatricians, whose patient base in large part was comprised of babies born at the Clinic. Nevertheless, pediatrics survived and thrived. After a 29-year absence, obstetrics reopened at the Clinic in 1995 (see Chapter 12).

In 1956, Mercer invited Mary Harmon, M.D., to join the staff. A specialist in metabolic abnormalities in babies, she established a unit which was designated by the State of Ohio as a center for the treatment of phenylketonuria (PKU) .

The department next added pediatric gastroenterology with the appointment of William M. Michener, M.D., in 1961. He left in 1968 but returned five years later to become Director of Education. He then resumed his pediatric practice on a part-time basis. His ability to distinguish chronic ulcerative colitis from Crohn's disease was highly valued. A second gastroenterologist was not added until the early 1980s, when Robert Wyllie, M.D., was recruited. The section quickly grew into one of the largest groups of pediatric gastroenterologists in the country, gaining national recognition in the treatment of inflammatory bowel disease, hepatitis, and gastrointestinal bleeding, as well as for endoscopy and liver transplantation. Wyllie set the national standards for pediatric endoscopy and was the senior editor of a major textbook in pediatric gastroenterology.

Mercer had participated in the first successful chemotherapy during his pathology residency at Boston Children's Hospital. The study in which he assisted included a large number of patients, and its success gave birth to the subspecialty of pediatric oncology. At

---

Staff" category was created in 1968, she was appointed to that position, as noted in the previous chapter.

Douglas S. Moodie, M.D., Chairman, Division of Pediatrics, 1994–

the Clinic, Mercer continued to care for cancer patients himself until his other pediatric patients and administrative duties necessitated looking for help. In 1962, he recruited Derrick Lonsdale, M.D., a pediatrician with a special interest in childhood cancer, to assume the care of the Clinic's young patients with leukemia and other childhood cancers.

In 1960 Mercer started one of the first laboratories in the state for the culture of cells and study of chromosomes. He felt he needed these studies to aid in diagnosis of certain congenital disorders. After a few years, he turned the laboratory over to the Department of Laboratory Medicine.

In 1971, residency programs began to graduate a new wave of physicians and surgeons with training in pediatric specialties, and the Clinic recruited two: Paul Dyment, M.D., a pediatric hematologist/oncologist, and Ronald L. Price, M.D., a pediatric ophthalmologist. Price joined the Department of Ophthalmology and received a joint appointment in Pediatrics. Dyment became a well known pediatric specialist and was appointed department chairman upon Mercer's retirement in 1980. These additions allowed the Clinic to begin offering the specialty care that has distinguished it in American medicine.

In 1973, the appointment of A. David Rothner, M.D., enabled the Clinic to establish the Section of Pediatric Neurology. Over the years, the section has grown and has developed particular expertise in the treatment of headaches, neurofibromatosis, learning disabilities, brain tumors, and metabolic and neuromuscular disorders. By the mid-1980s, so many children with epilepsy were being evaluated at the Clinic that a special childhood epilepsy service was established. The pediatric neurologists now offer a 24-hour, fully computerized epilepsy and sleep studies unit, and with their neurosurgical colleagues they have developed an international reputation in epilepsy surgery for children.

In 1977 Carl C. Gill, M.D., joined the staff to organize a pediatric cardiac surgery program. A year later, Douglas S. Moodie, M.D., a pediatric cardiologist who had worked with Gill at the Mayo Clinic, rejoined him as the first head of the Section of Pediatric Cardiology. Other cardiologists with expertise in pediatric electrophysiology, echocardiography, Kawasaki disease, and cardiac transplantation were subsequently added. The section has developed a unique program that provides continuity of care for patients with congenital heart defects from birth through old age. Today, the Clinic's pediatric cardiologists and cardiac surgeons care for the largest number of adult congenital heart disease patients in the country. Capitalizing on this expertise, they have developed fellowships in adult congenital heart disease (1993) and pediatric interventional cardiology (1994) — both unusual training programs in this country.

In 1986, Dyment left the Clinic to become chairman of pediatrics at the Eastern Maine Medical Center in Portland and was succeeded as department chairman by Moodie.

After Gill left Cleveland in 1987 to become chief of staff and then chief executive officer of Cleveland Clinic Florida, Eliot Rosenkranz, M.D., was named the new head of the Section of Congenital Heart Surgery. Renowned Australian surgeon Roger B. Mee, M.B. Ch.B., succeeded him, bringing with him an international reputation for excellence and innovation. A second congenital heart surgeon was added in 1993. Together, they doubled the number of pediatric open heart cases and at the same time achieved one of the lowest mortality and morbidity rates in the world.

Robert Kay, M.D., started the Section of Pediatric Urology in 1980, and quickly became known as an outstanding urologist. However, he became so busy with his responsibilities as director of medical operations for the Clinic that a second surgeon, Jonathan H. Ross, M.D., had to be added to the staff in 1992.

The first full-time pediatric surgeon at the Clinic was Hugh V. Firor, M.D., who arrived in 1981 and operated primarily on children with abdominal and bowel disease. He left the Clinic in 1991 and was replaced by Fred Alexander, M.D. Within two years, Alexander was performing more than 300 operations a year and investigating the feasibility of doing small bowel transplantation in children.

By the 1980s, the Clinic was becoming well known worldwide for pediatric specialty care, but was not known in the community for general pediatrics. A Section of General Pediatrics had existed since the appointment of Dr. Ruth Imrie in 1978, but it was part of Primary Care and existed to provide care for the children of staff and employees. In 1982, Michael V. Macknin, M.D., a highly regarded academic pediatrician was recruited, and a third pediatrician was added two years later. In 1991, Moodie brought the section into the Department of Pediatrics to give it a higher profile in the community.

Robert J. Cunningham, M.D., became head of pediatric nephrology in 1981, and assumed directorship of the pediatric residency program in 1985. He built the largest pediatric nephrology service in northeastern Ohio, was named vice chairman of Pediatrics, and is currently associate director of The Cleveland Clinic Children's Hospital. Needless to say, a second nephrologist was needed. When Ben Brouhard, M.D., joined the staff in 1988, he not only brought expertise in pediatric hypertension and renal transplantation; he also had a strong research background. Brouhard subsequently became director of pediatric research and developed an excellent program for both staff and residents. While only a quarter of the pediatric programs in the country require their residents to do research, The Cleveland Clinic requires pediatric residents to present the results of a research project each year. Brouhard also encouraged staff members to publish, speak, and spread their expertise as visiting professors. This activity has done much to improve their national reputation.

Although Neurosurgery chairman Donald F. Dohn, M.D., performed surgery on children, the first designated pediatric neurosurgeon was Joseph F. Hahn, M.D., who eventually succeeded Dohn as department chairman. In 1987 Hahn's patient-care capacity was reduced when he was appointed chief of the Division of Surgery while maintaining his departmental leadership. The growing need for a full-time pediatric neurosurgeon led Moodie to recruit the Clinic's first pediatric-trained neurosurgeon, Mark S. Luciano, M.D., in 1993.

A similar situation existed in Endocrinology. Department chairman O. Peter Schumacher, M.D., Ph.D., had developed a solid reputation in pediatric diabetes, but he had been trained in adult endocrinology. The Clinic's first pediatric endocrinologist, Geoffrey Redmond, M.D., arrived in 1982. When he left for private practice in 1991, he was replaced by Douglas G. Rogers, M.D., a specialist in pediatric diabetes. Rogers also became the first quality assurance officer for Pediatrics, a post he held until 1995 when it was assumed by gastroenterologist Marsha Kay, M.D.

Michael J. McHugh, M.D., was recruited to head pediatric intensive care in 1979, and became director of the new Pediatric Intensive Care Unit in 1992. He also took over directorship of the residency program from Cunningham in 1992. Under his leadership, the number of residents has more than doubled to 33. In addition, up to 60 medical students now rotate through Pediatrics every year, and fellowships have been developed in the pediatric subspecialties of nephrology, gastroenterology, allergy and immunology, critical care, interventional cardiology, psychology, and adult congenital heart disease.

Gynecologist Gita P. Gidwani, M.D., came to the Clinic in 1976 from Kaiser Permanente. She remains the institution's only gynecologist with special training in the problems of adolescence. She works closely with Ellen Rome, M.D., a specialist in adolescent pediatrics who joined the staff in 1994, and Ruth Imrie, who had developed an interest and expertise in the problems of teenagers over the years.

Under Moodie's direction, the Department of Pediatric and Adolescent Medicine took a quantum leap from a small but respected group of pediatric specialists to one of the largest and most comprehensive pediatric programs in the country. Existing sections were expanded, and the first pediatric specialists in many fields were added to care for the growing number of children. These included allergy (Alton L. Melton, M.D., 1988), infectious disease (Barbara Baetz-Greenwalt, M.D., 1988), dermatology (Teri A. Kahn, M.D., in 1992),[4] plastic surgery (Frank A. Papay, M.D., 1992), pulmonary disease (Paul C. Stillwell, M.D., 1992), rheumatology (Bernhard Singsen, M.D., 1993), otolaryngology (Diana Traquina, M.D., 1993) and neonatology (Jeffrey Schwersenski, M.D., 1994).

In 1987, the Clinic opened its Children's Hospital and became an associate member of the National Association of Children's Hospitals

---

[4] John B. Lampe, M.D., a general pediatrician recruited in 1991, had a special interest in pediatric dermatology and provided new expertise in this area. Kahn was the first trained pediatric dermatologist at the Clinic, and she had established the largest practice of its kind in northern Ohio.

and Related Institutions. This hospital-within-a-hospital occupies the third floor of the old hospital. In one unit, children under age 10 are cared for in single rooms. Each room provides space for the patient's own toys as well as a convertible chair bed to accommodate a parent. A rooftop play deck provides a safe outdoor play area for patients right off the hospital wing.[5] A separate unit, designed for adolescent patients, is staffed with nurses specially trained in treating teenagers. To make hospitalization as pleasant an experience as possible, the unit includes a recreation room with appropriate furniture, stereo equipment, and games. A four-bed special care unit, originally placed on this unit to treat patients needing more intense nursing care, has evolved into an epilepsy monitoring unit.

The pediatric intensive care unit opened in the fall of 1992 and quickly grew from six to nine beds. It is likely that additional beds will be necessary to accommodate the rapidly growing programs in pediatric cardiac surgery and neurosurgery. The Clinic opened a pediatric cardiac surgery operating room directly outside the intensive care unit and moved all pediatric cardiology and cardiac surgery services to an integrated space in the Children's Hospital at the end of 1994.

In 1994, the Department of Pediatrics, with a staff of 79 physicians, was granted division status to help coordinate and administer all pediatric activity at The Cleveland Clinic.

The future of pediatrics at The Cleveland Clinic promises to be exciting. The staff anticipates rapid growth in both the specialty and general pediatrics programs, the Children's Hospital facilities, satellite pediatric programs, and obstetrics. A common focus on providing the best possible care of sick children unifies these activities. Active research programs in many areas, including the study and treatment of genetic and immunologic diseases, will constantly reaffirm and support this goal.

---

[5] The Jennifer Ferchill Play Deck is a highly valued component of The Cleveland Clinic Children's Hospital. Located right off the pediatric hospital wing, its wide doors, flat surface, and oxygen hook-ups ensure that even wheelchair-bound and intravenous-tethered children can enjoy fresh air. A glass house between the outdoor portion and the hospital provides an outdoor-type setting where children can play during the winter. The play deck was donated by John Ferchill, a corporate developer, in gratitude for the care his young daughter had received at the Clinic during her battle with a brain tumor. Ferchill persuaded Cleveland's construction community to donate almost $700,000 worth of labor to construct the deck.

TWELVE

DIVISION OF SURGERY

The best surgeon is he that hath been hacked himself.
— *English Proverb*

When the Clinic opened in 1921, urology and otolaryngology (then called ear-nose-throat) were the only surgical specialties represented. General surgeons did all other operations. Urology had not, however, formally separated from general surgery, and Lower performed almost as many thyroidectomies, cholecystectomies, and general surgical procedures as urologic procedures.

The first otolaryngologist, and later, orthopedic, neurological, and ophthalmic surgeons, strictly limited their practices to their specialties. Eventually, specialists in plastic surgery, gynecology, thoracic surgery, vascular surgery, and colorectal surgery were added to the staff. General surgery gradually became one of the smaller services, limited in scope to the treatment of diseases of the upper abdomen, thyroid and breast, and to hernia repair.

Nevertheless, many of the physicians who helped shape The Cleveland Clinic Foundation in its early days were general surgeons. For this reason, the development of the Division of Surgery has been closely intertwined with the history of the Department of General Surgery and the practice of surgery as a whole in the 20th century.

GENERAL SURGERY

Thyroidectomies, for the most part, paid for the original Clinic and Hospital. In 1921, following the discovery that iodine made thyroidectomy possible for patients with Graves' disease, a backlog of

Joseph F. Hahn, M.D., Chairman, Division of Surgery, 1987–

suddenly operable patients was found to exist. Nontoxic goiters that were endemic in the Great Lakes Region generated additional patients. Improvements in surgical technique introduced by Crile and the Mayo brothers made thyroidectomy safe, and in 1927, Clinic surgeons were performing an average of ten a day. Their mortality rate for this procedure was the lowest ever reported.[1]

---

[1] The greatest danger at that time was thyroid crisis, a dramatic chain of events that was likely to occur when a patient with Graves' disease and severe hyperthyroidism was subjected to general anesthesia, surgery, infection, or even a bad fright. The patient's pulse rate would soar, the heart often fibrillated and the body temperature rose to 105° or 106°F. The patient literally was consumed in the fire of his own metabolism. Ice bags and oxygen tents sometimes helped; transfusions did not. The crisis tended to run its course, peaking on the second night after surgery, then, if the patient survived, subsiding.

Crile believed that fear could trigger such a crisis. To avoid it, he developed a system called "stealing the thyroid." The patient would not be told when the operation was to take place. Every morning, breakfast was withheld and the nurse anesthetist would go to the patient's bedside and administer just enough nitrous oxide to make the patient a bit giddy and confused. On the morning of surgery, the routine was the same except that the analgesia was a little deeper, so the patient took no notice when the team moved in. The neck was prepared with ether, iodine, and alcohol, then draped. A floor nurse or the patient's private nurse stood on a chair behind the head of the bed and illuminated the operative field with a shaded light held on the end of a pole.

With a single stroke, Crile would make a gracefully curved incision and then dissect the skin flap. He never stopped to clamp bleeders; that was the function of the first assistant. The sec-

Better surgical training and technique and improved anesthesia gradually enabled increasing numbers of these operations to be done in community hospitals. The introduction of iodized salt, better food transportation, antithyroid drugs, and radioactive iodine eventually obviated the need to operate on patients for Graves' disease. After 1927, the incidence of thyroidectomy at The Cleveland Clinic declined steadily.[2]

At the same time, the number of operations for cancer of the colon and rectum grew. Thomas E. Jones, M.D., an accomplished abdominal surgeon, returned from a trip to London having learned a one-stage combined abdominoperineal resection procedure, which he proceeded to perfect into a fine art. He could perform three or four of these complex operations in a morning when it took most surgeons three or four hours to do one.

Jones was operating in the days before sulfonamides or antibiotics, and mortality from colon resection with anastomosis was high everywhere. The fatal problem was peritonitis, which Jones avoided by not opening the bowel or anastomosing it. Cancers located well above the rectum were treated by abdominoperineal resection with end colostomy. After a resection of the left colon or transverse colon, he usually exteriorized the tumor over a Rankin clamp and performed an obstructive resection. There were no anastomoses except after resections of the right colon, which had few complications. The result was an astonishingly low mortality rate for surgery of the colon and rectum, but the price was a high incidence of colostomy.

Jones was a true general surgeon whose versatility encompassed not only abdominal surgery, but also gynecology, varicose veins, radical dissections of the neck, and some thoracic surgery. A pioneer in implanting radium and gold radon seeds into cancers, Jones mastered the techniques of surgical irradiation and was considered a leading authority on the treatment of cancer. He performed a successful local resection of a lung cancer several years before the first reported successful pneumonectomy for this disease, and pioneered the use of electrocoagulation with implantation of

---

ond assistant, hanging uncomfortably over the head of the bed, would retract the skin and cut the thread after the knots were tied. These 10-minute operations were bloody and unanatomic, but in the days before intravenous anesthesia, speed was necessary. A transfusion team was always available to give blood when there was excessive loss. The same team stood ready to do tracheotomies when necessary, since the incidence of injury to the recurrent laryngeal nerves was high. Postoperative hemorrhage was fairly common, too, because the main vessels were not tied.

[2] Despite the large number of thyroidectomies performed in 1927, not one patient was diagnosed to have hyperparathyroidism. In 1969 Clinic surgeons performed 32 operations on the parathyroid. By the 1990s, as the result of better diagnostic techniques and the reputation of Caldwell B. Esselstyn, Jr., M.D., over 100 operations for hyperparathyroidism were performed annually.

Thomas E. Jones, M.D., Chief of Surgery, 1943–1949

radon seeds in selected low-lying rectal cancers. Although his results were excellent, he never reported them.

After Jones's sudden death in 1949,[3] he was replaced by Robert S. Dinsmore, M.D., one of the two remaining general surgeons in the department. He held both titles until his own death in 1957. During that eight-year period, the hospital expanded. Dinsmore, wisely looking ahead, planned a 23-room operating pavilion. Many members of the staff felt that this was far too big, since antibiotics, antithyroid drugs, and radioactive iodine were rapidly drying up the source of thyroid operations. But by the time the building was finished, the operating rooms were fully used. Ten years later, after closure of the obstetrics department, six more rooms had to be opened to accommodate the growing number of cardiac cases.

Upon Dinsmore's death, Stanley O. Hoerr, M.D., was appointed chairman of the Division of Surgery, and George Crile, Jr., M.D., became chairman of the Department of General Surgery. They had

---

[3] In 1949, Jones was 57 years old and at the peak of his career when he collapsed in the surgeons' locker room from a ruptured left ventricle. Efforts to resuscitate him failed. At the time of his death, he was the principal surgeon in the Department of General Surgery and chairman of the Division of Surgery.

Robert S. Dinsmore, M.D., Chief of Surgery 1949–1957

been colleagues in the Department of General Surgery under Dinsmore. Thus arose a unique situation in which Hoerr was Crile's chairman in the division and Crile was Hoerr's chairman in the department. The arrangement worked, undoubtedly because the men respected each other and had no cause for conflict.

James S. Krieger, M.D., succeeded Hoerr as chairman of the Division of Surgery in 1971, and served until his retirement. Bruce H. Stewart, M.D., a urologist, held the position from 1980 until his untimely death from cancer in 1983. Ralph A. Straffon, M.D., Stewart's colleague and chairman of the Department of Urology, was then appointed chairman of the Division of Surgery. When Straffon was tapped to become Chief of Staff in 1986, Joseph F. Hahn, M.D., former chairman of the Department of Neurological Surgery, took over the position.

For more than six decades, Clinic surgeons have tried to find ways to avoid the morbidities associated with radical operations for cancer. In 1955, when the worldwide trend was towards more radical and therefore, extensive and deforming operations, Crile, Jr., began to treat selected patients with small breast cancers by wide local excision or partial mastectomy, usually combined with axillary dissection. He abandoned radical mastectomy, setting a national trend. In 1980, Caldwell B. Esselstyn, Jr., M.D., began to combine local excision of small breast cancers with specialized radiation. The Breast Center, opened in 1995, builds on this philosophy as it provides a multidisciplinary approach to treating breast cancer.

In 1968, Crile, Jr., who had always planned to retire at age 60, resigned as head of the Department of General Surgery and became a senior consultant. Hoerr served as head for one year before following in Crile's footsteps. Robert E. Hermann, M.D., a member of the staff with a special interest in teaching, was chosen to head the department. An exuberant man and an excellent surgeon, Hermann made friends for the Clinic all over the world. Under his direction, the breast cancer surgeons continued to evaluate and practice conservative operations, assembling a larger patient population with longer follow-up than any other institution in the country. Hermann also started a successful liver transplantation program that complemented the department's previous experience with liver surgery, major bile duct surgery, and surgery for portal hypertension (see Chapter 14).

With the cooperation of their colleagues in the Department of Gastroenterology, the general surgeons developed a Section of Surgical Endoscopy and moved smoothly into performing laparoscopic surgery. Their experience and expertise in placing indwelling venous catheters opened up home health care options for thousands of patients who require intravenous feeding, chemotherapy, or antibiotics.

Hermann resigned as chairman in 1989, but remained on the active staff for five more years. After a lengthy search, Scottish-trained liver surgeon J. Michael Henderson, M.B., Ch.B., was chosen in 1992 to head the department as well as the Transplant Center. Thyroid, parathyroid, breast, and hepatobiliary surgery, along with laparoscopic techniques, continue to be the major focuses of the department.

COLORECTAL SURGERY

After Jones's death, Rupert P. Turnbull Jr., M.D., performed most of the colon operations. Before long he became so expert in diagnosis and management that the Clinic established a Department of Colonic and Rectal Surgery in 1968[4] and named him chairman. He

---

[4] Later that same year the Board of Governors simplified the name to "Colon and Rectal Surgery."

introduced many innovations and operations that circumvented the need for permanent colostomy and reduced morbidity.[5]

Turnbull was succeeded by Victor W. Fazio, M.B., B.S., under whose direction the department has developed an international reputation. They were the first to use stapled ileal pouch anastomoses, and with 150 cases per year they have the largest experience with this procedure in the world.

The department has maintained its preeminence in surgery for Crohn's disease, and performs more operations for ulcerative colitis, especially the bowel-conserving strictureplasty than any other institution. The staff now has the world's largest experience with the advancement rectal flap operation for Crohn's anal and anovaginal fistula, as well as with the stapled valve-pouch operation for continent ileostomy. They were the first to use the advancement pelvic pouch anal anastomosis for fistula-stricture complications and the advancement rectal flap operation for Crohn's anal and anovaginal fistulas. The group also pioneered the combination strictureplasty technique for Crohn's stricture, and they perfected many new laparoscopic bowel surgery techniques which greatly shorten hospital stay and recovery time.

Much of the department's success stems from basic research on colorectal cancer and inflammatory bowel disease. A major program for research and clinical application of laparoscopic bowel surgery began in 1992 with a $1.7 million grant. Endowments also fund personnel for the familial polyposis and Crohn's disease registries, ulcerative colitis research, and laboratory technicians.

Peer recognition of these surgeons has been manifested by their election to positions in prestigious national and international subspecialty organizations. Fazio himself served as president of the American Board of Colon and Rectal Surgery in 1992, and he is the current president of the American Society of Colon and Rectal Surgery.

OTOLARYNGOLOGY

In 1921, ear, nose, and throat (ENT) surgeons were preoccupied with tonsils and adenoids. The concept of chronic infection as a

---

[5] Turnbull carried an extremely large hospital service, sometimes with as many as 50 or 60 patients at various stages of preparation for or recovery from surgery. Considering the complex nature of what he was doing and the potential frequency of unexpected (mostly bad) sequelae, the pressures on him were enormous. Nonetheless, he always exuded calmness and confidence, even in the operating room, where the norm for many of his contemporaries was considerably different. With his tall stature and flowing white hair, he seemed to float serenely above the fray.

cause of many illnesses was gaining popularity, and the tonsils bore the brunt of the surgeon's assault. In those days before sulfanilamide and antibiotics, the treatment of mastoid infections was a great challenge. The correction of deviated nasal septa, an easier procedure, was also in vogue.

Justin M. Waugh, M.D., was the Clinic's first ENT surgeon. After his retirement, William V. Mullin, M.D., took over and did much to develop the technique of operating on the mastoid. After Mullin's untimely death from an overwhelming bacterial infection, Paul M. Moore, M.D., headed the department. He was succeeded by Harold E. Harris, M.D., a young surgeon with superb technical skill and clinical judgment.

By the 1940s, cancer of the larynx was becoming increasingly common. Pediatricians and internists were beginning to take a second look at tonsillectomy and to wonder if the tonsils might be serving some useful function. Most importantly, an operation for otosclerosis, a disease that fused together the tiny bones of the inner ear, causing progressive deafness, was developed. When the surgeon who developed the procedure organized a course to teach other otolaryngologists how to do it, Harris was among the first to apply.

As a result of learning this new technique, he was swamped with patients. By 1955, the need for operations in which he had been trained (i.e., tonsillectomy, adenoidectomy, mastoidectomy and correction of the deviated septum) had all but disappeared. In their place were new operations for cancers of the larynx, tongue, and mouth. Competition for the care of patients with these cancers caused conflict with the newly formed Department of Plastic Surgery. Bronchoscopic operations, historically performed by the otolaryngologists who had developed the technique, were rapidly shifting into the domain of the thoracic surgeons, who could then operate on whatever pulmonary disease was visualized. Thus, a struggle developed, and resolution of this conflict seemed insoluble without casualties.

Fortunately, the Clinic's Surgical Committee, composed of the contestants' peers, acted discreetly and with tact. They took no action on bronchoscopy, believing that there would be enough to provide training for residents in both departments. They charged a subcommittee to review the results of neck dissections in the presence of the surgeons who had done them. It soon became clear that the plastic surgeons, who had been trained to do radical surgery, performed the operations in about one-third the time and with fewer complications. Soon, the plastic surgeons and otolaryngologists were cooperating, the latter doing the laryngeal part of the operations and the former doing the neck dissections assisted by ENT residents.

After Harris's death in 1975, Harvey M. Tucker, M.D., was named chairman of the Department of Otolaryngology and Communicative Disorders. By 1985, the department had six members who were specializing in head and neck cancers, nerve reconstruction, cosmetic surgery of the face, and hearing problems. Newer diagnostic tests for dizziness and hearing loss were implemented. The addition of otolaryngologists with special expertise in head and neck cancer ensured a steady flow of patients formerly referred to plastic surgeons.

Under the chairmanship of Marshall Strome, M.D., who assumed the post in 1993, the department's residency program was lengthened one year to accommodate a full year of research. Graduates now receive a master of science degree for their work during that year.

Further, the department added a Section of Pediatric Otolaryngology and a Center for the Professional Voice. New programs that have brought local and national recognition to the department include laser palatal surgery for snoring, phonosurgery for the larynx, cochlear implants, endoscopic sinus surgery alone and in conjunction with laser surgery, and skull base surgery.

An emerging research program is transforming this clinical department into a formidable academic center. Clinical studies have improved the understanding of autoimmune inner ear disease. The new Immunology Genetics Laboratory is carrying out clinical trials for treatment of advanced squamous cell carcinoma of the head and neck.

NEUROLOGICAL SURGERY

From the moment the Department of Neurological Surgery was founded by Charles E. Locke, Jr., M.D., in 1924, it was considered outstanding. The second chairman, W. James Gardner, M.D., enjoyed a long and brilliant career characterized by the combination of innovation with superlative skill. His contributions to the art and philosophy of neurologic surgery earned him a special place in his field. His achievements were not limited to neurosurgery, but included development of the pneumatic suit to maintain blood pressure or control bleeding, the pneumatic splint for fractures, and the alternating air pressure mattress for preventing bed sores. His associate for 30 years was Alexander T. Bunts, M.D., son of one of the four founders, who specialized in the surgery of protruded inter-vertebral disks and spinal cord tumors.

Gardner was succeeded by Wallace B. Hamby, M.D., who had trained under him and then developed a national reputation in the diagnosis and treatment of brain aneurysms.

After Hamby came Donald F. Dohn, M.D., who maintained the department's reputation for leadership with his proficiency in stereo-tactic surgery for symptoms of Parkinson's disease, surgery to con-trol excessive sweating, and pituitary destruction with implanted radioactive yttrium (^{90}Y). Dohn left the Clinic in 1981 to enter private practice in Mississippi, but was coaxed out of retirement in 1988 to start the Department of Neurosurgery at Cleveland Clinic Florida.

The vacancy he left in Cleveland was filled by Joseph F. Hahn, M.D., who was subsequently appointed chairman of the Division of Surgery in 1987.[6] During Hahn's tenure, the department grew to include not only clinical neurosurgeons, but also a neurointensivist and a director of neurological research. Hahn developed basic research programs in neuro-oncology, epilepsy surgery, vascular disease, and congenital defects. Taken together with programs in the Department of Neurology, the complete epilepsy program is now ranked among the best in the country. Over the past 10 years the department established a computer-assisted neurosurgery program, partially funded by a $10 million grant from the Department of Defense, part of a government effort to convert defense technology for civilian applications. The Clinic's program uses targeting soft-ware to pinpoint and eradicate lesions in the brain. To better exploit this and other new technologies for treating brain tumors, the department recently established a Neuro-Oncology Center.[7]

The Department of Neurological Surgery also developed the use of subdural and epidural electrodes in epilepsy surgery and the stereotactic wand for brain and spinal surgery. Both procedures are now used throughout the country.

ORTHOPEDIC SURGERY

Orthopedic surgery was introduced as a specialty at the Clinic in 1922 by James A. Dickson, M.D., a surgeon of great originality and

---

[6] John Little, M.D., held the post of department chairman from 1987 until he left in 1990, where-upon Hahn resumed the department chair in addition to his duties as chairman of the Division of Surgery.

[7] Two of the technologies under consideration for this center are the gamma knife and the Cyberknife.

international repute. Before it became common practice to insert metal hip joints, Dickson had perfected an elegant operation called geometric osteotomy, in which an unhealed fracture of the hip was rotated to promote healing. During his tenure, which lasted until 1954 when he was succeeded by James I. Kendrick, M.D., he witnessed the decline and fall of osteomyelitis as a major orthopedic problem, and the development of artificial joints and operations to correct arthritis.

Charles M. Evarts, M.D., replaced Kendrick as department chairman in 1970. He was one of the first proponents of internal fixation, the process of holding vertebrae in place by a metal prosthesis.

Sports medicine was introduced to the department by H. Royer Collins, M.D., who succeeded Evarts as chairman. Over the years, sports medicine increased in importance and visibility, reaching its peak under the direction of John A. Bergfeld, M.D., who joined the staff in 1973. Highly respected by athletes and trainers, Bergfeld has fostered many key relationships between the Clinic and major sports teams, including the Cleveland Browns[8] and the U. S. Olympic Ski Team.

Alan H. Wilde, M.D., a surgeon noted for joint replacements, took over the department in 1976 and served with distinction for 15 years. In 1991, he was succeeded by Kenneth E. Marks, M.D., an orthopedic oncologist and department member since 1975.[9]

Since the mid-1980s, the department has added a Foot and Ankle Center, an Upper Extremity Center, and a traumatology program. Musculoskeletal researchers in the Department of Biomedical Engineering, originally established by the department during Evarts' tenure, collaborate with the orthopedic surgery staff in studies of musculoskeletal biology, gait analysis, neuromuscular control, biomechanics, biomaterials, and image processing. Technology transfer is one of the department's priorities.

A number of new techniques and technologies have been developed in part or wholly at the Clinic. One example is the non-cemented joint prosthesis, which allows bone to grow into pores in the metal surfaces for better fixation. The sports medicine surgeons have led the way in developing techniques for reconstructing knee ligaments. This allows a common but complex operation to be done

---

[8] As of this writing, the future of the Cleveland Browns remains uncertain.

[9] Since his residency years at the Clinic, Marks has become legendary for his humorous, extemporaneous one-liners. Having on one occasion returned from a particularly arduous trip, his comment on airline food was that "...they should just put it directly into the airsickness bag and avoid the middleman."

mostly through an arthroscope, which translates into a shorter hospital stay and quicker recovery.

The department's Section of Musculoskeletal Oncology has developed methods for reconstructing the skeleton and soft tissues after massive limb-sparing cancer surgery. These include a new method for the functional attachment of bone or soft tissue to the metal endoprosthetic devices used to reconstruct hips and knees after tumor resection. Fresh and frozen allografts are used often in reconstruction after tumor resection, trauma, and surgery for arthritis; and a new device allows for congenital defects to be gradually reconstructed with vascularized bone segments. A new system for harvesting human osteoblastic progenitor cells by aspiration has played a critical role in the healing of fractures, the incorporation of bone grafts, and maintenance of the skeleton throughout life.

The cerebral palsy clinic helps maximize the function of children with neuromuscular disorders. A Rheumatology/Orthopedics Clinic improves the care of patients with rheumatoid arthritis, and a Foot and Ankle Clinic aids patients with a broad spectrum of conditions, including those related to diabetes. A geriatric orthopedic program helps patients stay mobile and independent as long as possible. Care for non-surgical orthopedic conditions of all kinds is provided by the addition of three family practitioners with special training in musculoskeletal disease.

UROLOGY

During The Cleveland Clinic's existence, scientific developments have transformed urology from a service concentrating on medical treatments and minor surgery to a major surgical specialty. At first, urologists were primarily occupied with treating gonorrhea and performing suprapubic prostatectomies. Then came transurethral resection of the prostate and of bladder tumors. William J. Engel, M.D., Lower's son-in-law, was a master of the transurethral resectoscope. Charles C. Higgins, M.D., who succeeded Lower as head of the Department of Urology in 1948, became renowned for his "acid ash diet," an effective way of preventing — and sometimes successful means of dissolving — kidney stones. He also pioneered an operation to transplant the ureter into the lower bowel of children with exstrophy of the bladder. He operated on more of these patients than anyone else in the world, and also had one of the world's largest series of cystectomies for bladder cancer.

In 1934, a Cleveland pathologist discovered that partial blockage of a renal artery was one cause of hypertension. Acting on this information, Eugene F. Poutasse, M.D., developed renal arteriography. He discovered that in many such patients renal hypertension could be corrected by removing the obstruction, grafting a new vessel, or removing the part of the kidney which the diseased artery supplied.

After Higgins and Engel retired, Ralph A. Straffon, M.D., became chairman of the department.[10] Collaborating with Willem J. Kolff, M.D., Ph.D., inventor of the artificial kidney and head of the newly formed Department of Artificial Organs, Straffon initiated a kidney transplant program. Within a few years the Clinic reported more successful transplantations of kidneys taken from cadaver donors than had ever been done elsewhere. Today, the Clinic's renal transplant program remains one of the largest and most successful in the world (see Chapter 14); it is supported by a large dialysis program and regional tissue-typing laboratory.

By 1984, the Department of Urology had begun the process of subspecialization. That year, Straffon relinquished his chairmanship to assume the post of Chief of Staff, and James E. Montie, M.D., took over. A highly regarded urologic oncologist dedicated to his patients, Montie served only 18 months before deciding that the demands of the position took too much time away from patient care. He returned to his position on staff and was replaced as chairman by Andrew C. Novick, M.D.

Under Novick's leadership, the department evolved into the largest and most subspecialized department of its kind in the country, with tertiary care expertise in every urologic subspecialty: female urology, urodynamics, endourology, stone disease, impotence, prosthetic surgery, urologic oncology, renal vascular disease, renal transplantation, adrenal disease, male infertility, reconstructive surgery, and pediatric urology. In recent years the Clinic has established a regional kidney transplant network that provides Clinic transplant urologists for affiliated hospitals. This approach has made the service locally available to many patients. A strong and broad program in laboratory research supports these activities.

Over the past few years, the department has pioneered nephron-sparing surgery in patients with renal cancer and continues to pioneer new techniques in renal vascular surgery. Working with

---

[10] Straffon was destined for surgical stardom. An All-Star football player during his days at the University of Michigan, he had both the intellectual firepower and the physical stamina to excel in whatever task he set for himself. His achievements were recognized nationally in 1991 by his election to the presidency of the American College of Surgeons, the most prestigious post to which a surgeon can professionally aspire, and one once held by the senior Crile.

staff members from Thoracic and Cardiovascular Surgery, the urologists have attained the world's largest experience in the use of cardiopulmonary bypass and deep hypothermic circulatory arrest for surgery on tumors of the vena cava. Working with the colorectal surgeons, they have developed methods for complete intestinal bladder replacement with anastomosis to the urethra. They have also gained widespread recognition in the development of advanced techniques that allow many women with incontinence to be successfully treated non-surgically.

GYNECOLOGY

Gynecology was introduced as a specialty in 1950 under the leadership of James S. Krieger, M.D., who arrived at the Clinic about the time that the Papanicolaou (Pap) smear became popular. Krieger was interested in the conservative treatment of *in situ* carcinoma of the cervix by conization. While gynecologists across the country were debating whether the condition should be treated by radical or conservative hysterectomy with or without radiation, Krieger collected data showing that simple conization could be as effective as the more complex procedures if the patients were followed by annual Pap tests. At first bitterly criticized, the concept gradually gained broad support.

After Krieger's retirement in 1974, the chairmanship was assumed by Lester A. Ballard, Jr., M.D. He increased the staff to seven physicians, who covered the areas of general gynecology, gynecologic oncology, child and adolescent gynecology, and microsurgery. He also started a program in assisted reproductive technologies. This program includes both cryopreservation of embryos for later reimplantation as well as routine in-vitro fertilization. In addition, the newest micromanipulation technique of sperm injection into the cytoplasm of the egg has enabled many previously barren couples to achieve pregnancy.

As a natural extension of this program, the Clinic re-established the obstetrical service in 1995 after a 29-year hiatus. The new obstetrics unit was located on the sixth floor of the original hospital building, just around the corner from the old obstetrics ward. The old delivery suite, which had served as an operating pavilion for cardiovascular surgery, then orthopedics, and finally ambulatory surgery, had come full circle with its reconversion to the original use.

Lack of options to treat a large number of patients with defects in the pelvic floor resulted in the establishment of a Center for Pelvic Support. This center unites the efforts of Clinic gynecologists, colorectal surgeons, urologists, and physical therapists to give better care for these difficult problems.

Although the Department of Gynecology has always had a strong clinical focus, it began to develop major commitments to research and education in the 1990s with the arrival of a new chairman, Jerome L. Belinson, M.D. The department now has an organized research effort with numerous funded projects in reproductive endocrinology, gynecologic oncology, and general gynecology.

PLASTIC SURGERY

With formal training programs established just before World War II, plastic surgery is one of the youngest surgical specialties. Soldiers wounded in World War I, who had recovered with serious deformities, challenged surgeons in the 1920s and 1930s to develop expertise in repair and reconstruction. These surgeons had a variety of surgical backgrounds, and so the emerging specialty was a hybrid.

Robin Anderson, M.D., was a general surgeon trained in St. Louis by some of the great American pioneers of plastic surgery.[11] When Hoerr felt the need to develop plastic surgery at the Clinic, he extended an invitation to Anderson, whom he had known for several years. Anderson joined the Department of General Surgery in 1951. By 1960, a second plastic surgeon had been added, and the department was separated from General Surgery with Anderson as chairman.

When Anderson retired in 1979, Melvyn I. Dinner, M.D., succeeded him. A move into more spacious facilities was followed by rapid growth. Dinner recognized the importance of developing subspecialties within plastic surgery, and encouraged the development of expertise in craniofacial, pediatric, hand, and microvascular techniques.

When Dinner left the Clinic in 1983 to enter private practice, Shattuck W. Hartwell, Jr., M.D., a longtime member of the department and former director of Professional Staff Affairs, was asked to serve as acting chairman while a search committee looked for a new permanent chairman. Earl Z. Browne, M.D., was appointed in 1985. He was succeeded by James E. Zins, M.D., who had been on the staff for nine years, in 1992, and Zins continues to serve in that role. Another prominent member of the department, Harry Moon, M.D.,

---

[11] Anderson's technical prowess was not limited to the operating room. Like many noted physicians, he had a profound interest in music. He expressed this by building fine harpsichords in his spare time, many of which are still in existence.

was among the original staff of "pioneers" who moved to Fort Lauderdale in 1988 to open Cleveland Clinic Florida. Moon subsequently became Chief of Staff for the Florida operation, assuming many important administrative duties there (see chapters 9 and 20).

DENTISTRY

In 1982, a Section of Dentistry and Maxillofacial Prosthetics was established within the Department of Plastic Surgery to provide support for the treatment and rehabilitation of patients with head and neck cancer as well as deformities of the jaw, face and skull. Salvatore J. Esposito, D.M.D., was recruited to head the section, which included prosthodontists, an oral and maxillofacial surgeon, and a general dentist.[12]

In 1991 the section had attained departmental status, and Esposito became chairman of the newly formed Department of Dentistry. To support their multidisciplinary approach to patient care, Sections of Maxillofacial Prosthetics, Oral and Maxillofacial Surgery, Oral Medicine, Cosmetic Dentistry, Dental Oncology, Orthodontics, and Sports Dentistry were established.

The department's residency and fellowship positions are highly sought after. It was the first in Ohio to offer a dental oncology fellowship which, funded by the American Cancer Society, is one of only five in the country. The department's general practice residency is funded by the NIH. Among the new techniques residents learn are dental implantation, craniofacial implantation and the carbon dioxide laser for removing intra-oral soft tissue lesions and gingival hyperplasia.

VASCULAR SURGERY

The Department of Vascular Surgery was started in 1957, and it was one of the earliest of its kind in the country. In 1952, Crile, Jr., had visited St. Mary's Hospital in London, where he saw the world's first homograft (allograft) artery bank. Impressed with the success of replacing a blocked artery with a patent one from a cadaver, he decided this procedure should be brought to the Clinic. Upon his return, he persuaded Dinsmore to select a surgeon to learn this technique. Since the vessels in the lower extremity would be the main ones grafted, they chose Alfred W. Humphries, M.D., a junior mem-

---

[12] Dentistry had existed as a department, led by Dr. Charles Resch, from 1934 until his retirement in 1966. Between 1966 and 1982 consultants provided dental care at the Clinic.

ber of the Department of Orthopedic Surgery. They felt he had the skill, stamina, knowledge of the anatomy, and (perhaps most importantly) would be able to amputate the leg if the graft failed. Fortunately, Humphries proved to be an innovative technician with a keen intellect, and he made bold progress in a new field that was virtually uncharted in the 1950s. [13]

Within a year Humphries was working full time at vascular surgery, and his knowledge about all types of arterial reconstructions and their complications had become widely recognized. He was the first surgeon in the area with an artery bank. He then promoted the use of plastic grafts, and through the years had great success treating all types of aneurysms. With the assistance of anesthesiologist John Homi, M.D., he devised a technique to increase blood flow to the brain by having patients inhale carbon dioxide, thus enabling operations on their carotid arteries that previously had often led to brain damage from anoxia.

In 1961 he added a second member to his staff, Edwin G. Beven, M.D., whose surgical skill as a resident was legendary. Beven succeeded Humphries as chairman in 1973. His first staff appointee, Norman R. Hertzer, M.D., was another Clinic graduate who would eventually succeed him as chairman in 1989. Hertzer currently serves as president of the Society for Vascular Surgery, and Beven, who remains an active staff member, is president of the International Organization of Spanish-Speaking Vascular Surgeons.

The staff now numbers five surgeons. Recent additions include a surgeon with special training in catheter-based endovascular inter-

---

[13] Crile, Jr., was not alone in his interest in establishing this service at The Cleveland Clinic. Victor G. deWolfe, M.D., former chairman of the Department of Vascular Medicine, writes:

"Early in 1952, I made a visit to Dr. Robert S. Dinsmore, the Chief of the Department of Surgery, and explained to him that, just as heart and kidney surgery were rapidly advancing, so was the new specialty of vascular surgery, and we should get into the act. Shortly after this, Dr. Barney Crile returned from England with news about Dr. Charles Rob's artery bank and his early work in replacing vessels with freeze-dried arteries. He urged Dr. Dinsmore to take action...

"Due to Barney's enthusiasm, Dr. Dinsmore wasted no more time in solving this dilemma. He came to a very logical solution. On the staff at that time was a young orthopedic surgeon, Alfred Humphries... Initially he would do vascular work in the extremities. Ausey Robnett was a young general surgeon, newly appointed to the staff, who had an interest in abdominal surgery and proved himself to be skillful in that area, and he would work in the belly. These two young surgeons would operate together and each would teach the other about his area of expertise...

"Humphries did his first operation in 1952, when he successfully treated a popliteal aneurysm and replaced it with a section of the patient's saphenous vein. By 1957, 280 patients had been operated on with a 90% success rate in the larger arteries and 80% in the arteries below the groin...

"The department, created from spare parts, has continued the well-established tradition of careful selection, meticulous technology, and outstanding results."

vention, a procedure which may soon make it possible to repair aneurysms with synthetic grafts inserted percutaneously. The department has also published a series of studies that revolutionized the preoperative cardiac assessment of patients with peripheral vascular disease.

THORACIC AND CARDIOVASCULAR SURGERY

The growth of cardiac surgery has been one of the most dramatic developments in the history of the Clinic. In 1948, Donald B. Effler, M.D., was appointed head of the Department of Thoracic Surgery. At that time lung cancers were still rare, and thoracic surgeons were mainly occupied with draining empyemas and lung abscesses and performing thoracoplasties for tuberculosis. With the findings that penicillin was effective in controlling pneumonia and streptomycin reduced the need for thoracoplasties, surgery for these diseases all but vanished. However, the rising incidence of lung cancer — first treated by total pneumonectomy in 1932 — soon filled the gap. Then came the pioneering work of surgeons in Boston and California on congenital heart disease and mitral stenosis, and the specialty of cardiac surgery was born.[14]

The Clinic's thoracic surgeons were poised to participate in heart surgery. They found that some cardiac defects could be corrected or improved by relatively simple operations, but others required a machine to maintain circulation during surgery. Such machines existed, but they were large and cumbersome. Clinic staff member Willem J. Kolff, M.D., Ph.D., constructed a membrane oxygenator which permitted open heart surgery to be performed on children, who do not have a large volume of blood. Once heart-lung machines were improved, the latitude of relatively safe operations increased, but other problems remained. Kolff had done animal experiments in which he temporarily stopped the heart's action by injecting a solution of potassium into the coronary arteries. This technique was adapted for clinical use, and open heart surgery became a reality. Congenital and rheumatic valve defects were soon successfully corrected, and prosthetic valves were inserted into the heart.

As soon as Clinic cardiologist F. Mason Sones, Jr., M.D., used his new angiography technique to demonstrate that an internal

---

[14] The California surgeon was John Jones, M.D., brother of the Clinic's Chief of Surgery Tom Jones.

Leaders in the treatment of coronary artery disease. Standing: Willem J. Kolff, M.D., Ph.D., Artificial Organs (far left). Donald B. Effler, M.D., Thoracic and Cardiovascular Surgery (5th from left). Laurence K. Groves, M.D., Thoracic and Cardiovascular Surgery (6th from left). Donald E. Hale, M.D., Anesthesiology (4th from right). F. Mason Sones, Jr., M.D., Cardiology (far right) (photographed in 1956)

mammary artery implanted in the heart muscle could form connections with coronary arteries, there was great demand for this operation. Occasionally, a narrowed portion of a coronary artery was excised and a vein inserted, or the narrowed area was slit lengthwise and a tapered gusset inserted to widen the narrowed portion. Both procedures resulted in increased blood flow through the coronary arteries.

In May 1967, René G. Favaloro, M.D., an Argentine-born and educated surgeon on the Clinic staff, began using sections of saphenous veins to bypass coronary artery obstructions. The symptoms were often relieved and the graft usually remained open. Operative mortality was low from the start and decreased further with time; since 1971 the Clinic's overall operative mortality rate for non-emergency coronary artery bypass surgery without valvular disease or other serious complications has been less than one percent.

Favaloro returned to his homeland in 1971, where he remains an internationally acclaimed surgeon. Effler retired to a more relaxed

Drs. René G. Favaloro and F. Mason Sones, Jr. (photographed in 1982)

practice in 1975 and was succeeded by Floyd D. Loop, M.D. Loop's contributions included improvement of operative techniques, extensive follow-up studies on bypass patients, and approaches to control the cost of hospitalization for cardiac surgery. His confirmation of the superiority of the internal thoracic artery as a bypass vessel was a major advance. Beginning under his direction and continuing today, the Department of Thoracic and Cardiovascular Surgery has developed and refined many important surgical support strategies for blood conservation, myocardial protection, cardiopulmonary perfusion, and automatic drug administration. These have contributed to consistently safer cardiac operations as well as an operative mortality rate that sets the standard worldwide.

In addition to bypass surgery, Clinic surgeons have led the world in valve repair and replacement. Techniques to repair the mitral valve were developed by Delos M. Cosgrove III, M.D., in the mid-1980s. He subsequently developed a mitral valve retractor and annuloplasty ring that affords a more effective repair. With the assistance of intraoperative Doppler echocardiography, which has helped to optimize the results, there has been only one death at the Clinic from isolated mitral valve repair since 1990. Certain aortic valve conditions in selected patients can now be repaired with encouraging results.

Clinic surgeons have also become known for the repair of thoracic great vessel aneurysms and aortic dissections. In collaboration with the cardiac perfusionists, Bruce W. Lytle, M.D., introduced and refined a technique that extends the safe interval of total circulatory arrest necessary to perform these complex surgeries without neurological complications.

Although surgery for congenital heart disease was performed early in the department's history, the treatment of acquired heart disease demanded the most attention. A resurgence of referrals for the study and correction of cardiac defects followed the appointment of Carl C. Gill, M.D., a congenital heart surgeon, to the staff in 1978. Over the next decade, the Clinic developed a national reputation for the correction of congenital heart defects in patients of all ages. In 1988, Gill was appointed chief executive officer of Cleveland Clinic Florida and chairman of the Department of Cardiothoracic Surgery. The current head of the Cleveland program is the internationally renowned Australian surgeon Roger B. B. Mee, M.B., Ch.B., who performed 250 congenital heart operations with outstanding results in 1994 alone.

In the late 1960s, Clinic cardiac surgeons performed two successful heart transplants. But it was not until 1984 that a new era of intense transplantation activity was launched by Robert W. Stewart, M.D., who formed a highly organized medical and surgical team to care for these patients. In the mid-1990s, the team was performing more than 60 heart transplants a year, making it one of the top four programs in the country (see Chapter 14).

As an adjunct to the transplant program, the department has become one of the nation's leading centers in the use of mechanical assist devices to support patients waiting for a heart transplant or needing to rest the heart after bypass surgery. Transplant surgeon Patrick M. McCarthy, M.D., has worked closely with pioneer Leonard A. R. Golding, M.B., B.S., on research directed at the clinical use of these and other technologies.

In December 1991, the Clinic joined a multicenter group using the HeartMate® implantable left ventricular assist device (LVAD) as a bridge to transplantation. Patients who were candidates for a heart transplant but who were not expected to survive the wait for a donor were placed on the LVAD. Despite the fact that all were in cardiogenic shock and many were moribund, 75 percent recovered and subsequently underwent transplantation. The Clinic's program quickly became the most active in the U. S. and obtained some of the best clinical results.

In 1993, The Cleveland Clinic was one of three centers selected by the National Institutes of Health to continue research towards an electrically powered total artificial heart. This device will be used on patients who are not candidates for an LVAD and will initially be used as a bridge to transplantation. Both the HeartMate® and total artificial heart are designed to serve as an alternative to heart transplantation as well as therapy for patients with end-stage heart disease.

In 1986, a formal Section of Thoracic Surgery was established under Thomas W. Rice, M.D. A second surgeon, Thomas J. Kirby, M.D., was added in 1990. Together, they have made significant achievements, including the first lung transplant in Ohio and almost 100 single and double transplants since that time. Their pioneering work in video-assisted, thoracoscopically performed lobectomies and the use of ultrasound to further the clinical staging of esophageal cancers has improved results.

The department's extensive surgical activity has provided a fertile resource for its computerized cardiovascular information data bank [Cardiovascular Information Registry (CVIR)]. Established in 1971, it is the oldest and one of the country's largest. The information entered on every patient has helped the surgeons to track the results. In 1986, the data bank was instrumental in confirming the long-term benefits of the internal thoracic artery bypass graft, thus influencing the choice of grafts for future patients.

In 1989, Loop became chairman of the Board of Governors and Chief Executive Officer. Paul C. Taylor, M.D., then served as acting chairman of the Department of Thoracic and Cardiovascular Surgery until Cosgrove was selected as chairman the following year. A staff member since 1975, Cosgrove had developed an international reputation in valve repair and replacement, and he was a pioneer in blood conservation techniques. His methods reduced the average amount of blood transfused during bypass surgery from several pints to nearly none. Cleveland Clinic cardiothoracic surgeons continue to develop mechanical devices to assist circulation; refine the heart and lung transplant programs; and maintain their undisputed leadership in bypass reoperations as well as the correction of congenital defects and abnormalities of the heart's conduction system.

Under Cosgrove's direction, The Cleveland Clinic has become the largest open heart surgery center in the U. S.[15] The staff also performs the largest number of valve operations. In addition to caring for several thousand patients a year and conducting extensive research, members of the Department of Thoracic and

---

[15] In 1994, members of the department performed 3,420 cardiac operations!

Cardiovascular Surgery have tackled the challenges of a more efficient and cost-effective surgical practice. Despite the facts that 48 percent of the patients are over age 65, 30 percent undergo reoperations, and the majority of cases are complex, the overall length of stay has been reduced by allowing stable patients to enter the hospital on the day of surgery and discharging many earlier than is traditional. A total quality management program ensures consistency in the quality of care provided. For this reason, The Cleveland Clinic is proud to have been the first hospital in the country to voluntarily release outcome data and mortality statistics to the public.[16]

CONCLUSION

An overview of the Division of Surgery shows that Clinic surgeons have been both innovative themselves and quick to exploit the best ideas of others. Moreover, some have shown how medical or office treatment could replace an operation previously considered necessary. This ability to think of surgery as only one way of treating the patient is encouraged by the fact that there is no incentive for Clinic surgeons to perform a large number of operations; their salaries depend more on their peers' estimation of the quality of their work than on the dollars received as a result of it. It has been helpful, too, to have the cooperation of skilled colleagues who spend their time in research as well as readily available, high-quality support from medical services. The tradition of innovation started so many years ago by Bunts, Lower, Crile, and Phillips has flourished in an environment well suited to the study of clinical problems and to the discovery of their solutions in the operating room, clinic, and laboratory.

---

[16] The first of The Cleveland Clinic's award-winning *How to Choose a Doctor and Hospital* series dealt with coronary artery surgery. In these brochures, various Clinic services are evaluated according to six quality indicators (credentials, experience, range of services, research and education, patient satisfaction, and outcomes) showing Clinic data vs. national benchmarks when available.

THIRTEEN

DIVISION OF ANESTHESIOLOGY AND CRITICAL CARE MEDICINE

*We are more sensible of one little
touch of a surgeon's lancet than of
twenty wounds with a sword in the
heat of fight.*

— *Montaigne, 1588*

From 1921 to 1946, the administration of anesthetics at The Cleveland Clinic was handled by nurses, who dropped ether onto gauze laid over patients' airways or used chloroform to "put them under." Physicians did not begin to specialize in anesthesiology until just before World War II, when the control of breathing and pain through endotracheal intubation was being developed.

Following the war, the Clinic established a Department of Anesthesiology in the Division of Surgery. Donald E. Hale, M.D., was appointed chairman. A practicing surgeon before entering the field of anesthesiology, Hale obtained board certification in both specialties and later published one of the first textbooks on anesthesia in the United States.

With a myriad of new techniques to practice, no physicians to assist him, and an extensive surgical schedule, Hale faced a daunting task. To solve his manpower crisis, he initiated a training program in anesthesiology. One of his early trainees was Carl E. Wasmuth, M.D., who replaced him as chairman in 1967, but served only two years before being elected chairman of the Board of Governors. Wasmuth also served as president of the American Society of Anesthesiologists from 1968 to 1969.

Wasmuth's vacancy in the Department of Anesthesiology was filled by J. Kenneth Potter, M.D. Under Potter's chairmanship, anesthesiology was withdrawn from the Division of Surgery and granted division status of its own.

Potter was succeeded by John F. Viljoen, M.D., a specialist in the care of patients undergoing surgery for heart disease. When Viljoen stepped down in 1976, Potter was called out of retirement to lead the division until a replacement could be found. The search committee recommended Azmy R. Boutros, M.D., a professor of anesthesiology at the University of Iowa, who accepted the position. Boutros subsequently reorganized the division and added staff to accommodate increasing clinical and educational responsibilities. In six years, the number of staff physicians doubled to 30.

Fawzy G. Estafanous, M.D., chairman of the Department of Cardiothoracic Anesthesiology, was appointed chairman of the Division of Anesthesiology upon Boutros's retirement in 1987. Renamed to reflect the scope of its services, the Division of Anesthesiology and Critical Care Medicine today oversees 50 operating rooms and more than 70 surgical intensive care beds.

CARDIOTHORACIC ANESTHESIOLOGY

In response to the Clinic's growing recognition as a heart center, the Department of Cardiothoracic Anesthesiology was formed in 1976 with Estafanous as chairman. It was the first subspecialty department of its kind in the country. As a cardiac anesthesiologist with an active interest in clinical and basic research, Estafanous played an important role in the evolution of cardiac anesthesia as a specialty. Not only did he build his department into one of the most respected in the world, he also made significant contributions in the areas of post-myocardial revascularization hypertension, the hemodynamic effects and clinical effects of opioids and muscle relaxants, blood conservation, and the limitations of hemodilution.

In 1986, the department offices moved to the new hospital wing, adjacent to eleven state-of-the-art cardiac operating rooms and three cardiovascular intensive care units (CVICU) built to the department's specifications. Today, the 55-bed CVICU accommodates 14,000 patient days per year, providing the department's 12-year-old registry with a rich resource for outcomes research.

Upon Estafanous's appointment as chairman of the Division of Anesthesiology, Norman J. Starr, M.D., a staff member since 1979, was tapped to be chairman of the Department of Cardiothoracic Anesthesiology. Under Starr, the department has grown to include

F. George Estafanous, M.D., Chairman, Division of Anesthesiology and Critical Care Medicine, 1987–

17 full-time, board-certified cardiac anesthesiologists, nine certified registered nurse anesthetists, 43 respiratory therapists, and a five-member clinical engineering department.

Today, nearly one-fourth of all cardiac surgery patients at The Cleveland Clinic have undergone one or more previous cardiac operations, putting them at higher risk than ever before. Yet advances in technique and technology combined with the experience of both the anesthesiologists and surgeons have led to the Clinic's reputation as the world's premier site for cardiac surgery. In addition, the Clinic's designation as a major center for heart and lung transplantation has provided the cardiac anesthesiologists with extensive expertise in the use of advanced ventricular support devices, the forerunners of a successful artificial heart.

GENERAL ANESTHESIOLOGY

Upon his appointment as chairman of the Division of Anesthesiology, one of Estafanous's first acts was to establish a Department of General Anesthesiology and appoint Arthur Barnes, M.D., chairman. Barnes formalized the department structure, establishing clinical subspecialty sections, appointing section heads, and creating new protocols to distribute resources. He also arranged for additional space to accommodate pre-surgical evaluations and the School of Nurse Anesthesia.

Armand Schubert, M.D., a neuroanesthesiologist with a strong background in clinical research, succeeded Barnes as department chairman in 1993. Schubert expanded the Acute Postoperative Pain Service to make epidural analgesia routinely available.

Today, the Department of General Anesthesiology is a dynamic group of more than 40 physicians with a remarkable breadth and depth of talent. They are supported by 36 nurse anesthetists, five School of Nurse Anesthesia faculty members, five clinical engineers, and 19 nurses and nurse specialists.

The rapidly growing need for sophisticated post-surgical intensive care is met by the department's Section of Critical Care, which has four staff members certified in critical care medicine as well as anesthesiology.

In 1989, the department developed an ambulatory anesthesia service headed by R. John Anderson, M.D. This unit, now under the direction of Walter G. Maurer, M.D., cares for 45 percent of all noncardiac surgical patients at the Cleveland Clinic.

A simultaneous rise in the number of same-day surgeries created a need for improved anesthesia clearance procedures. The problem was solved by adding a Pre-Surgical Services Center in the Crile Building.

When Kaiser Permanente members began to use Cleveland Clinic facilities in 1993, the number of surgical cases increased dramatically. Procedure rooms were added in the Crile Building, an area formerly restricted to local anesthesia, to accommodate more patients. The department was consulted on the development of these rooms, which serve the Eye Institute, the Department of Orthopedic Surgery, and the Department of Plastic and Reconstructive Surgery.

In 1995, 24 state-of-the-art operating rooms were built on the second floor of the new Emergency Medicine and Access Center building, where the department has taken new space. The number of emergency cases and trauma resuscitations are growing as a result of the new Emergency Department, which opened in 1994. And for the first time since 1966, the department is providing anesthesia for women in The Cleveland Clinic's new obstetrical suite.

PAIN MANAGEMENT

In the 1970s, The Cleveland Clinic established a formal program for the management of postoperative pain. In 1988, the program was expanded to include chronic pain. Michael D. Stanton-Hicks, M.B., B.S., was appointed director of the Pain Management Center. Its physician staff of eight stresses a multidisciplinary approach to pain. Seventy-five percent of their chronic pain patients receive physical and/or occupational therapy, and 55 percent require psychological evaluation. The self-contained center, now located on the second floor of the former Woodruff Hospital, has six block rooms and an eight-bed recovery unit. The center receives many referrals from the Bureau of Workers' Compensation, the Reflex Sympathetic Dystrophy Syndrome Association, and The Cleveland Clinic's Spine Center, Cancer Center, Department of Physical Medicine and Rehabilitation, and Department of Gynecology. Some of the latest pain management techniques offered include spinal cord stimulation, the implantation of infusion systems, and the introduction of highly specific diagnostic tests using enhanced fluoroscopic imaging.

Postoperative pain management remains a key service. The staff oversees the placement of epidural catheters prior to anesthesia, which allows patients to continue analgesia postoperatively as long as necessary. In the future, the acute pain service plans to expand beyond surgical pain management to include acute non-surgical and pediatric pain.

To better serve these patients, the Pain Management Center is preparing to become a separate department within the Division of Anesthesiology. The physicians are also planning to start an Institute of Pain Rehabilitation with their colleagues in the Department of Physical Medicine and Rehabilitation. This comprehensive program will help restore independence and improve the quality of life for many Cleveland Clinic patients.

CLINICAL ENGINEERING

In 1977, the Department of Cardiothoracic Anesthesiology formed the nation's first clinical engineering group within an operating room complex. Headed by John Petre, Ph.D., the group was charged with providing instrumentation management for cardiac surgery as well as the cardiac recovery units. Six engineers and technicians are now employed.

A similar technical support program was initiated for the general anesthesia operating rooms in 1986. Robert Koch, M.S., and his staff of five support this large area. Both groups are responsible for the daily management and service of all equipment and provide technical support for clinical research projects as well as new equipment design and development. By working directly in the operating rooms, the engineers have been able to apply their technical skills more effectively to benefit both the medical staff and patients. Their input has been invaluable in the design and construction of the Clinic's operating room complexes and support areas. Not surprisingly, their technical expertise has led to patents on nine pieces of medical equipment, several of which were developed into commercial products. Manufacturers continue to solicit their technical expertise for the co-development of new products.

EDUCATION

Estafanous delegated the responsibility for educating anesthesiology residents to Arthur Barnes. Under Barnes's tutelage, the program has achieved a high level of excellence, culminating in 1990 with a five-year unconditional approval by the national Residency Review Committee. Graduates of the program are highly sought after and continue to attain prominent positions worldwide.

The Clinic's cardiothoracic anesthesiology fellowship program trains 15 residents a year, making it the largest in the United States. Also holding this title is the pain management fellowship with 10 fellows. The program prepares them for the two examinations offered in pain management. The division also operates one of only 22 accredited surgical intensive care fellowships in the country, training five fellows per year. All are required to participate in a research project and produce a paper at the end of their fellowship.

NURSE ANESTHESIA

With the large number of anesthesiologists on staff and volume of operations performed daily at The Cleveland Clinic, nurse anesthetists play an important role and are considered invaluable members of the team. The Cleveland Clinic School of Nurse Anesthesia, started in 1969, graduated its 216th student in July 1995. It was a hospital-based, 24-month certificate program until 1989, when it affiliated with the Frances Payne Bolton School of Nursing at Case Western Reserve University. Graduates now receive an M.S. degree and are qualified for certification as a nurse anesthetist after completing the 28-month course.

RESEARCH

The Division of Anesthesiology is committed to establishing one of the nation's top 10 anesthesiology research programs. The

J. Kenneth Potter, M.D., Chairman, Division of Anesthesiology, 1970–1973

cornerstone of this program is the Center of Anesthesiology Research, which was founded in 1994 under the direction of Paul Murray, Ph.D., to coordinate and administer all research activity. The center occupies 3,500 square feet in the Research Building and includes six laboratories and six offices.

Murray's own research focuses on the fundamental mechanisms of pulmonary vascular regulation, the effects of anesthetic agents on pulmonary vasoregulation, and chronic changes in pulmonary vascular regulation following lung transplantation. Two other staff members concentrate on various aspects of cardiac function. Three more are being recruited to begin research in selected areas. The center also has seven full-time research fellows.

Funding for research has a high priority. Although division projects have attracted significant funding from the pharmaceutical and medical technology industries as well as grant-giving organizations such as the National Institutes of Health and American Heart Association, the establishment of a $4 million Anesthesiology Endowment Fund is under way. Income from the endowment will be used to start new programs and recruit new scientists.

FOURTEEN

CENTERS OF EXCELLENCE

*Men of genius do not excel in any profession
because they labour in it, but they labour in
it because they excel.*

— *William Hazlitt, 1823*

At The Cleveland Clinic, the term "Center of Excellence" is more than a marketing term. These multidisciplinary groups exemplify the Clinic's realization of the core concept of group practice: "to act as a unit."

While centers of excellence exist within most specialties (and the term is used broadly to encompass the Clinic's medical and surgical departments devoted to major body systems and the diseases that affect them, such as cardiovascular disease, digestive diseases and cancer), this chapter is devoted to the five multidisciplinary Centers of Excellence designated by the Board of Governors: the Center for the Spine, the Transplant Center, the Mellen Center for Multiple Sclerosis, the Cancer Center, and the Eye Institute.

CENTER FOR THE SPINE

The Center for the Spine was established in November 1984 as a cooperative effort of the Departments of Orthopedic Surgery and Neurosurgery under the joint leadership of Frank Boumphrey, M.D., and Russell Hardy, M.D. Specialists from the Departments of Neurology and Rheumatic and Immunologic Disease who shared an interest in studying and treating patients with spinal conditions were included. It was conceived as a "center without walls," and relied on a central triage system to refer patients to the appropriate

Daniel J. Mazanec, M.D., Director, Spine Center, 1991–

physician. The entire group met regularly to discuss and develop new approaches to the diagnosis and management of patients with back pain.

As the number of referrals grew, Boumphrey developed a questionnaire to identify patients needing urgent care during the appointment process. It was successful, and between 1986 and 1990, patient volume increased 30 percent. The multidisciplinary group of physicians and physical therapists involved in their care grew accordingly to meet the demand.

In 1990, a task force appointed by the Board of Governors recommended that the Center for the Spine be reorganized as a medical department "with walls." They concluded that placing a medical director, physicians, and physical therapists at a single location would further the Center's development as a model program for the treatment of spinal disorders through conservative patient management and rehabilitation. Its core concept was an initial evaluation by a medical specialist, rather than a surgeon.

In July 1991, rheumatologist Daniel J. Mazanec, M.D. was appointed director of the Center for the Spine. Shortly thereafter, a close collaboration with the recently reconstituted Department of Physical Medicine and Rehabilitation began. In 1994, this resulted in the W. E. R. C. (Work Evaluation and Rehabilitation Clinic), an innovative, multidisciplinary program for injured and disabled back patients aimed at restoring function and a return to work. With more than 90 percent of patients who complete the program achieving this goal, the W.E.R.C. has become one of the most successful programs of its kind in the country.

The Center for the Spine has attracted a growing number of workers' compensation patients seeking alternative approaches or second opinions on work-related injuries. Center physicians collaborate extensively with the Department of Physical Medicine and Rehabilitation and the Pain Management Center to meet these patients' needs.

The interdisciplinary nature of the Center for the Spine has enabled it to serve as a focal point for clinical activities, research, and education. Involved members of the Departments of Orthopedic Surgery, Neurosurgery, Radiology, Pain Management, Psychiatry, and Physical Medicine and Rehabilitation are focused on the development of clinically superior, cost-effective diagnostic and management methods for spinal disorders, emphasizing the appropriate use of technology.

MELLEN CENTER FOR MULTIPLE SCLEROSIS

A comprehensive center for the treatment of multiple sclerosis (MS) was the brainchild of Neurology chairman John Conomy, M.D., who had a specialty interest in the disease. It was realized through the generosity of the Mellen Foundation and Mr. John Drinko.

The Mellen Center for Multiple Sclerosis opened on February 11, 1985, in two rooms in the Department of Neurology. In addition to Conomy, the staff included three neurologists, each of whom dedicated one day a week to MS patients. Within three months, the Center also had a full-time nurse, occupational therapist, physical therapist, psychologist and social worker, making it one of the most comprehensive clinical teams ever assembled to tackle the disease. But conditions were so crowded that staff members often saw patients together. Every patient was evaluated by every team member, and a comprehensive set of treatment recommendations were made. This method of operation continued for about two years until demand for services made it impractical.

By mid-1986, the Mellen Center was moved into a facility of its own in the former Woodruff Hospital. Richard A. Rudick, M.D., was recruited as full-time director, and the program entered a rapid growth phase.

Richard A. Rudick, M.D., Director, Mellen Center for Multiple Sclerosis, 1987–

Space and resources allowed the development of a number of novel clinical programs, including water exercise, special aerobics exercise, functional electrical stimulation, and adapted cooking. Psychology groups were formed for stress management and coping strategies, and specialized programs for children and adults were started. Educational programs to teach patients and their families about MS were developed, often in conjunction with the local MS Society. At the same time, programs were initiated to train students in nursing, occupational therapy, and social work to help patients cope with the disease.

Clinical and basic research programs began in 1988 and quickly flourished. Studies encompassed medications, memory impairment, cognitive function, physical function, and emotional status. The Center received grants to develop new devices to assist in managing symptoms and adapting computer equipment.

The Mellen Center established a separate service for MS patients needing hospitalization. At the same time, outpatient services were expanded to include neuropsychological assessments as well as counseling about the impact of MS-related cognitive impairment on daily function. A project to design and fabricate custom seating was implemented along with programs designed to help patients maximize their independence and continue to enjoy their favorite activities. In 1990, the center started a day treatment program to provide social and therapeutic activities for patients with severe physical or cognitive impairment, and to afford a respite for their caregivers.

Basic research continued to grow and won national recognition. The influx of patients for treatment and clinical trials necessitated new recruitment and reorganization of staff and facilities. Finally, the Mellen Center staff extended their expertise by initiating postdoctoral fellowship programs to train the next generation of neurologists, psychologists, and scientists.

The Mellen Center played a major role in founding the Consortium of Multiple Sclerosis Centers, of which there are now 67. Conomy was named its first executive director, and Jill S. Fischer, Ph.D., served as president from 1992 to 1993. Other Mellen Center staff members have been elected to the administrative staff and continue to serve as committee chairmen.

In 1994, the Mellen Center attracted a well-known myelin researcher, Bruce Trapp, Ph.D., to chair the newly formed Neuroscience Department. It is now one of the top multiple sclerosis research groups in the world. The addition of other key staff members has allowed clinical health psychology services and the testing of experimental medications to expand.

The Mellen Center has a growing reputation as one of the world's premier multiple sclerosis centers. While the staff is proud of its accomplishments, it is humbled by the challenges that lie ahead. They hold to the belief that the team approach will enable them to fulfill their mission to provide compassionate, innovative care to patients and families affected by multiple sclerosis, to conduct important clinical and basic research, and to educate other clinicians, scientists, and the public about the disease.

TRANSPLANT CENTER[1]

The concept of organ transplantation had long interested Clinic surgeons looking for ways to extend natural organ function without the use of artificial materials. The first successfully transplanted organs were the kidneys. The Clinic's renal transplant program was developed by Ralph Straffon, M.D., when he was chairman of the Department of Urology. During the 1980s and 1990s, major technical improvements, advances in immunosuppression, and better patient

---

[1] This center is devoted to whole organ and bone marrow transplantation, not the transplantation of pieces of organs, such as corneas or skin.

J. Michael Henderson, M.D., Director, Transplant Center, 1992–

selection criteria made successful transplant programs in heart, heart/lung, kidney/pancreas, bone marrow, liver, and lung a reality.

The Cleveland Clinic views transplantation as an essential component of a broad strategy to offer all patients with advanced diseases the most appropriate therapy. To coordinate all activities in this rapidly developing specialty, the Clinic opened a Transplant Center in 1985. It is currently directed by J. Michael Henderson, M.B., Ch.B., a liver transplant surgeon who chairs the Department of General Surgery. Henderson also serves on the boards of LifeBanc and the Ohio Solid Organ Transplant Consortium.

KIDNEY TRANSPLANTATION

The kidney transplant program was initiated in January 1963, as an outgrowth of Kolff's pioneering efforts to develop and refine hemodialysis. At that time renal transplantation was considered experimental and had relatively low patient and graft survival rates. From 1963 to 1967, The Cleveland Clinic, under Straffon's direction, performed about 10 percent of all cadaver kidney transplants. Advances in tissue matching techniques, the use of living donors, and a reduction in the surgical morbidity soon gave the program an edge which resulted in more successful transplants than any other institution.

Andrew Novick, M.D., became director of renal transplantation in July 1977. The following year he initiated the first approved post-graduate fellowship training program in transplantation.[2] In 1985, he was appointed chairman of the newly established Cleveland Clinic Organ Transplant Center, a position he held until Dr. Michael Henderson assumed the role in 1992.

During the 1980s, the Clinic made important contributions to the field of renal transplantation through the use of pediatric cadaver kidneys for transplantation, the development of microvascular surgical techniques to enable the transplantation of kidneys with abnormal vascular supply, and the use of anti-lymphocyte globulin for immunosuppression. Two basic research laboratories were established to support the program.[3]

Today, Clinic urologists perform approximately 160 kidney transplants a year at The Cleveland Clinic and its affiliated transplant programs in Youngstown, and Akron, Ohio, and Charleston, West Virginia. These programs, which are staffed by full-time Clinic kidney transplant surgeons, were developed to better serve patients and help secure cadaver kidneys.

The Cleveland Clinic's patient and graft survival rates following kidney transplantation are above the national average: the one-year patient survival rate is approximately 95 percent, and the one-year graft survival rate is 93 percent following live donor transplant and 86 percent following cadaver transplant. Besides Novick, who also serves as chairman of the Department of Urology and has performed more than 1,000 kidney transplants himself, the Clinic's renal transplant program now includes five board-certified urologists with postgraduate training in transplantation, three full-time Ph.D. investigators, three postgraduate physician trainees, five clinical nurse specialists, and three research nurses.

KIDNEY/PANCREAS TRANSPLANTATION

In the mid-1980s, physicians realized that a combined kidney and pancreas transplant could be used to manage diabetic renal dis-

---

[2] It was the first program to receive approval by the Education Committee of the American Society of Transplant Surgeons and has trained 28 urologists in renal transplantation. Many are now directing their own programs.

[3] One laboratory, directed by Nicholas Stowe, Ph.D., investigates renal ischemia and preservation; and the other, directed by Robert Fairchild, Ph.D., explores the mechanisms underlying graft acceptance and rejection.

ease and treat end-stage renal disease of diabetes for some patients. The Clinic performed its first kidney/pancreas transplant in 1985, and had done 14 by 1989, when the procedure was put on temporary hold due to the high rate of complications.

After reassessing the immunologic and surgical aspects of the procedure, the program was resumed at The Cleveland Clinic in 1993 under the direction of James Mayes, M.D. Today, improved patient selection and better understanding of immunosuppressive agents make the procedure a viable option for selected patients.

BONE MARROW TRANSPLANTATION

The Cleveland Clinic's first bone marrow transplant was done in 1977, but the program did not begin to grow in earnest until Roger Herzig, M.D., was recruited in 1982. Brian Bolwell, M.D., was named director of the program after Herzig left the Clinic in 1988.

During the 1990s, bone marrow transplantation experienced remarkable growth. The Clinic was a founding member of the National Marrow Donor Program, which coordinates the search for unrelated donors for patients in need of allogeneic marrow transplants. Since these transplants are complicated by a high incidence of graft-versus-host disease, the Clinic's bone marrow transplant program continues to investigate novel methods of depleting the donor marrow of T cells to reduce the incidence and severity of this problem.

In 1992, the Clinic's autologous bone marrow transplant program began to surge under Bolwell's direction. With about 200 transplants now performed annually (the majority autologous), it is one of the most active programs of its kind anywhere.

Initially, autologous bone marrow transplantation was most successful in patients with non-Hodgkin's lymphoma and Hodgkin's disease, but it has been increasingly employed in the treatment of high-risk breast cancer. Procuring marrow cells from the peripheral blood has reduced the need to harvest marrow, shortening the length of stay for autologous transplantation from five weeks to about three weeks, and dropping induction mortality rates from 20 percent to less than two percent.

HEART TRANSPLANTATION

The Clinic's first experience with cardiac transplantation came in 1968. Over the next year, Lawrence K. Groves, M.D., René G.

Favaloro, M.D., and Donald B. Effler, M.D., performed four heart transplants. Although one of these patients survived for more than one year, national results were discouraging and the Clinic's program, like most others in the country, was shelved for nearly 15 years.[4]

In August 1984, Robert W. Stewart, M.D., renewed the effort, and the Clinic became the first medical center in Ohio to resume the procedure. Six transplants were performed the first year, and the second patient remains alive more than 11 years later.

Over the next five years, Stewart and Leonard A. R. Golding, M.B., B.S., performed nearly 100 heart transplants. Their efforts were supported by a transplant team that included two cardiologists and a program coordinator. Members of the Departments of Infectious Disease, Anatomic Pathology, and Cardiothoracic Anesthesiology provided invaluable assistance.

With fewer than 20 transplant programs in the country in the mid-1980s, donors were available in areas without programs, and the Clinic's team frequently traveled to other states to procure donated hearts. These trips were arranged with private air carriers on short notice, and regularly involved coordinating private jets, helicopters, and ambulances. Landing at wrong airports and hovering over cities while asking directions to heliports were all too common. At least once, the team landed in a cornfield.

In the early days of the program, immunosuppressive regimens were more intense than current protocols; heart recipients remained in isolation within specially constructed rooms both in the intensive care unit and afterwards on the nursing floor. Protected by surgical masks, the recipients were conspicuous as they were transported through the Clinic.

In the 1990s, patient activity grew dramatically, and a second surgeon, Patrick M. McCarthy, M.D., and two more cardiologists were added to the heart transplant program. The rate of growth is best illustrated by comparing the first five-and-a-half years, when 100 heart transplants were performed, with the second five-and-a-half years, when 300 were performed. One-year survival has always exceeded 80 percent and currently exceeds 90 percent. The Clinic's program was certified by Medicare in 1988 and has been considered one of the top five in the United States since 1991.

---

[4] The discovery of the immunosuppressive agent cyclosporin A made transplantation of various organs in addition to the kidneys practical.

LUNG AND HEART/LUNG TRANSPLANTATION

Thomas J. Kirby, M.D., the Clinic's lung transplant program director, performed Ohio's first single lung transplant in February 1990, and the state's first double lung transplant sixteen months later. The Clinic's program remains the only one in Ohio, and with more than 100 transplants, it is one of the busiest in the country. Patients with a variety of end-stage respiratory diseases are now considered potential lung transplant candidates and can expect survival rates of 70 percent after one year and 50-60 percent after three years.

The shortage of donors has led to an interest in living-related lung donation and xenotransplantation,[5] which is expected to become a reality within 10 years. Other research is being done in lung volume reduction for patients with end-stage emphysema who are not candidates for transplantation or for whom this procedure could delay the need for a transplant. The Clinic is also active in researching new methods of respiratory support for these patients using an intravascular oxygenator and long-term "heparinless" extracorporeal membrane oxygenator.

On February 14, 1992, Patrick McCarthy, M.D., director of the Clinic's heart-lung transplant program, performed the first heart-lung transplant in Ohio. Candidates for this rare type of transplant have either complex congenital heart disease with severe pulmonary hypertension, or combined end-stage heart and lung disease. Due to the lack of donors, only 30-50 of these operations are performed in the entire country every year. By July 1995, four patients had received heart-lung transplants at The Cleveland Clinic.

LIVER TRANSPLANTATION

Robert E. Hermann, M.D., and Edwin G. Beven, M.D., performed the first liver transplant at the Cleveland Clinic in the late 1960s. It was an auxiliary transplant, and the patient's own liver was not removed. The patient, a child, died 24 hours after the operation. This was one of only 100 liver transplants that had been attempted worldwide by 1975.

By 1985, 42 centers in the U. S. were performing liver transplants. The Clinic's first transplant that involved removing a dis-

---

[5] Xenotransplantation refers to the use of organs from donors of different species, *e.g.*, baboons.

eased liver and replacing it with a donor organ was carried out in 1984. Since that time and especially since 1990, the program has grown steadily. As of July 1995, 280 transplants had been done at the Clinic. The one-year survival rate is now 83 percent, and fewer than eight percent of patients require retransplantation. This success is attributable to improvements in immunosuppression, organ preservation, recipient selection and management, and postoperative care.

Planning for the Clinic's first orthotopic liver transplant had begun 18 months earlier. In 1983, following the success of the kidney transplant program, the Board of Governors appointed a Transplantation Committee to study the possibility of beginning such programs for other organs. The involved departments began assembling transplant teams.

General surgeon David Vogt, M.D., director of the Clinic's liver transplant program, attended the Consensus Conference on Liver Transplantation at the National Institutes of Health. The panel determined that transplantation was a viable therapeutic option for selected patients with end-stage liver disease, and Vogt returned to the Clinic to share the good news with other prospective members of the team. Their need for additional training was solved by sending each member of the team to Pittsburgh to study with transplantation pioneer Thomas Starzl, M.D.

Starting in the spring of 1984, Vogt practiced his technique in the animal laboratory to become familiar with both the donor and recipient procedures. Since decompression of the portal venous system was also necessary, the perfusion team became involved. By fall, the program was ready to accept human patients. It was agreed that all candidates would be evaluated by the liver transplant team, which met weekly and consisted of hepatologists, surgeons, social workers, psychiatrists, bioethicists, the program coordinator, and a representative from the business office.

Hermann and Vogt worked together on the first four transplants, with Hermann preparing the recipient while Vogt retrieved the donor liver. These tedious, grueling operations lasted overnight and took an average of 12 hours.[6] With many administrative duties

---

[6] Fortunately, in 1987 the discovery of a new organ preservation solution doubled the permissible cold ischemia time to 24 hours. This not only allowed donor organs to be preserved longer, but gave them better function after transplantation and reduced the average length of the recipient's operation to nine hours. With some exceptions, the recipient could be taken to the operating room at 6 a.m. the morning following the donor organ retrieval. This meant that only half the surgical team was up all night.

that needed attention during the day, Hermann quickly decided to relinquish his place on the surgical team. By the end of 1989, 66 liver transplants were performed.

In 1992, Henderson, an experienced liver transplant surgeon from Emory University, came aboard as chairman of the Department of General Surgery and head of the Transplant Center. In January 1993, the staff was further augmented by the arrival of James T. Mayes III, M.D., who had received formal fellowship training in multiple abdominal organ transplantation and was adept in liver, pancreas, and kidney transplantation.

Since that time, better patient selection criteria, surgical experience, and meticulous anesthesia management have decreased the operative time to an average of six to eight hours. Blood usage has fallen from an average of 25 units to less than 10, and patients are able to go home in about 25 days. The three-year survival rate is 73 percent. As a reflection of the program's success, the Clinic was approved by the Health Care Financing Administration as a liver transplant center for Medicare patients in 1992.

HISTOCOMPATIBILITY LABORATORY

The Cleveland Clinic's kidney transplant program was in its infancy when a tissue-typing laboratory was opened to support it. William E. Braun, M.D., was recruited in 1968 to head the laboratory and serve on the staff of the Department of Hypertension and Nephrology. Under Braun the laboratory achieved international prominence in HLA typing for solid organ and bone marrow transplants as well as disease associations and paternity testing. In recognition of these achievements, Braun was elected the first president of the American Society of Histocompatibility and Immunogenetics in 1974.

Today, under the direction of Daniel J. Cook, Ph.D., the Histocompatibility Laboratory uses state-of-the-art technology, such as flow cytometry, to perform more than 40,000 tests a year. This sensitive technique helps better identify the presence of antibodies against a potential organ donor that may increase the risk of organ rejection, and monitors the effectiveness of post-transplant treatment in preventing rejection. The laboratory's use of high-resolution HLA typing that identifies components at the DNA level was critical in obtaining a contract to type the DNA of potential bone marrow donors through the National Marrow Donor Program.

Maurie Markman, M.D., Director, Cancer Center, 1992–

CANCER CENTER

Throughout its history, Cleveland Clinic physicians and surgeons have made major contributions to advances in the care of cancer patients. George Crile, Jr., M.D., was one of the earliest and most influential advocates of less-than-radical surgery for breast cancer, having begun to doubt the need for radical mastectomy in the early 1950s. Rupert P. Turnbull, Jr., M.D., discovered that isolating diseased tissue during surgery for colon cancer would prevent the further spread of cancer cells. By the 1980s, his "no-touch" technique was widely accepted as reducing the risk of death from metastatic disease following colorectal surgery.

Since the term cancer refers to a group of more than 100 diseases characterized by the abnormal growth and spread of cells, the treatment of patients with cancer at The Cleveland Clinic was originally incorporated into the services of various departments throughout the institution. The first attempt to organize a centralized cancer program was made in the 1970s by pathologist William A. Hawk, M.D. Hawk focused on aspects of malignant disease that were not yet well represented within the institution, such as basic research, epidemiological studies, cancer rehabilitation, and continuing care.

The program was conceived in collaboration with Case Western Reserve University, which had an established program in basic cancer research and could contribute to the community-wide programs necessary for epidemiological studies and rehabilitation. The emphasis on programs not well represented on the Clinic's campus, however, resulted in an initial effort that had little relationship to the cancer treatment services under way in the various departments.

In the early 1980s, the Board of Governors perceived the need for a cancer center that could coordinate all cancer treatment and research under way at The Cleveland Clinic. Distinct programs had already been established in the Departments of Hematology and Medical Oncology and Radiation Therapy. Surgical oncology fell under no specific departmental umbrella. The Board of Governors eventually recruited general surgeon John H. Raaf, M.D., in 1985 to be the center's first full-time director.

As the cancer program expanded, surgical departments began to create formal oncology sections. This increased the number of cancer patients. To serve them best, the Department of Hematology and Medical Oncology, then chaired by James K. Weick, M.D., began to recruit staff members with special organ expertise. The first was David J. Adelstein, M.D., an expert in aerodigestive tract malignancies, who joined the group in 1989. After Weick transferred to Cleveland Clinic Florida, Maurie Markman, M.D., a medical oncologist with a major interest in gynecologic malignancies, was recruited as chairman of the Department of Hematology and Medical Oncology and director of the Cancer Center in 1992.

In the mid-1980s, the opening of the A Building[7] had a significant impact on the Cancer Center. Several departments vacated space in the original Clinic building and Main Clinic building when they moved to their new quarters. Fortunately, this space was adjacent to Radiation Therapy. Weick immediately recognized the value of such a space where related clinical specialties could practice in proximity, and decided to relocate Hematology and Medical Oncology to the third floor of the original Clinic building. A portion of the floor was reserved as space for interdepartmental use where related services, such as neurological assessments and postoperative follow-up of cancer patients, could take place.[8] The area was

---

[7] The A Building was later rechristened the Crile Building. See Chapters 8 and 9 for further information about this landmark structure.

[8] Even in the absence of physical proximity, some oncologists had organized interdepartmental clinics before 1985 by making departmental space available for patients scheduled to be seen

renovated and dedicated as the Cleveland Clinic Cancer Center in June 1987.[9]

By 1994, the Cleveland Clinic Cancer Center had the largest cancer treatment program in Ohio and surrounding states. In only 10 years, the number of patients at the Clinic with cancer had grown from one in six to one in four inpatients, and from one in twelve to one in nine outpatients. This volume permitted subspecialists to develop substantial expertise in dealing with some relatively rare forms of cancer.

Besides coordinating existing cancer programs, the Cleveland Clinic Cancer Center is working with other departments to develop new programs. One successful example is the establishment of screening and detection programs for patients without symptoms within departments that previously focused on the diagnosis and treatment of symptomatic patients. By 1994, the Clinic was offering site-specific screenings for cancers of the breast, cervix, colon and rectum, mouth, prostate, and skin.

Treatment advances since 1971 have increased the number of patients surviving five or more years by one-third. Many of these patients at the Cleveland Clinic participate in a peer-support group, which was founded in 1988 by Cancer Center nurse counselor Barbara Gustafson. They also celebrate National Cancer Survivors Day yearly with major festivities on campus.

Unfortunately, the lack of basic understanding about how cancer is controlled means that progression of the disease is still a reality for many patients. For this reason, the Cancer Center is committed to helping poor-prognosis patients control their symptoms. The Palliative Care program began in 1987 when T. Declan Walsh, M.D., was recruited jointly by the Cancer Center and Department of Hematology and Medical Oncology. Initially established as a consulting service for hospitalized patients, the program grew to include a dedicated outpatient clinic, home care services, and certified hospice. In 1994, a generous gift from the Harry R. Horvitz Family Foundation made it possible to add a 23-bed inpatient unit, which has been recognized by the World Health Organization.

---

by staff members from other departments. One example is urologic oncology, where patients were seen weekly by a team that consisted of a urologic oncologist from the Department of Urology and a medical oncologist from the Department of Hematology and Medical Oncology.
[9] The subsequent catalytic impact of the physical identity for the Cancer Center resulted eventually in the creation of several additional discrete centers, including the Breast Center on the ground floor of the Crile Building, and the Center for Prostatic Diseases in the Department of Urology.

Comprehensive cancer care requires a team approach that combines the contributions of physicians with those of allied health professionals, especially nurses and social workers. In 1985, the Department of Nursing established a Cancer Nursing Section with six clinical nurse specialists assigned to interdepartmental cancer teams. Today, cancer nursing care throughout The Cleveland Clinic is carefully coordinated. Social workers, who were available only to hospitalized cancer patients and their families before 1985, are now provided in the Cancer Center clinics for outpatient counseling, follow-up in the community, and leadership of peer support groups.

Since the analysis and interpretation of results is critical to controlling cancer, The Cleveland Clinic Research Institute's Department of Biostatistics and Epidemiology established a new Section of Biostatistics in 1985 to help with this process and track cancer patients enrolled in clinical trials. Since 1986, the section has directed the work of the Cleveland Clinic Tumor Registry, which collects baseline and follow-up information on all cancer patients seen at the Clinic. In 1994, it was expanded to include a registry for studies involving families with a strong history of cancer. Today, the Section of Cancer Biostatistics, under the leadership of Paul Elson, D.Sc., provides collaborating clinical researchers with biostatisticians, systems analysts, and data management study coordinators.

In 1993, the Cleveland Clinic Cancer Center assisted in recruiting Roger Macklis, M.D., to chair the Department of Radiation Therapy. A funded investigator in radiation biology and radiation physics as they relate to targeted delivery of cancer therapy, Macklis was interested in many of the Cancer Center's programs. For this reason, the new department was transferred from the Division of Radiology to the Cancer Center and renamed the Department of Radiation Oncology. Within the first two years, the new department received a gift that allowed it to begin planning a Center of Oncologic Robotics and Computer-Assisted Medicine, where one of only six prototype linear accelerators mounted on a robotic arm will be housed. This design will reduce the need for rigid immobilization of patients undergoing lengthy and recurring treatments for brain cancer.

New basic research insights have been applied to the care of cancer patients at the Clinic for almost 20 years and are an integral part of the Cancer Center's success. Cancer research reached a new level of institutional prominence when Bernadine Healy, M.D., was named chairman of the Division of Research (soon thereafter renamed the Research Institute) in 1985; she immediately established a Department of Cancer Biology in the division and recruited

Bryan R. G. Williams, Ph.D., to head it (see Research). Its importance was further underscored when George R. Stark, Ph.D., a researcher with interests in gene amplification and interferon, succeeded Healy as chairman. He received the Research Institute's first National Cancer Institute basic sciences program project award for an inter-departmental investigation into signal transduction. Today, dozens of Clinic researchers work closely with Cancer Center clinicians to find better ways of preventing and treating all forms of this group of diseases.

As the century draws to a close, the Clinic continues to build upon its leadership role in the care of cancer patients through a wide array of experts and specialized services. The Cleveland Clinic Cancer Center provides a single, integrated approach to the control of cancer for patients throughout the Foundation. A major addition to the Cancer Center and new research laboratories in the Research Institute are expected to be completed by the year 2000, and this will ensure that the Clinic has optimal facilities to meet the challenges of this disease in the coming years.

EYE INSTITUTE

Ophthalmology was introduced at The Cleveland Clinic in 1924 under A. D. Ruedemann, M.D., a capable surgeon with a dynamic personality. He acquired an enormous following and saw an extra-ordinarily large number of patients on a daily basis. An independent thinker who often locked horns with the chief of surgery, Ruedemann left the Clinic in 1947 and was succeeded by Roscoe J. Kennedy, M.D., a respected physician who served with distinction.

When Kennedy retired in 1969, Froncie A. Gutman, M.D., a vit-reoretinal specialist, was appointed department chairman. The only other staff member at that time was a general ophthalmologist named James Nousek, M.D., whom Kennedy had hired in 1957.

Under Gutman's leadership, the Department of Ophthal-mology began to expand and modernize, adding subspecialty trained physicians, implementing new technology, strengthening the educational programs, and expanding clinical research activity. By 1988, the department included specialists in corneal and external disease, neuro-ophthalmology, uveitis, pediatric ophthalmology, glaucoma, ophthalmic plastic and reconstructive surgery, and general ophthalmology, in addition to a vitreoretinal staff of four. They developed busy and challenging clinical practices which provided the resources and environment for resident and fellowship training as well as clinical investigation. Many of the staff have been recog-

Hilel Lewis, M.D., Chairman, Eye Institute (Division of Ophthalmology), 1992–

nized as leaders through their appointment or election to office in professional ophthalmic organizations. Gutman himself was elected chairman of the American Board of Ophthalmology and served as president of the American Academy of Ophthalmology.

Ophthalmic technicians, laboratory services, and optometry were introduced to support the clinical programs. In 1970, the Department of Ophthalmology opened the first ophthalmic laboratory in Cleveland with a full-time staff of photographers who performed fluorescein angiography studies. New laboratories for ophthalmic electrophysiology and ultrasonography soon made additional diagnostic services available. The department established an ophthalmic technician training program to supply a pool of trained individuals who could assist in patient evaluations and ancillary testing. The addition of optometrists and an optical dispensary rounded out the department's primary care service.

In 1992 Hilel Lewis, M.D., a talented vitreoretinal specialist from California, succeeded Gutman as chairman. With his appointment, the department parted company with the Division of Surgery and became a new division.

Lewis's goal is to create one of the leading eye research and patient care facilities in the country, and the division's name change to the Eye Institute reflects this commitment. Recruitment is under way to assemble a group of world-class physicians in 10 clinical departments and ophthalmic research. Since recent developments in outpatient eye care have rendered the Clinic's hospital-based eye service obsolete, a free-standing building is planned to house the Eye Institute. It will include facilities to treat 100,000 patients a year more comfortably and cost-effectively as outpatients. Special eye research facilities will allow the scientists to focus on finding a cure for diseases that are not well understood, such as retinitis pigmentosa, glaucoma, and macular degeneration.

CONCLUSION

Each of the Centers of Excellence brings together professionals from a variety of disciplines in a common setting to address all aspects of a complex clinical problem. Group practice lends itself well to the creation and smooth operation of such centers, and The Cleveland Clinic has been particularly successful in implementing this approach to health care delivery, research, and education.

FIFTEEN

DIVISION OF PATHOLOGY AND LABORATORY MEDICINE

A physician can sometimes parry the scythe
of death, but has no power over the sand
in the hourglass.
— *Hester Lynch Piozzi, 1781*

To say that the laboratory is key to the practice of medicine is an understatement. Perhaps it is better to say that the laboratory is at the very heart of scientific medicine. Much of today's most advanced medical technique and technology is put to use in the clinical laboratories, making possible the diagnosis and rational treatment of disease.

During its long and illustrious history, The Cleveland Clinic's Division of Pathology and Laboratory Medicine has undergone remarkable growth and development. The division currently consists of two departments, Anatomic Pathology and Clinical Pathology. Anatomic Pathology provides diagnostic services based on the histologic and cytologic microscopic features of tissue and cellular samples obtained by biopsy, smear, surgery, or autopsy. The Department of Clinical Pathology is composed of five sections: Biochemistry, Blood Banking and Transfusion Medicine, Laboratory Hematology, Immunopathology, and Microbiology. In addition, Laboratory Information Systems and the Primary Laboratory Center support division activities. Through the Reference Laboratory, top-quality laboratory services available to Clinic patients are offered outside the institution as well.

Under the leadership of William R. Hart, M.D., chairman since 1992, the division supports a professional staff of 35 M.D.'s and

179

William R. Hart, M.D., Chairman, Division of Pathology and Laboratory
Medicine, 1992–

Ph.D.'s, and a technical staff of 562. They perform nearly all laboratory testing for The Cleveland Clinic's hospital, clinic, and satellite
facilities, processing more than three million tests annually, including more than 45,000 surgical pathology and 24,000 cytopathology
cases. With the exception of phlebotomy stations, a handful of small
satellite laboratories, and the operating room suite where surgical
specimens are dissected and frozen sections performed, all division
facilities are housed in the 164,000-sq. ft. Laboratory Medicine
Building. This volume surely could not have been foreseen in 1921.

ANATOMIC PATHOLOGY

In the early days, Cleveland Clinic surgeons were supported
solely by Allen Graham, M.D., who joined the organization in 1928
as head of tissue pathology. He was respected for his abilities as a
diagnostician, teacher, and expert in diseases of the thyroid. Trained
first as a surgeon, he was a valued consultant in the operating room.

The quality of Graham's work is evident in his files. An acute
observer, he was able to identify several abnormal conditions whose
corresponding diseases were not described until many years later.
He preferred to work alone, even doing his own photomicrography

John Beach Hazard, M.D., Chairman, Division of Laboratory Medicine and Chief
of Pathology, 1946–1970

and developing his own prints and films. However, this often
delayed autopsy reports by months. Faced with a growing workload
and unable to delegate, Graham became overwhelmed by his burden and left the Foundation in 1943.

During the next few years, pathology services were supplied by
Harry Goldblatt, M.D., an outstanding pathologist at the Western
Reserve University School of Medicine. Routine activities within the
department were carried out by Betty Haskell, one of the original
technologists. Although Clinic surgeons felt the quality of pathology reports was excellent, they missed having the support of a
pathologist in the operating room.

Fortunately, several staff surgeons had become acquainted with
a pathologist named J. Beach Hazard, M.D., either through World
War II or through Boston City Hospital. In 1946, Hazard was invited to join the staff as head of the Department of Tissue Pathology. As
part of the Division of Surgery, the department was located in a
small area adjacent to the operating room where surgeons could
freely seek consultations. In the beginning, Hazard was the only
physician in a department of technicians.

He set about organizing his department with the enthusiasm
and goodwill that characterized his leadership of 24 years. Whereas

Graham had sometimes worked for days without speaking, Hazard was always eager to talk. His knowledge spanned a wide range of interests, and so he was approached by colleagues and fellows from many departments as well as his own trainees. He made pathology come alive. And although he foresaw the wisdom in combining the clinical laboratories with his department, he made no move to implement any objective that would appear self-serving. Anyway, the clinical laboratories were working efficiently for the time being, and he had enough to do carrying the load in anatomic pathology.

Growth of The Cleveland Clinic's surgical facilities and hospital eventually created a demand for anatomic pathologists. In 1951, Lawrence J. McCormack, M.D., joined Hazard. It was a good match, since Hazard specialized in diseases of the thyroid, and McCormack's interests encompassed diseases of the lung, kidney, bone and brain, as well as the developing field of cytology. William A. Hawk, M.D., a specialist in gastrointestinal disease, became the third member of the team five years later. To ensure order among this rapidly growing group of physicians, the Division of Surgery relinquished the Department of Tissue Pathology to the new Division of Pathology in 1957. It included both the clinical laboratories and anatomic pathology under Hazard's direction.

In the early 1970s, Hawk added Howard S. Levin, M.D., and Bruce A. Sebek, M.D., to the staff. These two stalwart pathologists carried much of the caseload themselves for years, at the same time advancing the fields of genitourinary, endocrine, breast, and head and neck pathology.

In 1981, William R. Hart, M.D., replaced Hawk as chairman of Anatomic Pathology. He had come to the Clinic from the University of Michigan, where he had specialized in surgical pathology and gynecologic pathology after stints at the Armed Forces Institute of Pathology and the University of Southern California. Under his direction, growth in the overall size of the department and specialization accelerated. New staff members were recruited to develop general surgical pathology, cytology, cardiovascular pathology, dermatopathology, endocrine pathology, gastrointestinal pathology, gynecologic pathology, hematopathology, hepatic pathology, nephropathology, neuropathology, orthopedic pathology, pulmonary pathology, and soft tissue pathology. The use of diagnostic electron microscopy was expanded. New technologies were rapidly incorporated into the diagnostic armament of the anatomic pathologists, including immunohistochemistry, morphometry, DNA-ploidy and cell cycle analysis, flow cytometry, and molecular pathology.

During the 1980s, the department established a national and international reputation. It became one of the first fully computerized anatomic pathology facilities of its kind in the country. Staff members gained recognition through scientific publications and presentations, workshops, and seminars held at their professional society meetings, and leadership positions in national and international organizations.

In 1993, after Hart was appointed chairman of the Division of Pathology and Laboratory Medicine, Robert E. Petras, M.D., was promoted to chairman of Anatomic Pathology. He had joined the staff after completing his training at the Clinic and developing expertise in gastrointestinal pathology.

CLINICAL PATHOLOGY

The original clinical laboratories were designed by David Marine, M.D., who never occupied them.[1] They opened in 1921 under the medical supervision of Henry J. John, M.D., a diabetologist with an interest in chemical analysis.

After John left the Clinic in 1933, the laboratories were supervised for 10 years by Russell L. Haden, M.D., head of the Division of Medicine. Haden was a hematologist noted for developing several instruments used in the examination of blood. He organized and occupied a laboratory for the study of blood diseases, while carrying a heavy clinical load as well. The various other clinical laboratories were also under Haden's direction, but were actually run by technicians.

In 1944, a new Department of Clinical Pathology was created in the Division of Medicine, and Lemuel W. Diggs, M.D., was appointed chairman. His ideas were incorporated into the design of the modern laboratories within the new clinic building. He also established a blood bank.

When Diggs left in 1947, John W. King, M.D., Ph.D., was appointed head of the department. With a doctorate in bacteriology and a degree in medicine, King was well qualified for the post. At this time, increasing specialization, an explosion in basic medical research, and the development of new techniques were paving the way for a rapid expansion of the Clinic's laboratory services. Only 20 laboratory tests were routinely performed in 1940, but the

---

[1] Marine and Graham served together as resident pathologists at Lakeside Hospital and Western Reserve University School of Medicine. Marine left Cleveland in 1920 to become director of pathology at Montefiore Hospital in New York.

increased use of blood, plasma, plasma products, and antibiotics during World War II profoundly influenced the practice of medicine. Surgeons demanded support from clinical laboratories, and physicians in all specialties required accurate, fast results from new, often complex tests.

King recognized that subspecialization within the laboratory was needed to meet these demands, and he established a Section of Bacteriology and Serology and a Section of Biochemistry. Later, an endocrine laboratory was added. King himself headed the Section of Bacteriology and Serology, as well as the Blood Bank. Adrian Hainline, M.D., was named head of Biochemistry, and soon a subsection of microchemistry was formed. The number and range of tests offered by Haden's original "special hematology" laboratory was expanded.[2]

Increasing specialization continued, and George C. Hoffman, M.D., was appointed head of Laboratory Hematology in 1959. Although morphologic hematology already had reached a high degree of excellence, exciting new approaches to bleeding disorders and the hemolytic diseases were being developed. Hoffman worked closely with the clinical hematologists to ensure that their patients received state-of-the-art care.

For many years the hematology laboratory was Hoffman's domain alone. Five colleagues eventually joined him, each specializing in different diseases of the blood. These included the structure and chemical processes within normal and abnormal blood cells, hormone control of red blood cells, sickle cell anemia and other abnormalities of hemoglobin, and abnormal blood clotting.[3] When Hoffman was named division chairman in 1981, Ralph G. Green, M.D., was recruited from the Scripps Clinic to succeed him in Laboratory Hematology. He served until 1993, when he was replaced by Michael L. Miller, D.O., a former fellow in hematopathology and member of the staff since 1986.

In 1961, Donald A. Senhauser, M.D., was named head of Microbiology. He subsequently introduced new techniques in the field of immunopathology. In 1964, a Section of Immunopathology was created with Sharad D. Deodhar, M.D., Ph.D., as head. The

---

[2] When Haden left the Clinic in 1949, supervision of the laboratories by hematologists rather than clinical pathologists was preserved. John D. Battle, M.D., directed the laboratory, and in 1953, James S. Hewlett, M.D., was invited to share these duties.

[3] Two of Hoffman's young staff members later assumed leadership positions within the Clinic: Andrew J. Fishleder, M.D., became chairman of the Division of Education, and Fred V. Lucas, M.D., became the first chairman of Pathology and Laboratory Medicine at Cleveland Clinic Florida.

Laboratory Medicine Building, 1980

same year, Charles E. Willis, M.D., was appointed head of Biochemistry. Three years later, when Senhauser left the Clinic, Thomas L. Gavan, M.D., replaced him as chairman of Microbiology.

Upon Hazard's retirement in 1970, McCormack was appointed division chairman. The name was changed to the Division of Laboratory Medicine, and its sections were renamed departments.

With all this growth, space was becoming a problem. Laboratories were scattered throughout the Clinic's buildings. The need for additional space was temporarily met by moving some of the laboratories into the old Research Building while a new building was designed and constructed. In 1980, the majority of laboratories were finally consolidated in a Laboratory Medicine Building.

Robert S. Galen, M.D., was brought to the Clinic as chairman of Biochemistry in 1982 following Willis's retirement. Under Galen, the laboratory developed a number of specialized functional sections: Quality Control; Lipids; Nutrition and Metabolic Diseases; Automated/Acute Care Chemistry; Applied Clinical Pharmacology; and Enzymology. Highly automated and sophisticated instrumentation capable of handling high volumes of routine as well as specialized chemical analyses were introduced and became the laboratory standard. Galen left in 1988 and was replaced by Frederick Van Lente, Ph.D., a biochemist he had brought to the Clinic to head the automated and acute care laboratories. Van Lente became the division's first non-physician department chairman.

Sharad Deodhar, M.D., Ph.D., headed the Department of Immunopathology from its inception until his retirement in 1993. Under his guidance, the Clinic became a national leader in the field of immunopathology. Departmental activities encompassed such areas as the functional study of the immune system, cellular immunity, radioimmunassay, immune mechanisms in rheumatic diseases, tissue typing for organ transplantation, paternity testing, and cancer immunology with emphasis on controlling metastatic disease. Raymond R. Tubbs, D.O., a member of the anatomic pathology staff with special expertise in immunopathology, was chosen to succeed Deodhar.

The Blood Bank prospered under King's direction, meeting the enormous need for blood required by the Clinic's expanding cardiac surgery program. In order to ensure a steady supply of well-trained technologists, he also founded the John W. King School of Medical Technology, which, more than 35 years later, graduates six highly qualified lab technologists every year.

Following King's retirement in 1981, Gerald A. Hoeltge, M.D., was promoted to department chairman. Although innovations in blood conservation during cardiac surgery reduced some pressure on the Blood Bank, the demand for blood products escalated as the overall volume of surgical procedures rose and organ transplants became more commonplace. New techniques in hemapheresis and immunohematology have made blood safer than ever before, as have serological testing for viruses such as hepatitis and HIV, and autologous blood donation. Hoeltge also runs the cytogenetics laboratory, in which the chromosomal abnormalities of diseases such as leukemia and lymphoma are identified.

Under the direction of Thomas L. Gavan, M.D., the Department of Microbiology incorporated the Sections of Bacteriology and Serology. Staff members were recruited for the newly appointed sections of Anaerobic Microbiology, Parasitology, Mycobacteriology, Mycology and Clinical Virology. The staff actively pursued interests in computerization, automation, and antibiotic susceptibility testing.

Following Gavan's appointment as division chairman in 1986, John A. Washington, M.D., was recruited from the Mayo Clinic to chair the Department of Microbiology. Washington expanded virology activities, and the department soon became a leader in the development and use of molecular techniques for the identification of viruses, most notably the human immunodeficiency virus (HIV). With Hart's restructuring of the division in 1992, all clinical laboratory departments were consolidated, and Washington was named chairman of the new Department of Clinical Pathology.

LABORATORY INFORMATION SYSTEMS

During the years when McCormack was division chairman, an innovative general laboratory computer system was installed. In 1984, David Chou, M.D., was recruited to run it and was named director of Laboratory Information Systems (LIS) upon McCormack's retirement the following year. Under Chou's guidance, computerization flourished within individual departments as well as division-wide. In 1995, the original laboratory information system was replaced with a more sophisticated one that linked several independent departmental systems — such as the ones in Microbiology (the first computerized laboratory in the Division) and the Blood Bank — with the central LIS and a new hospital information system.

REFERENCE LABORATORY

In response to the rapidly changing medical environment of the 1980s, the division expanded its facilities to provide high-quality, cost-effective laboratory services to the community. In 1989 the Reference Laboratory, which had grown out of McCormack's small regional laboratory, was partnered with a national commercial laboratory. The venture offered esoteric clinical laboratory testing to hospitals and institutions within a six-state area. Washington served as medical director of the laboratory until 1994, when a new business plan was adopted, the partnership dissolved, and a general manager recruited. Today, the independent Cleveland Clinic Reference Laboratory provides the full range of routine and esoteric tests for hospitals, nursing homes, home health care services, physician offices, and industry.

CONCLUSION

Since World War II an explosion of medical knowledge has unleashed a new and exciting world of technique and technology. The Division of Pathology and Laboratory Medicine has responded to these challenges through increasing subspecialization, computerization, and automation. The division continues to dedicate itself to finding new and better ways to provide the most timely, accurate test results possible for millions of patients a year both within and outside The Cleveland Clinic.

SIXTEEN

DIVISION OF RADIOLOGY

Beware lest you lose the substance by
grasping at the shadow.

— Aesop, Sixth Century B.C.(?)

When the The Cleveland Clinic first opened, radiology was a relatively young medical specialty.[1] The founders selected Bernard H. Nichols, M.D., to be the first head of the Department of Radiology which was positioned in the Division of Medicine. This choice was a singularly fortunate one, for Nichols was one of the

---

[1] At least one of the founders of The Cleveland Clinic had reason to believe that good diagnostic radiology was essential to the practice of medicine. In 1902, when Crile was still operating at St. Alexis Hospital, one of the trustees of the hospital woke up at midnight, choking, and felt certain that he had swallowed his lower denture. For an hour and a half he clawed at his throat, mistaking the hyoid bone for the missing teeth. He succeeded in so traumatizing the throat that he could no longer swallow, even his saliva. A roentgenogram was made (this was only seven years after Roentgen's discovery of the x-ray), and the film showed some calcifications in the aortic arch which were interpreted as being the missing teeth. The patient was by this time in serious condition as a result of his own and his physicians' attempt to locate and remove the teeth. Finally Crile was called and was prevailed upon to operate.

Shortly after the operation the teeth were found in an obscure corner of the patient's room. The next day the patient died, and the story hit the headlines throughout the country: "Death Due to Operation. Patient Who Didn't Swallow His Teeth Is Dead." Crile in his autobiography summarized the diagnostic problem as follows:

"The positive statement of an intelligent man, a benefactor of the hospital, one whom we had known for a long period, that he had not only swallowed his teeth but that he had touched them a number of times with his fingers and at one time had almost succeeded in removing them; the firm belief of his doctor, a physician of wide experience, that the teeth were still in the throat; the statements of the family that the teeth were not in the room, and their reiterant belief that the teeth had been swallowed; the rapid increase and gravity of the symptoms of the patient during the first day, seemingly out of proportion to the exploratory traumatism; and lastly the positive x-ray diagnosis, overruled our negative findings at the exploration. In consultation the various doctors who had been interested agreed that an operation was indicated."

country's pioneers in diagnostic radiology. He practiced medicine first in Youngstown, Ohio. He then moved to White Hospital (now Robinson Memorial Hospital) in Ravenna, Ohio. There he met Bunts, Crile, and Lower, who were also on the staff and often operated there. Nichols became interested in radiology when a Ravenna manufacturing company began making x-ray machines of the primitive hand-cranked variety and one of these machines was put at his disposal.

Nichols entered the Army Medical Corps during World War I and, after completing a course in bone pathology, served as a radiologist. With this background, he joined the staff as a specialist in radiology in 1921. Over the next 15 years, he wrote 50 papers on diagnostic radiology, 23 of which concerned the diagnosis of diseases of the genitourinary tract. Energy, honesty, and an amused affection for people combined to make him a popular member of the staff. He had a goatee that gave him such a distinguished air that he was commonly referred to as the "Duke of Ravenna," the town in which he lived.

In 1922, the Department of Radiology was strengthened by the appointment of U. V. Portmann, M.D., as director of radiation therapy, and by the purchase of the Cleveland area's first 250,000-volt radiation therapy machine. Tall, massively built, handsome, and somewhat intimidating, Portmann generated confidence. He soon became a national figure in radiotherapy, writing as extensively as Nichols did, chiefly on the measurement of radiation dosage and its use in treating cancers of the thyroid and breast. He also wrote a widely read textbook on radiotherapy.

A third pioneer in radiology, Otto Glasser, Ph.D., was a biophysicist and a member of the Research Division. He was described by a colleague as "a giant radiation physicist." Glasser first formulated the concept of a condenser dosimeter for measuring the amount of radiation delivered by a diagnostic or therapeutic radiation device. This instrument was used for calibrating x-ray equipment, a safety measure for the patient and medical personnel. Previously, radiotherapists estimated the dosage on the basis of reaction of the skin, the amount of radiation required to redden the skin being considered to be an "erythema dose." Glasser's concept was implemented by the Clinic's brilliant engineer, Mr. Valentine Seitz, who constructed a practical unit that was used clinically by Portmann. Thus, the talents of a radiotherapist, a biophysicist, and an engineer were combined to produce one of the fundamental advances in radiology. A prototype of the dosimeter is in the collection of scientific discoveries in the Smithsonian Institution.

Michael T. Modic, M.D., Chairman, Division of Radiology, 1989–

Glasser was responsible for control of the radon (radium) seeds used in the treatment of certain types of cancers. He was also a prolific writer of scientific papers and editor of a massive three-volume work entitled *Medical Physics*. He also wrote a definitive biography of Wilhelm Conrad Roentgen, the man who discovered the x-ray in 1895. Later in his career, Glasser's interest turned to radioactive isotopes, and again he made important contributions. He was urbane but not pretentious, and he was kindly and considerate to all, relating to those of modest station in life as easily and sincerely as to those of exalted status. His human qualities matched his scientific achievements.

C. Robert Hughes, M.D., became head of the Department of Radiology in 1946. Hughes had training in surgery before his interests changed to radiology, and this clinical background combined with his technical knowledge gave him insights valued by both internists and surgeons, who consulted him frequently about problem patients.

Hughes was a born planner and inventor whose talents were not confined to medicine. At the time of his appointment, the Clinic was on the threshold of an explosion in growth and Hughes, working with Charles L. Hartsock, M.D., of the Department of Internal

Otto Glasser, Ph.D., Head, Department of Biophysics, 1923–1964

Medicine, designed a new and innovative x-ray department. Hughes wanted original ideas to supplement proven concepts, so the two planners came up with a unique department design that served efficiently for many years with little modification — a great accomplishment in an ever-changing field. The Department of Radiology was originally confined to the Clinic Building. Only portable equipment was used in the hospital, at the bedside, or during operations. An additional radiology facility was opened in the hospital in 1947. Surgical operations were becoming more complex, and often it was desirable to obtain intraoperative radiological examinations, and so x-ray facilities were included in many of the operating rooms when a new surgical pavilion was built in 1955.

In 1960, the Board of Governors established a Division of Radiology, removing Radiology from the Division of Medicine. Hughes was appointed to head this new division. In 1966, the Division of Radiology was defined by the Governors to include a Department of Hospital Radiology, including radiology performed in the operating pavilion, a Department of Clinic Radiology, and a Department of Therapeutic Radiology and Isotopes. At this time, Thomas F. Meaney, M.D., a former radiology fellow under Hughes, was appointed to chair the Division of Radiology and manage the hospital department with Hughes taking responsibility for the clinic department and A. R. Antunez, M.D., chairing therapeutic radiology and nuclear medicine. Hughes continued as clinic department chairman until 1970 when he was replaced by Anthony F. Lalli, M.D. The current clinic department chairman, George H. Belhobek, M.D., assumed this responsibility in 1983. Meaney turned the hospital department chair over to Ralph J. Alfidi, M.D., in 1970 and continued on as division chairman until 1987. The current hospital chairman, Gregory P. Borkowski, M.D., was appointed in 1985.

Meaney, an innovative young man with great vision, became division chairman coincident as tremendous advancements in x-ray technology and practice were occurring. He was already recognized for his work with the newly developed procedure of angiography, a technique with which he became familiar during a sabbatical leave in Sweden in 1963. Over the next several years, Meaney was instrumental in developing angiographic and interventional procedures for use not only at the Cleveland Clinic but across the nation. His collaborative work with Harriet Dustan, M.D., in the Department of Hypertension and Nephrology and Lawrence McCormack, M.D., in the Department of Pathology in the mid-1960s resulted in multiple publications outlining the role of renal vascular disease in hypertension.

Over the next 20 years, radiologists expanded their arsenal of interventional procedures to include biliary drainage, abscess drainage, embolization and clot lysis, and percutaneous lung, kidney, and bone biopsies. Thus, interventional radiologists emerged with an active role in patient treatment as well as diagnosis.

DIAGNOSTIC RADIOLOGY

In 1972, Meaney visited England to evaluate a newly developed device which was capable of directly imaging pathology of the brain in a cross-sectional display. The technique, computerized axial tomography (CAT), was just being introduced to the world at that time. Seeing its great promise, Meaney purchased the fourth such device in the world for the Clinic. This original machine, which was limited to scanning the brain quickly, had a profound effect on the practice of neurology and neurosurgery. Ten months later, a CAT scanner (now referred to as CT scanner) designed for body imaging was installed at the Clinic, greatly increasing the scope of this technology. Numerous generations of CT scanners have been developed since that time with the latest technology providing images of very thin tissue thickness obtained with sub-second imaging times.

C. Robert Hughes, M.D., Chairman, Division of Radiology, 1960–1969

Digital subtraction angiography was the next innovative technology to hold a primary research focus in the Division of Radiology during Meaney's tenure. This computerized technology allowed individual arteries to be visualized with a generalized injection of intravenous water-soluble contrast material, thereby decreasing the need for the more invasive catheter arteriography in some cases.

A third technological breakthrough was brought to The Cleveland Clinic by Meaney in the early 1980s. Nuclear magnetic resonance imaging, soon to be called magnetic resonance imaging (MRI), was first utilized for imaging internal organs in 1973. Based on the principle of nuclear magnetic resonance, development of this technique was slow. By the early 1980s, however, there was a growing excitement that this non-invasive means of visualizing internal organs without the use of ionizing radiation used in x-ray-based techniques would have great promise in examining the soft tissues of the body including the brain and spinal cord. Meaney once again recognized the potential value of an emerging technology and purchased a unit for the Clinic in 1983. The Cleveland Clinic's Department of Diagnostic Radiology led the way in the ongoing development of this major imaging technology. A magnetic resonance spectroscopy research program under the guidance of Thian C. Ng, Ph.D., was added in 1984.

Meyer Medical Magnetic Resonance Center, 1983

A corollary of the dramatic growth of radiology activities in the 1970s and 1980s was the need to enlarge the physical facilities of the diagnostic radiology departments. In 1974, the Hospital Radiology Department was moved from the 8th floor of the original hospital to a vastly expanded facility in the basement of the new hospital building. Further expansion of radiology facilities came with the development of an outpatient department in the Crile Building, which opened in 1985. A large gift from Mr. E. T. Meyer (president of The Cleveland Clinic Foundation, from 1969 to 1972) made possible the construction of the Meyer Center for Magnetic Resonance in 1983, a facility uniquely designed to house the Clinic's magnetic resonance scanners.

Following Meaney's retirement in 1987, a search committee was convened to identify a new division chairman. After an intensive review of nationally known candidates, Michael T. Modic, M.D., a former resident in diagnostic radiology at the Clinic, was selected to fill this important position.[2] Modic, a neuroradiologist, was well known for his research work with MRI, especially its applications to diseases of the spine. He came with the reputation of being a clear,

---

[2] Between Meaney's and Modic's chairmanships, Arthur Rosenbaum, M.D., a neuroradiologist from Johns Hopkins University, served for a brief but fractious period.

decisive thinker. A man of action, he was charged with maintaining The Cleveland Clinic's position on the cutting edge of diagnostic imaging and supporting an environment that would foster active research activities while providing excellent clinical care and educational opportunities. With a staff of 36 subspecialty-oriented diagnostic radiologists, Modic forged ahead into the 1990s. New challenges were soon encountered, however. While the traditional goals of excellent patient care, productive research, and effective education were still considered high priorities, stricter control of operational costs also became increasingly important. The addition of five Clinic satellite radiology facilities and a new enlarged and more active Emergency Department with radiography and CT capabilities increased the demands on the Division.

Modic recognized that traditional radiology practice had to be re-evaluated and that new practice methods including electronic image transfer (teleradiography) and filmless radiography (digital radiography) needed to be considered. The demands of modern practice would also require more plain hard work. The division was ready to accept these challenges and move ahead.

RADIATION ONCOLOGY

After Portmann's retirement, several radiologists led the radiation therapy activities within the Department of Radiology until A. R. Antunez, M.D., was appointed chairman of the Department of Therapeutic Radiology and Nuclear Medicine in 1963. Like Meaney, Antunez was a builder. As in the case of diagnostic radiology, radiation physicists and engineers were developing new equipment, and Antunez acquired the latest equipment, sometimes raising funds to pay for new devices by personally attracting large gifts from philanthropists and grateful patients.

Antunez's department acquired a state-of-the-art cobalt therapy unit and high-voltage linear accelerators. He obtained computers for treatment planning and a simulating device to permit calculation of the maximal dose delivery to the desired location. He also arranged for the Lewis Research Laboratories of the National Aeronautics and Space Administration to make their Cleveland cyclotron available for neutron beam treatment of Clinic patients. In 1991, a major expansion of radiation therapy space was necessary to keep up with practice demands.

In 1993, shortly after the arrival of the present department chairman, Roger Macklis, M.D., radiation therapy was moved administratively from the Division of Radiology into the Cleveland

Clinic Cancer Center.[3] Radiation oncologists and medical oncologists had long been combining their talents to provide effective treatment protocols for the Clinic's cancer patients. The positioning of these two groups within the Cancer Center further strengthened this working relationship. With the recruitment of Macklis from the Harvard Joint Center for Radiation Therapy, the re-named Department of Radiation Oncology began another expansion phase. By 1995, it had become the largest and most technically sophisticated clinical radiotherapy department in Ohio, treating over 2,500 patients a year at the main campus and satellite sites. New personnel, new equipment, and a new clinical and research pavilion constructed at the corner of Euclid Avenue and E. 90th Street added to the department's momentum.

NUCLEAR MEDICINE

The use of radioactive iodine in treating thyroid disease had interested Glasser in the early days of the Division of Radiology. With his knowledge of physics and the technical skills of Mr. Barney Tautkins, a hand-constructed rectilinear scanner for imaging the thyroid gland following the uptake of radioactive iodine was developed. The device worked well, and, thus, isotope imaging studies at The Cleveland Clinic began. A physician was needed to interpret these scans, and since the Radiation Therapy Department was in close proximity to the scanner, this responsibility naturally fell to the staff in this department.

Eventually the gamma camera replaced the slower rectilinear scanning devices, and a multitude of radioisotopes useful for organ imaging were developed. The scope of nuclear medicine was rapidly increasing so that in 1978 a separate Department of Nuclear Medicine was created within the Division of Radiology. Sebastian A. Cook, M.D., was named its first chairman.

Raymundo Go, M.D., succeeded Cook as department chairman in 1983, and he continues to hold this position. He presently administers a department consisting of highly sophisticated computerized technology applied by a staff of six nuclear medicine physicians, a nuclear physicist, nuclear pharmacist, bioengineer, and a nuclear chemist. They have been especially active in the investigation of cardiac radionuclide diagnostic techniques and PET[4] scanning under

---

[3] Two chairmen, Frank Thomas, M.D., and Melvin Tefft, M.D., each led the department for brief periods between Antunez's departure and Macklis's appointment.
[4] PET = positron emission tomography, yet another advanced imaging technology.

the guidance of W. James MacIntyre, Ph.D., an internationally respected authority on nuclear instrumentation. Although a relatively new medical field, nuclear medicine has already contributed greatly to the modern practice of medicine.

CONCLUSION

Nichols, Portmann, and Glasser would be amazed that from their small beginnings the Division of Radiology has grown to include 43 staff physicians, 33 physicians in training, four physicists, two computer scientists, five research staff, and 359 employees who support their work. They have achieved many significant accomplishments over the years, and many accolades have been bestowed on individual staff members. Under Modic's leadership, the Division of Radiology is shaping itself to meet the challenges of the future. We expect that the next 75 years will be as productive and promising as the previous 75 have been.

SEVENTEEN

NURSING: DIVISION OF PATIENT CARE OPERATIONS

I enjoy convalescence.
It is the part that makes the
illness worthwhile.

— *George Bernard Shaw, 1921*

Throughout the history of The Cleveland Clinic, the importance of nursing in providing "better care of the sick" has never been challenged. It is universally acknowledged that the dedication, professionalism, and compassion of Cleveland Clinic nurses have played a key role in making it one of the world's leading health care institutions. Nursing, like all medical professions, has changed drastically over the years as a result of advancements in medical technique and technology as well as changes in the way health care is financed. Florence Nightingale could never have foreseen many of the duties and programs undertaken today by Cleveland Clinic nursing personnel.

The Cleveland Clinic opened in 1921 with four clinic nurses on staff.[1] The 184-bed hospital, which opened in 1924, had a nursing staff of 75, which included seven head nurses, 42 general duty nurses, and four operating room nurses. All direct patient care was provided by graduate (*i.e.* registered) nurses who were assisted by orderlies and ward maids. For many years, the hospital nursing

---

[1] Many of the clerical functions usually handled by a doctor's office nurse were done by secretaries at the Clinic.

staff was supplemented by private duty nurses who contracted directly with patients.[2]

The position of the ward maid eventually evolved into that of the nursing unit assistant (NUA). Floor hostesses, the precursors of unit secretaries, were added in 1947. The first practical nurses were hired in the hospital in 1954, and five years later, there were as many practical nurses as general duty R.N.'s on the hospital staff. Practical nurses were also added to the Clinic nursing staff, along with patient care assistants.

By 1985, the number of nursing personnel had risen to 350 in the outpatient departments and 1,725 in the hospital. More than 400 patients per day were being tended in the operating room and treatment areas alone. Increasing numbers of nurses were breaking with traditional roles and practicing as clinical nurse specialists or departmental assistants in outpatient medical departments.[3]

With a nurse functioning as superintendent over all departments in the hospital, nursing was represented at the highest level of hospital administration. However, when long-time superintendent Abbie Porter, R.N., retired in 1949 and was replaced by Mr. James Harding (not a nurse), the heads of the Nursing Department and Operating Room Department became the Clinic's highest-ranking nurses. In 1970, the Department of Nursing was decentralized into seven areas headed by directors, leaving the hospital without a unified nursing department. The director of nursing had, in a sense, become a committee.

This situation lasted until 1981, when the Board of Governors reunified nursing activities under the leadership of Sharon L. Danielsen, M.S.N., R.N. The new Department of Nursing encompassed Operating Room nursing as well as Nursing Education and Nurse Recruitment. Within the next few years, Ms. Danielsen organized the department according to a clinically oriented scheme. By 1985, it consisted of three clinical divisions — Surgical Nursing, Medical Nursing, and Operating Room and Treatment Areas — and a support division called Nursing Resources. She met regularly with the four division heads, the director of program planning, and the

---

[2] At first, nurses were mostly white females. This began to change slowly in the 1950s, gaining momentum thereafter as racial and ethnic minorities (especially African-Americans) and men appeared in larger numbers in nursing unit assistant and patient care assistant positions.

[3] Certified registered nurse anesthetists (CRNAs) worked outside the Department of Nursing. From the first, they had administered all anesthetics at the Foundation until a physician-headed Department of Anesthesiology was created in 1946. Nurse anesthesia was never phased out as it was in so many hospitals after World War II, and a school for nurse anesthetists was established at the Clinic in 1969.

Sharon J. Coulter, M.S.N., M.B.A., R.N., Chairman, Division of Patient Care
Operations, 1987–

fiscal coordinator as the Nursing Administrative Group to make
decisions about nursing policy and practice.[4]

In 1986, Isabelle Boland, head of the operating room and treatment areas, served as acting head of nursing during a nationwide
search for a new director of nursing. Sharon J. Coulter, M.S.N.,
M.B.A., R.N., was chosen for the position and assumed her duties in
May 1987. The Board of Governors immediately approved her
request for divisional status. The new Division of Nursing encompassed all inpatient facilities, surgical services, and the Emergency
Department. It did not, however, include clinic nursing or departmental assistants.

Coulter reorganized the administrative structure of nursing to
reduce its cumbersome management hierarchy to three levels: head
nurse, clinical director, and division chairperson. She retained nursing operations managers (similar to nursing supervisors) and assistant head nurses to handle administrative and managerial responsi-

---

[4] Surgical Nursing was headed by Linda J. Lewicki, M.S.N., R.N.; Medical Nursing by Francine
Wojton, M.S.N., R.N.; Operating Room and Treatment Areas by Isabelle Boland, M.S.N., R.N.;
Nursing Resources by Shirley Moore, M.S., R.N.; and Program Planning by Sandra S. Shumway,
M.S.N., R.N.

bilities on the off-shifts. The Department of Nursing Resources and the Operating Room nursing structure were also streamlined.

By 1988, Coulter chaired the Nursing Management Group (successor to the Nursing Administrative Group and predecessor to the Nursing Executive Council), which included the clinical directors for medical nursing; neuro/ortho/ENT nursing; critical care nursing; surgical nursing; operating room nursing; cardiac nursing; as well as the support department directors for physical and environmental resources; nursing research and nursing education; the fiscal coordinator; and the assistant to the chairman. Clinical directors for oncology and critical care nursing were added in 1989 and 1991.[5]

The basic table of organization was subsequently modified. By 1993, the Division of Nursing had six departments: medical/surgical nursing; cardio-thoracic nursing; critical care nursing; surgical services; the Center for Nursing, which included nurse recruitment and retention, nursing education, quality management, staffing and scheduling, nursing operations managers and information systems; and Nursing Research.[6]

In 1993 the Division of Nursing broadened its scope by absorbing the Pharmacy Department and changing its name from the Division of Nursing to the Division of Patient Care Operations.

CLINIC NURSING

Throughout the years, clinic nursing has remained separate from hospital nursing. The clinic nurses have traditionally reported directly to the medical departments for which they work and have no nursing management *per se*. After World War II a director of nursing was appointed, but it was not until the long tenure of Corinne Hofstetter, R.N., that the department firmly established its own

---

[5] By 1988, the Nursing Management Group had the following membership: Ms. Coulter as chair; clinical directors Mary Ann Brown, M.S.N., R.N. (medical nursing), Cathy M. Ceccio, M.S.N., R.N. (neuro/ortho/ENT nursing), Angela Janik, M.S.N., R.N. (critical care), Linda J. Lewicki, M.S.N., R.N. (surgical nursing), Marian K. Shaughnessy, M.S.N., R.N. (operating room nursing), Gayle Whitman, M.S.N., RN (cardiac nursing); support department directors Kathleen Lawson, B.S.,R.N. (physical and environmental resources), Deborah M. Nazdam, Ph.D., R.N. (nursing research), and Elizabeth Vasquez, M.S.N., R.N. (nursing education); and two staff, Amy Caslow Maynard (fiscal coordinator) and Sandra S. Shumway, now assistant to the chairman. Meri Beckham (Armour), M.S.N., R.N., was named clinical director of oncology nursing in 1989. Madeline Soupios served as acting director of critical care nursing for most of 1991 until a permanent director, Deborah Peeler (Charnley), M.N., R.N., was hired.

[6] By 1993, medical/surgical nursing was headed by Meri Beckham Armour, M.S.N., R.N., cardio-thoracic nursing by Gayle Whitman, M.S.N., R.N., critical care nursing by Deborah Peeler Charnley, M.S.N., R.N., surgical services by Betty Bush, B.S.N., R.N., the Center for Nursing by Maureen Donnelly, M.B.A., R.N., and nursing research by Christine Wynd, Ph.D., R.N.

identity and stability. After Hofstetter's retirement in 1986, E. Mary Johnson, B.S.N., R.N., assumed the directorship.

In 1990, a significant gap between clinic and hospital nursing closed when Johnson, who had long supported the idea of closer ties among Cleveland Clinic nurses, accepted an invitation to join the Nursing Management Group as a voting member. This improved communication for policy-making between the Division of Nursing and Clinical Nursing. Ambulatory (clinic) Nursing, however, remained administratively separate from the Division of Nursing. With decentralization in 1991, the nurses reported directly to the medical department chairmen.

Health care financing and technology has had a substantial effect on ambulatory nurses. Pushed by third-party payers and the development of new technologies, such as flexible endoscopy, an increasing number of procedures can now be done outside the hospital. In addition, nurses in the outpatient clinics have seen their patient loads grow as managed care becomes more prevalent.

NURSING DELIVERY CHANGES WITH THE TIMES

The Cleveland Clinic nursing staff has evolved in response to the scientific and technological advances that are transforming medical practice. In the 1920s, no antibiotics were available to treat postoperative patients or those with infections. Today, nurses administer antibiotics daily by mouth as well as by intramuscular or intravenous injection. Infection control removed one obstacle to the performance of increasingly invasive, delicate, and effective surgical procedures. Operating room nurses, who had themselves manufactured some of the supplies and equipment used in the operating room well past the mid-century, now became responsible for the purchase, care, and readiness of a fortune's worth of surgical instruments and supplies. But the high cost of more sophisticated care has provoked increased pressures for cost containment and a new emphasis on outpatient care.

In the Cleveland Clinic Hospital, the delivery of nursing care was originally organized according to function: nurses received specific assignments, such as pouring and passing medications for all patients on their units. During the 1960s and 1970s, nursing leadership implemented team nursing, with R.N.'s heading small teams that included L.P.N.'s and N.U.A.'s who were responsible for the complete care of a group of patients. In the late 1970s, the Nursing Department began to encourage primary nursing, whereby a nurse was assigned to each patient. The idea was that primary nursing would enable each patient to identify his or her nurse, give nurses increased responsibility for patient care, and provide better continuity of care.

In 1987, an expense reduction program at The Cleveland Clinic resulted in a substantial cut in budgeted staff positions.[7] While the Division of Nursing was not required to reduce its number of positions, limits placed on the division's overall expenses, together with a review of activities by the new leadership, resulted in the elimination of some job categories and a reduction in others as responsibilities and tasks were shifted. The Medicus-based patient classification system helped determine staffing levels, and the float pool of R.N.'s and L.P.N.'s expanded to increase flexibility in staffing.

At the same time a change in the handling of intravenous therapy gave more responsibility to unit staff R.N.'s. The division's intravenous team, which had responded to routine calls for intravenous services throughout the organization, was reduced in size and its mission redirected towards complex intravenous care and difficult starts. R.N.'s were trained to handle all routine starts on their own units.

Each unit had a head nurse and, in most cases, two assistant head nurses. In 1992, the title was changed to Nurse Manager, clarifying their responsibility for managing 50 or more employees as well as the unit's patients and budget. The following year, the title of Ambulatory Nursing Coordinator was also changed to Nurse Manager to reflect the same level of responsibility within the clinic.

The Patient Care Technician (PCT) position was developed during this period. First proposed by the Cardiothoracic Nursing Department in the late 1980s, it was implemented in the intensive care units by 1992. PCTs were used to perform some of the technical tasks needed in the ICU setting as well as the traditional duties of the NUA, freeing R.N.'s to concentrate on patient assessment, care planning, and patient education.

As in all hospitals, the need for nurses to be on duty 24 hours a day, seven days a week often caused difficulties. Cleveland Clinic nurses rated shift rotation and working weekends as major reasons for job dissatisfaction. Nursing leadership concluded that various types of flexible scheduling would increase nurse satisfaction and help the Clinic recruit and retain nurses.

In response to the challenge, a "Weekender Option Program" was implemented in 1990. It attempted to solve one part of the prob-

---

[7] This effort predated the Economic Improvement Plan (see Chapter 8) by nearly two years.

lem by allowing part-time R.N.'s and L.P.N.'s to work two 12-hour shifts during the weekend, as well as additional hours during the week. The option was so popular that by 1991, full-time nurses in most areas were working only one out of every three to six weekends. When a shift incentive program was instituted that year to encourage more nurses to work straight evenings or nights, 130 nurses signed up to participate. This helped stabilize staffing and reduced the need for rotating shifts.

Unit staff nurses had more freedom to determine their monthly work schedules through "self-staffing" or "self-scheduling." The program also relieved head nurses and assistant head nurses of the thankless, time-consuming task of scheduling. Ambulatory nurses gained more independence in setting their own hours as well when they were placed on salaries in 1991.

By the late 1980s, the impact of managed care on nursing had become obvious. The importance of nurse documentation in tracking the patient's progress and response to nursing interventions was understood and acknowledged. But suddenly, lack of documentation began to have a negative financial effect. In some cases, third party payors would refuse reimbursement if portions of the record had not been completed properly. For better compliance, new forms replaced old ones and new charting methods were adopted.[8]

In 1988, the Division of Nursing began to focus on a case management system for care delivery. Case management was expected to be especially useful where many long-term or high-risk cases existed, as has always been the situation in the Cleveland Clinic Hospital. Nurse case managers would be assigned to track patients throughout the course of their care, ensuring that they were recovering according to schedule. Nurses were to be held accountable for the outcome of nursing care.[9]

Facing the impact of managed care, the Division of Nursing was under pressure to control costs while managing a significant

---

[8] By 1992 the PIE charting system, which centered around a "nursing progress record," was in use. This provided a format for recording the assessment, planning, intervention, and evaluation (PIE) of the nursing process for the individual patient. An associated "problem list" recorded the results of the assessment in terms of nursing diagnoses, and followed the diagnosed problems to record their resolution — or lack thereof — during the patient's hospital stay.

[9] In 1991, the division appointed a project director for case management and formed a committee. During the following months, the committee examined a mechanism for evaluating the results of case-managed care. They extended the system throughout the hospital, with all units developing care tracks for their most common diagnosis-related groups (DRGs). More case manager positions were created, and in 1993, staff nurses became more involved in the case management process. Clearly, both the health of the patient and the financial health of the hospital benefitted when recovery stayed on track.

increase in numbers of patients. With labor costs responsible for a large part of hospital expenses, they could not hope to increase staffing in any significant way. New ways of delivering care were needed.

One solution was the Short Stay Unit, which opened in 1990 to care for patients whose conditions warranted very short periods of hospitalization for observation. This allowed for rapid turnover of patients, better utilization of beds, and reduced denials by payers. The project also introduced the "generic health care worker," who handled secretarial, housekeeping, and dietary duties.

The division became interested in the increasingly popular idea of the "patient-centered hospital." This concept shifted attention away from rigid job descriptions and toward the needs of patients. It involved cross-training workers from different departments to perform similar tasks. Although nurses were not necessarily cross-trained, they had a significant role in directing and coordinating this new work structure on their units. The Cleveland Clinic began a patient-centered unit pilot project in 1993.

BUILDING RELATIONSHIPS

Although nurses in the 1990s spend more time than ever before with computers and record-keeping, their relationships with patients and colleagues still provide the greatest satisfaction of their professional lives. While the patient's immediate physical needs continue to demand the most time, new value is being placed on patient education. Family members are included in this process as the core of the patient's social network. Paradoxically, scientific and technological advances, once expected to decrease personal contact with patients, have in some cases enhanced holistic care. For example, new anti-emetic drugs have allowed oncology nurses to spend less time managing the side effects of chemotherapy and more time ministering to the emotional needs of cancer patients and their families.[10]

In an effort to improve working relationships between nurses and their physician colleagues, a Nurse/Physician Collaboration Committee was established. In 1991 they instituted "Partners in Care," a program that matches new residents with nurse mentors who help introduce them to their units or areas. This establishes

---

[10] Programs such as Patient Pride, piloted in 1990, have added a new, gratifying facet to patient care. Directed by Corinne Hofstetter, the retired head of Clinic Nursing, Patient Pride uses volunteers to help hospitalized women boost their self-esteem and decrease loneliness.

good nurse-physician communication from the start. The "One-to-One" program, a resident-nurse orientation program for new residents, and "Can We Talk" nurse-resident-staff physician forums also open communication and promote collaboration among physicians and nurses. The annual Nightingale Physician Collaboration Award initiated in 1992 is bestowed annually by the Division of Nursing on the staff physician who most exemplifies this effort.

The division makes serious attempts to increase awareness of the role of nursing at The Cleveland Clinic and throughout the community. The Nursing Image Committee assumed responsibility for positioning Cleveland Clinic nursing as the highest quality patient care in the market, creating a positive image of the Clinic among nurses as well as a positive image of nurses among the general public. A task force on business and professional attire selected uniforms for unit secretaries and revised uniform and dress code policies for all nursing personnel. The Nursing History Committee examined the role of the nurse at The Cleveland Clinic since 1921, and prepared to host the annual meeting of the American Association for the History of Nursing in 1996. The Nursing Publications Committee produces the division's semi-annual journal, *Cleveland Clinic Nurse*, submits articles by Clinic nurses to the Cleveland-area monthly *Nursing News*, and keeps the lay media informed about noteworthy accomplishments.

Internally, outstanding nursing personnel are recognized through awards presented annually during Nurses' Week. The Clinical Excellence Awards Committee and the Nursing Unit Excellence Award Committee choose the recipients. All nursing personnel are eligible for these awards, which by 1994 included the Emma Barr Award for Clinical Excellence (R.N.), the Elizabeth Minnick Award for Clinical Excellence (L.P.N.), the Edward E. Rogers Award for Nursing Unit Assistance Excellence, the Karen Bourquin Award for Unit Secretary Excellence, the Abbie Porter Leadership Award, the Poinsetta Jeffery Humanitarian Award, the Hannah Boland Pediatric Clinical Excellence Award, the Ambulatory Nursing Unit Excellence Award, the Marilyn Tetonis Nursing Unit Excellence Award, the Sharon J. Coulter Patient Support Service Collaboration Award, and the Kathleen O. Currie Preceptor Excellence Award.

Interaction with the community, especially the minority community, has become especially important for The Cleveland Clinic and its nurses. During the past three decades, the neighborhoods surrounding the Clinic have become predominantly African-American, and many Clinic employees live in this area as well as other parts of greater Cleveland. In 1987, the Foundation entered into an agreement with nearby John Hay High School to create a health careers program aimed at enhancing the educational opportunities of Cleveland students as well as promoting the training of future health care workers. A popular feature has been the summer employment of students as nursing associates and unit hostesses and hosts.

NURSING EDUCATION AND RESEARCH

In the 1920s, the largest Cleveland hospitals had their own "nurses' training schools." At the best schools nurses received education in both the classroom and clinical setting. At the better hospitals, graduates might serve as head nurses. But in hospitals with training schools, the staff nurses were often students. Early on, The Cleveland Clinic made a conscious decision not to follow this pattern, but to staff both the clinic and hospital with graduate nurses. The founders felt that an experienced nursing staff would provide the best patient care.

Formal educational opportunities for nurses at the Clinic existed from the beginning, but these were limited to a few postgraduate positions on staff. However, the severe nursing shortage caused by World War II led to the hiring of a few undergraduate nurses. In 1954, the hospital entered into its first formal affiliation with a nursing school, which allowed students to receive clinical experience at The Cleveland Clinic's hospital. In subsequent years, a number of local diploma, associate degree, bachelor and graduate programs as well as licensed practical nursing schools have arranged to send their students to the Clinic for clinical observation and practice.

At first, overseeing these affiliation programs fell to the assistant director of nursing, who was also responsible for orientation and continuing medical education as well as for nurse recruitment, staffing, and scheduling. In the late 1960s this position was divided into three: recruitment, continuing education, and patient care. The Departments of Nurse Education and Nurse Recruitment grew from the first two, and the Division of Nursing absorbed them in the mid-1980s.

By the 1988-89 academic year, the Division of Nursing was affiliated with seven college- and university-based nursing programs.[11] Thirty-three Cleveland Clinic nursing staff members were pursuing A.D.N., B.S.N., or M.S.N. degrees with the help of tuition grants administered through the division.

---

[11] These were Case Western Reserve University's Frances Payne Bolton School of Nursing, Cleveland State University, Cuyahoga Community College, Kent State University, Lakeland Community College, the University of Akron, and Ursuline College.

The division strengthened its ties with the Frances Payne Bolton School of Nursing at Case Western Reserve University when the latter reinstated its B.S.N. program in 1990. The Clinic, along with University Hospitals of Cleveland and Cleveland Metropolitan General Hospital (now called MetroHealth), agreed to collaborate in the program by providing tuition support and clinical experience to the students, who would commit to serve at the sponsoring hospitals after graduation. Sharon Coulter was named an assistant dean at the Frances Payne Bolton School of Nursing, which graduated its first B.S.N. class in 1994.

The Division of Patient Care Operations (formerly Nursing) also offers education to nurses outside the Clinic. Nurses from around the world visit the Foundation regularly to observe nursing practice and organization. Cleveland Clinic nurses travel widely, offering their expertise in clinical specialties, procedures, or management to clinics, hospitals and professional groups at home and abroad. An international nurse scholar program offers clinical fellowships to foreign nurses.[12]

In the mid-1980s, a formal program for nursing research was established under the jurisdiction of Nursing Resources. First, a process for approving nursing research proposals was established, then a Nursing Research Committee was formed. The committee reviews research proposals with an eye towards projects that enhance the quality of nursing and institute new approaches to patient care.[13]

Both the educational and research missions of the division are supported by patients' gifts to the Nursing Education and Research Fund.

LOOKING AHEAD

Since 1995, the director of nursing sits on the Cleveland Clinic's Institutional Review Board. The hospital has forty nursing units, and nurses work in the operating rooms and perioperative areas, the Emergency Department, and Infection Control. They work in the clinic, as departmental assistants, as research nurses, as nurse anes-

---

[12] For example, an annual "Dimensions in Cardiac Critical Care Nursing" symposium, started in 1981, attracts hundreds of nurses from around the country and spotlights the expertise of the Clinic's nurses in an area for which The Cleveland Clinic is renowned.

[13] Approved projects have included studies on pressure ulcers and skin care, which corresponded with the development of an ongoing program aimed at preventing pressure ulcers in hospitalized patients. It resulted in the development of a Skin Care Team, which by the end of 1993 included unit-based skin care nurses who monitored the patients in their areas.

thetists, as administrators and managers, and as staff in other departments and offices, such as Central Supply and Home Health Care.

Changes in health care have forced Cleveland Clinic nurses to grow beyond their traditional roles as well as the confines of the campus. Changes in the way services are reimbursed require nurses to care for sicker patients in a shorter period of time and take responsibility for the outcome. Perioperative and surgical nurses account for a greater share of the inpatient nursing care than in the past. Some nurses have gone full circle and now provide house calls to patients through Cleveland Clinic Home Health Care. Clinic nurses, who focus on maintaining wellness as well as caring for illness, answer patients' questions and triage more than 70,000 calls per year through the Nurse On Call program.

Although many of their duties are changing, Cleveland Clinic nurses remain focused on their nursing mission: to help patients perform activities contributing to health or its recovery (or to a peaceful death) that they would perform unaided if they had the strength, will, or knowledge, and to help patients become independent as quickly as possible.

Clearly nurses have been an essential part of the care delivery team at The Cleveland Clinic from the beginning. Their role will expand further as the Clinic moves back into obstetrics and enlarges its primary care capacity, and as the State of Ohio develops a more enlightened regulatory approach to advanced practice nursing. The future for nursing at The Cleveland Clinic has never been brighter.

EIGHTEEN

DIVISION OF EDUCATION

The roots of education are bitter, but the fruit is sweet.
— *Aristotle, Fourth Century B.C.*

At the opening of The Cleveland Clinic in 1921, Dr. Frank Bunts said, "We hope . . . that as we have after many years been allowed to gather together able associates and assistants to make this work possible, so in time to come, those men, taking the place of their predecessors, will carry on the work to higher and better ends, aiding their fellow practitioners, caring for the sick, educating and seeking always to attain the highest and noblest aspirations of their profession."

It is not surprising that the founders placed so much emphasis on teaching, since all served on the clinical faculties of one or more Cleveland medical schools. From the time it opened, the Clinic had graduate fellows-in-training, now called residents. The first medical resident was Charles L. Hartsock, M.D., who trained from June 1921 to June 1923 and then joined the staff and served with distinction until his death in 1961. The first surgical resident was William O. Johnson, M.D., who spent June 1921 to June 1922 at the Clinic, then returned in 1924 after the hospital opened and served with another surgical resident, Nathaniel S. Shofner, M.D. Fellowships in research were also established soon after the Clinic opened, and a number of traveling fellowships were awarded for residents to visit other clinics and medical centers in this country and abroad.

In the Clinic's early years, the absence of American specialty boards made training programs more flexible than they are today. Residents[1] could finish a year or two at one hospital and then apply

---

[1] In those days the terms "residents" and "fellows" were used interchangeably. Because the training programs at the Clinic were called "fellowships" then, the term "fellow" was often used where we would now use the term "resident."

Andrew J. Fishleder, M.D., Chairman, Division of Education, 1991–

to another to train with someone else. The system had no formal rules, rotations, or examinations. Today, the rigid requirements of the various specialty boards make transferring from one institution to another difficult.

In the 1920s, most interns and residents in teaching hospitals were underpaid or not paid at all. The Clinic paid relatively high salaries for that era and supplied competent technicians to perform time-consuming laboratory studies. Consequently, there was no shortage of applications for the limited number of fellowships offered. Both residents and staff benefitted from an apprentice-like arrangement.[2] Although formal postgraduate courses had not been established, more than 12,000 physicians spent various periods of time at the Clinic between 1924 and 1937. To support teaching, lecturing, and the presentation of papers, a medical library, medical illustrators, and medical photographers were available.

---

[2] Dr. William Proudfit recalls, "The entire formal educational experience when I was in training was a weekly lecture for fellows — all the fellows, regardless of specialty. This was held in the evening, and the same program was repeated annually (an advantage, for we learned what lectures to miss!). How that contrasts with the present programs! An internist or a surgeon was expected to be competent in all subspecialties (except, perhaps, allergy for internists and neurosurgery and orthopedics for surgeons)."

In 1935, the Clinic formalized education by establishing the Frank E. Bunts Educational Institute with Cleveland Clinic staff as faculty. The stated purpose of the new institute was "to maintain and conduct an institution for learning, for promoting education, and giving instruction in the art, science and practice of medicine, surgery, anatomy, hygiene and allied or kindred sciences and subjects."

During the Clinic's early years, the fellowship program was administered through a Fellowship Committee, which was organized in 1924. Robert S. Dinsmore, M.D., of the Department of General Surgery served as chairman until 1936. He was succeeded by Alexander T. Bunts, M.D., a neurosurgeon who held the post with distinction for 10 years. Bunts (son of the founder) was succeeded by William J. Engel, M.D., of the Department of Urology. Engel's service ended with the establishment of the Education Foundation in 1962.

By 1944, expanding educational activities pointed out the need for a full-time director of medical education. Howard Dittrick, M.D., a well-known Cleveland physician, was chosen for the role. For the next three years he was in charge of the editorial department, library, postgraduate courses, preparation of exhibits, and art and photography departments. He also became editor of the *Cleveland Clinic Quarterly*, which had been publishing scientific papers by the Clinic staff since 1932.[3]

Upon Dittrick's retirement, an editor at the American Medical Association named Edwin P. Jordan, M.D., was appointed to replace him. He held the position from 1947 to 1950, when he was replaced by Stanley O. Hoerr, M.D. Then Fay A. LeFevre, M.D., served as acting director of education from 1952 until 1955, when Col. Charles L.

---

[3] In 1982 the *Cleveland Clinic Quarterly* published its fiftieth anniversary issue. The following remarks are summarized from an article by James S. Taylor, M.D., editor, on the history of the *Quarterly*.

"In the first year of publication, the *Quarterly* published six original articles and the balance consisted of reprints. Because of the great depression, the *Quarterly* did not appear in 1933 or 1934. On November 28, 1934, the Medical Board met and decided that the *Quarterly* would no longer publish papers that had appeared in other journals.

"Some outstanding contributions to the world literature have been published in the *Quarterly*. The *Quarterly* is distributed without charge to physicians and medical libraries throughout the world. In 1982, circulation exceeded 16,000. It is sent to approximately 2600 alumni of The Cleveland Clinic Educational Foundation and to 1000 medical libraries and medical schools. The remainder are sent to other physicians requesting the journal.

"The *Cleveland Clinic Quarterly*, a refereed, indexed journal, is an integral part of the educational activities of the Cleveland Clinic and is underwritten solely by The Cleveland Clinic Educational Foundation. The journal is indexed in *Index Medicus, Chemical Abstracts, Biological Abstracts, Current Contents,* and *Nutritional Abstracts*. It is also microfilmed by University Microfilms International."

Howard Dittrick, M.D., Director, Frank E. Bunts Educational Institute (now
Division of Education), 1944–1947

Leedham, M.D., was recruited from the Armed Forces to assume the directorship.

With the development of American specialty boards and increased regulation by the American Medical Association's Council on Medical Education, formal training programs had to be established for candidates to meet the requirements of the various specialties. The division established a Faculty Board within the Bunts Educational Institute in 1956 to oversee the quality of the educational programs and develop policies governing them. The nine-member group was comprised of the division chairmen, director of research, chairman of the Board of Governors, director of education, and two members-at-large. They made appointments and promotions within the Clinic teaching staff, determined educational policies and curricula for graduate education, established criteria for their selection, and established standards for granting certificates for academic work performed.

In 1962, the name of the Bunts Education Institute was changed to The Cleveland Clinic Educational Foundation to help physicians here and abroad more closely recognize its relationship with The

Cleveland Clinic.[4] Walter J. Zeiter, M.D., former executive secretary to the Board of Governors, was appointed director and held the position until 1973.

As the years passed, the growth of the Cleveland Clinic naturally resulted in an expansion of educational activities. However, the Clinic lacked adequate physical facilities to support them. The solution came in the form of a generous gift from the estate of Martha Holden Jennings, which provided funds for the construction of a seven-story Education Building and an endowment to maintain it. The building, which opened in 1964, contained an auditorium, seven seminar rooms, a medical library, editorial and administrative offices, and on-call accommodations for house staff.

In 1973, William M. Michener, M.D., was appointed director of education following Zeiter's retirement. A former Clinic staff member, Michener returned after spending five years as a professor of pediatrics and assistant dean of graduate education at the University of New Mexico.

Under Michener's leadership, education programs flourished. By 1981, the division clearly needed reorganization, and a task force was formed. Two years later it made many excellent recommendations which the Board of Governors adopted. These included replacing the Faculty Board and its committees with a peer review group. Called the Education Governing Group (EGG), it was charged with reviewing, monitoring, and evaluating all existing and proposed education activities and training programs; establishing educational policies and program priorities; and proposing programs and budgets to the Division of Education.

At the same time, the division formed councils for allied health and nursing education, management and training, and physician education. Michener also appointed a vice chairman to oversee the Physician Education Council. Later, a Continuing Medical Education Council was added.

It was also agreed that The Cleveland Clinic Educational Foundation should formally function as a division of the institution. Patient Education became a department within the new Division of Education. Most importantly, the Board of Governors affirmed that teaching should become an integral part of the annual professional

---

[4] There was another reason for changing the name: Crile did not wish to be memorialized in any way that would set him apart from the other founders. Some felt that this policy should extend to Bunts as well. Also, with Dr. Alexander Bunts's retirement, Dr. George Crile, Jr., was the only remaining descendant of the founders on the staff. Dr. William J. Engel, who was soon to retire, was Lower's son-in-law.

review process for staff members involved in education, and that consideration should be given to the quality and quantity of their educational performance. With great foresight, the task force recommended that Cleveland Clinic training programs in collaboration with one or more medical schools be considered in the future.

Graduate Medical Education programs also thrived during Michener's tenure. With advances in medical technology stretching the curriculum of core residencies to capacity, the Clinic expanded subspecialty fellowships in a broad range of medical and surgical areas. Residency training programs grew in size, reflecting the growth of the institution and its professional staff. In order to ensure the maintenance of high quality education programs, the Clinic responded to recommendations from the Accreditation Council on Graduate Medical Education by establishing an internal review of training programs and documenting the evaluation of resident performance and staff teaching. By 1994, 650 residents were registered at the Clinic, with approximately 250 graduating each July.

Clinic graduates have gone on to practice in a broad range of medical environments throughout the United States and world. Under the jurisdiction of the Division of Education, the Office of Alumni Affairs maintains contact with more than 6,500 alumni to help the institution remain responsive to their evolving needs.[5]

In addition to the strong focus on residency training, the education of medical students began to play a more prominent role starting in 1974. The first year, 125 students enrolled in the senior medical student electives at the Clinic. In 1975, the number jumped to 280. By 1994, 600 third- and fourth-year students from American medical schools were rotating through the Clinic. They provide a broadened academic stimulus to the residents and staff and serve as an important source of candidates for residency positions. An average of 40 percent of the Clinic's first year positions in the National Residency Match are now filled by these students, who know firsthand the value of training at The Cleveland Clinic Foundation.

In 1986, the Clinic expanded its medical student commitment through a formal affiliation with the Pennsylvania State University Medical School in Hershey. The agreement provided for their third-year medical students to spend required clerkships in neurology, internal medicine, and pediatrics at the Clinic. Both students and faculty continue to rate the experience highly, and it has helped enhance the academic focus of residency training in these areas.

---

[5] The Alumni Association was transferred back to the Division of Education in 1993 after being revived and reinvigorated under Frank J. Weaver's leadership during the 1980s.

Education Building, 1964

The signing of a broad-based academic partnership with The Ohio State University in 1991 was a milestone for The Cleveland Clinic. Prompted by interests in medical student education and research, the agreement facilitated potential cooperation in many areas of mutual benefit. As of 1994, more than 150 Clinic staff members had obtained full faculty appointments at The Ohio State University College of Medicine. The partnership, entitled The Cleveland Clinic Health Sciences Center of The Ohio State University, also has facilitated the development of several joint research programs, most notably in biomedical engineering. Joint activities in pharmacy, nursing, biostatistics, and health policy studies are under way. Although the partnership is a major academic affiliation, it is not exclusive, and strong relationships continue with Case Western Reserve University and Morehouse School of Medicine. The Morehouse arrangement, initiated in 1992, seeks to enhance the Clinic's exposure to minority medical students with the goal of increasing the number of minority students, residents, and staff physicians at The Cleveland Clinic.

The Clinic's strong commitment to medical education also extends to practicing health care professionals. With the opening of an Education Building and Bunts Auditorium in 1964, the number of continuing medical education courses offered at the Clinic increased substantially. In the 1970s and 1980s, growth was stimulated by state requirements that licensure renewal be accompanied by documentation of attendance at continuing medical education courses. Taking that cue, programs sponsored by the Cleveland Clinic grew from 20 per year in the mid-1970s to more than 60 per year in 1993, with over 7,000 physicians, nurses, and allied health professionals attending annually from throughout the medical community. They position the institution as a resource for this expertise.

When the *Cleveland Clinic Quarterly* was started in 1932, there were relatively few medical research journals that provided an opportunity for physicians to share scientific expertise gained at the Clinic with other physicians. In 1987, the *Cleveland Clinic Quarterly* was renamed the *Cleveland Clinic Journal of Medicine*, and publication increased to six times per year. In response to a changing health care environment, the Journal is now focusing on articles dealing with the practical issues of medical care faced by practicing physicians everywhere.

In 1991, Andrew J. Fishleder, M.D., was appointed chairman of the Division of Education. A graduate of the Clinic's pathology training program, Fishleder's interest in education was well known through his service on the Physician Education Council and Education Governing Group. In recognition of the tremendous growth that had taken place in education, and with a desire to develop new programs that support the institution's educational mission, Fishleder added directors of patient education, medical student education, and allied health education to those in graduate medical education and continuing medical education. Vice chairpersons appointed to oversee these areas were charged with developing strategic initiatives aimed at enhancing the quality and diversity of their educational activities. At the same time, he focused significant energy on ensuring appropriate recognition for staff educational efforts through the development of an annual educational activities

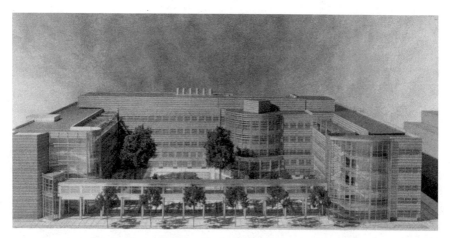

Research and Education Institute (artist's drawing)

report provided to the Office of Professional Staff Affairs during the Annual Professional Review process.

As the 21st century approaches, the Division of Education has broadened its activities even further. Practice management seminars have been developed to better prepare senior residents for the rapidly changing health care environment. Increased computerization has been utilized to enhance the development and distribution of health information to physicians, patients, and their families. On-site continuing medical education courses have been supplemented by the production of videotaped programs and proactive multimedia medical education programs aimed at clarifying evolving practice guidelines have been implemented. In response to projected needs for physician extenders, programs to train nurse practitioners and physician assistants[6] were slated for introduction in the fall of 1995. Finally, in 1994, the division initiated an Office of Faculty and Curriculum Development in an effort to support the continuing enhancement of program quality. The first director of that office, Mariana Hewson, Ph.D., was appointed in January 1995 and started the Clinic's Seminars in Clinical Teaching program.

The Division of Education looks forward to having new facilities to support a program that now includes 700 residents in 50 specialties, medical students rotating from around the country, and more than 250 students in 34 allied health fields. Despite the financial pressures of decreasing reimbursement, The Cleveland Clinic

---

[6] The Clinic previously operated a physician assistant training program in collaboration with Lake Erie College from 1969 to 1987.

remains committed to its educational mission. It recognizes that through education, the Clinic creates an environment that attracts and stimulates the finest physicians to provide the highest quality medical care while maintaining its commitment to train the health care practitioners of tomorrow. The new Research and Education Institute, now under construction, will stand as a monument to this commitment for years to come.

NINETEEN

RESEARCH INSTITUTE

*Science is the attempt to make the chaotic
diversity of our sense-experience correspond
to a logically uniform system of thought.*

— *Albert Einstein, 1950*

Both basic and clinical research have been fundamental to the mission of The Cleveland Clinic since the beginning. The Clinic's founders firmly believed that they could provide the best patient care by conducting active programs of medical research in the new Clinic. In 1921, they agreed among themselves that no less than one fourth of the net income from the new organization would be devoted to research and indigent care.[1]

Of the Clinic's founders, all of whom participated in research, George Crile, Sr., M.D., was its strongest advocate. He was convinced that laboratory discoveries were essential in providing a scientific basis for modern clinical practice. From his own investigations had come the original thesis linking the activity of the adrenal glands to physiologic stress.

Hugo Fricke, Ph.D., was the first scientist to be put in charge of research in biophysics, a field that interested Crile. The latter's "bipolar theory of living processes" was based on the differences in electrical charges between the brains and livers of animals, as well as between the nuclei and cytoplasms of individual cells. Fricke, and later Maria Telkes, Ph.D., measured the thickness of cell membranes and showed their relationship to electrical charges in living

---

[1] Later, this percentage was substantially increased, and in 1928, the trustees approved construction of a building for medical research.

George R. Stark, Ph.D., Chairman, Research Institute, 1992–

cells. Their studies were widely recognized contributions to this complicated field.

In 1930, the biophysics group was replaced by a team of biochemists headed by D. Roy McCullagh, Ph.D. McCullagh persistently tried to isolate a hormone from the testicle believed to inhibit the enlargement of the prostate gland. Although the quest was tantalizing, no solid results ever materialized. McCullagh did, however, become a pioneer in the measurement of thyroid function through iodine levels in the blood. He collaborated with his brother, Clinic endocrinologist E. Perry McCullagh, M.D., in studies of pituitary and sex hormones.

The original Research Building was designed for types of research that no longer exist today. By 1945, it was largely abandoned, except for several small laboratories. During the late 1930s and early years of World War II, Crile's leadership waned, and although the laboratories remained partially serviceable until the end of the War, they had neither the resources nor the inspiration they enjoyed during the peak of Crile's influence.

By the mid 1940s, it had become clear that a research leader was needed. In 1945, to the everlasting credit of the trustees, they persuaded Irvine H. Page, M.D., to become director of the Clinic's new Research Division. They had become acquainted with Page through his treatment of Charles Bradley, a prominent Clevelander, for high blood pressure. Russell L. Haden, M.D., chief of medicine at the Clinic, had referred Mr. Bradley to Dr. Page, a chemist and clinician whose work had addressed the cause of high blood pressure and paved the way for treatment.

In an effort to foster the cooperation of scientists in several disciplines, Page did not permit departmentalization in the Division of Research. Patient observations, animal experimentation, and work in the chemical laboratory were melded. His disdain of committees, excessive meetings, and other administrative distractions freed everyone to concentrate on research.

Page brought two colleagues, Arthur C. Corcoran, M.D., and Robert D. Taylor, M.D., with him from Indianapolis, where cardiovascular disease, and specifically arterial hypertension and atherosclerosis, had been their main focus. Page had begun his work in 1931 at New York's Rockefeller Institute after spending three years as head of the brain chemistry division of the Kaiser Wilhelm Institute (now called the Max Planck Institute) in Munich, Germany[2]. Corcoran left Montreal's McGill University to join Page in New York, where he studied renal aspects of hypertension. His use of sophisticated methods to study kidney function in hypertensive patients opened the door to the search for effective antihypertensive drugs and animal models in which new drugs could be tested. Taylor joined Page and Corcoran after they had moved to Indianapolis in 1937.

At the Clinic they developed a multidisciplinary approach aimed at solving problems in cardiovascular disease. Their unique plan called for physicians with specialized training in the basic sciences to work full-time with clinical researchers. This cooperation, which continues today, is responsible for some of the most significant findings in cardiovascular medicine.

Until that time, heart disease had gone largely unstudied; with the exception of the rheumatic and syphilitic varieties, it received little attention. High blood pressure was also generally considered to be a relatively harmless consequence of aging. But by the 1940s, the incidence of heart attack, stroke and hypertension, and their interrelationship, had become evident.

During the 1920s, a number of investigators had tried to produce renal hypertension in dogs with varying success. In 1934, Dr. Harry Goldblatt at Cleveland's Mt. Sinai Hospital produced the first reliable model by clamping the renal artery and partially blocking it.

---

[2] The Kaiser Wilhelm Institute led the world in early research into the chemistry of the brain.

Page later developed a simple practical method of causing severe hypertension by encapsulating the kidney in cellophane, making an inelastic hull that restricted normal pulsation.

Before coming to the Clinic, Page had worked on isolating a substance formed when blood is clotted, a substance known to have a strong effect on circulation. He continued this work in Cleveland and, with the collaboration of Clinic colleagues Arda A. Green, M.D., and Maurice Rapport, Ph.D., discovered a compound that proved to be 5-hydroxytryptamine. They called it "serotonin." Few biological agents have proven to have as many varied actions as serotonin, among them, profound effects on the brain as a transmitter of nerve impulses, and an active role in the formation of certain intestinal tumors.

A long series of investigations by Page and his associates led to the isolation of a substance that the group named "angiotonin."[3] Concurrently, a group directed by Braun-Menéndez in Buenos Aires isolated the same compound. Friendly dialogue between them led to an agreement on the name "angiotensin." It has formed the basis of thousands of studies worldwide, and has proven to be a fascinating participant in hypertension as well as the chief regulator of hormone secretion from the adrenal gland. Angiotensin became widely available for study after it was synthesized at the Clinic by F. Merlin Bumpus, Ph.D.[4] This major breakthrough helped spur research that led to the development of antihypertensive drugs.[5]

During the 1970s and 1980s, research at The Cleveland Clinic was divided into two categories: program research, which was done by members of the Division of Research and until 1966, concentrated solely on cardiovascular disease; and project research, which was conducted by physicians in the clinical departments. The plan for each project had to be submitted in writing and approved by the Research Projects Committee before funds and space were made available. Each project depended on the investigator's individual interest and was not necessarily related to any program research.

For many years, The Cleveland Clinic Foundation was the sole source of research funds. The prospect of accepting any government support was met with active antagonism. But in the late 1950s, increased competition, escalating costs, and the need for recognition

---

[3] The discovery of this substance took place in 1939 while the group was still working in Indianapolis.

[4] It was synthesized simultaneously by Robert Schwyzer, Ph.D., in Switzerland.

[5] Bumpus theorized that blocking the renal-adrenal blood pressure control mechanisms would lower pressure. He demonstrated this by developing the first molecular antagonists to angiotensin. This encouraged pharmaceutical companies to develop angiotensin-converting enzyme inhibitors that have evolved into useful drugs for lowering blood pressure.

caused the trustees to relax their policy. In 1962, the National Heart Institute of the National Institutes of Health awarded a major program grant to the Clinic instead of to individual investigators, as was customary. Since staff salaries were paid by the Clinic, the money was used to defray operating expenses. From this point on, grants became critical to growth, as did gifts from individuals and foundations, which helped to defray operating expenses, fund exploratory studies, and build an endowment fund.

As Page began to shape the Research Division, he added Dr. Arda Green, who had just crystallized phosphorylase-A in St. Louis, Georges M. C. Masson, Ph.D., from Montreal and in 1950 Willem J. Kolff, M.D., Ph.D., from the Netherlands. Three younger scientists, F. Merlin Bumpus, Ph.D., Harriet P. Dustan, M.D., and James W. McCubbin, Ph.D., came to the Clinic as associate staff or postdoctoral fellows and developed illustrious careers.

Kolff had spent the war years in Holland working on an artificial kidney. With the same stubborn determination that allowed him to continue doing research while his country was under German occupation, he worked against great odds in Cleveland to obtain funds for his projects. Initially, only The Cleveland Clinic funded the artificial kidney, a project that seemed so unlikely that few wanted to invest in it. Eventually, private foundations saw its potential, and, together with the National Institutes of Health, later became prime sources of funds.

Both Page and Kolff had strong convictions, a trait that would later lead to conflict. Separation eventually became necessary, and Kolff continued his research in the Division of Surgery until Page's retirement in 1966.

While Kolff was working on applied research projects, Page and his group were establishing the Cleveland Clinic Research Division as the mecca for studies in high blood pressure. Early on, they showed how the principle of feedback was part of an intricate mechanism that controls blood pressure. After many experiments, they developed a general theory of hypertension, which they called the "mosaic theory." It postulated that hypertension rarely has one single cause, but rather results from shifts in the equilibria among its many component causes.[6]

---

[6] Carlos Ferrario, M.D., joined Page and McCubbin in 1966. Although Page retired soon thereafter, the investigations they had begun culminated in a brilliant series of cooperative experiments involving a former associate, Dr. D. J. Dickinson, in London. Ferrario, McCubbin, and Dickinson proved that the brain was a regulator of blood pressure. Later, Ferrario and McCubbin showed where and how angiotensin enters the brain. The blood vessels, heart, sympathetic nervous system, brain, pituitary gland, and kidneys are among the contributors to hypertension. Their interrelationships are still being explored.

Irvine H. Page, M.D., Chairman, Research Division, 1945–1966

Under Page, one of the division's major innovations was to integrate care, clinical study, and laboratory investigation.[7] This allowed an extensive study of the effects of new antihypertensive drugs on previously studied patients, and led to the development of many effective medications.

Hemodynamics, the study of flow and pressure within the cardiovascular system, has been one of the cornerstones of hypertension research. High blood pressure is a hemodynamic abnormality, and an understanding of its problems requires accurate evaluation of hemodynamic patterns associated with a rise in arterial pressure. Frederick Olmsted, a biomedical engineer assisting Page and McCubbin, was instrumental in the early design, development, and application of electromagnetic flowmeters to measure cardiac output, regional blood pressure, and other facets of circulation in healthy animals. This did much to advance understanding of the

---

[7] A main contribution to the understanding of renal hypertension was made with the collaboration of Clinic urologist Eugene F. Poutasse, M.D., who showed that surgical removal of an obstruction in a renal artery effected a cure. Radiologist Thomas F. Meaney, M.D., provided the angiograms that were critical to the visualization and evaluation of these obstructions.

highly complex mechanisms controlling blood flow to each organ.[8] Blood oxygenation was another product of the same laboratory and played an important role in the development of cardiac surgery at The Cleveland Clinic.

The Research Division has had an equally long history of research in atherosclerosis. When it became apparent that increased blood fat levels were associated with atherosclerosis under certain conditions, work was directed towards modifying fat levels by changing the diet. Promising results in the laboratory then prompted a pioneering clinical investigation: a small group of cooperative medical students consumed experimental diets under the supervision of Helen B. Brown, Ph.D. It was found that certain diets were effective in decreasing fat levels. The U.S. Public Health Service became interested in the program and offered substantial financial assistance, eventually assuming the complete cost of a greatly expanded, expensive program. This project, called "The National Diet-Heart Study," showed the feasibility of a much larger, long-term program that would involve the cooperation of many institutions nationwide. It ultimately provided the basis for recommending that Americans change their diet to reduce cholesterol and raise polyunsaturated fats in order to prevent heart attack and stroke. This study was the forerunner of the Framingham Study, which continues today.

Page was also known for his filtration theory of the deposition of lipoproteins in the blood vessels. This was the first attempt to explain how cholesterol is deposited in the blood vessel wall during the development of atherosclerosis.

Before joining Page at the Clinic, John R. Shainoff, Ph.D., was among the first to demonstrate the deposition of lipoproteins in atherosclerotic tissue. But Shainoff's interests changed, and he began approaching atherosclerosis from another angle, believing that both the initial lesion and final closure of the diseased vessel wall involved the transformation of fibrinogen to fibrin to form blood clots. Virtually nothing was known about this. He devised methods to assess the conversion based on the freeing of "fibrinopeptides," which are soluble side products of the reaction. This enabled him to discover that fibrin could be carried in a soluble form loosely linked with fibrinogen in blood, and that these complexes are normally cleared without forming clots except when produced above a critical threshold. Today,

---

[8] Cardiac enlargement has always been a problem in uncontrolled hypertension. Robert C. Tarazi, M.D., and Subha Sen, Ph.D., were the first to show the effectiveness of various antihypertensive drugs in reversing cardiac hypertrophy.

analysis of fibrinopeptides and fibrin complexes remains the principal means for diagnosing intravascular fibrin formation.

As the story unfolded, an additional path to the formation of clot-like deposits from fibrinogen was discovered and found to be associated with tissue damage and repair. A simple and inexpensive approach to profiling these derivatives in blood samples is now being studied as a way of assessing the transition from atherosclerosis to thrombolytic vascular disease.

The continuing challenge of cardiovascular disease was stimulating to investigators and clinicians alike. It provided the excitement and drive necessary for everyone to participate in the understanding of these diseases, which are statistically among the most prevalent illnesses, and in the care of patients suffering from them.[9]

Without the strength of basic programs involving cooperation among scientists, the Clinic would not have attained its position as a national leader in medicine. Although project research was highly credible, the history of the Division of Research shows that coordination and cooperation have been the keys to success.

From 1945 to 1966 the philosophy of the Division of Research had been steadfastly to maintain the cardiovascular program and add approved research projects from any department. After Page retired, Bumpus was named chairman of the division, a post he retained until his own retirement in 1985.[10] Bumpus created the departments of Immunology, Artificial Organs (including Biomechanics), Biostatistics, and Clinical Science,[11] and he broke the long tradition of seeking no outside funding.[12]

By the mid-1970s, the Division of Research contained loosely structured sections of specific research focus: Artificial Organs, Arteriosclerosis and Thrombosis, Cardiovascular Research, Immunology, and the Clinical Research Projects Committee, which evaluated projects originating in the clinical departments.

---

[9] As a result of the growing national interest in cardiovascular disease, the American Foundation for High Blood Pressure was founded in 1945. It later became the Council for High Blood Pressure Research of the American Heart Association.

[10] He continued to serve in the Department of Cardiovascular Research, by then renamed the Department of Cardiovascular Biology, as emeritus staff, consultant, and researcher on the newly discovered substance, "human chymase," until his death in 1993.

[11] Artificial Organs was actually a legacy from Kolff's time. His associate, Yukihiko Nosé, M.D., Ph.D., continued his experimental and developmental work with artificial kidneys and hearts. When Kolff left the Clinic in 1967, the laboratory was turned over to the Division of Research.

[12] Departing from tradition has proven to be more effective than was anticipated. In 1995, the Division of Research had a $52 million budget, half of which was funded by the Clinic. Ensuring the continued success of the Research Institute will require maintaining an excellent record of extramural support and inaugurating new collaborations with government, industry, and biomedical scientists in academia.

The Department of Immunology was a natural evolution in the Clinic's growing interest in organ transplantation, autoimmune diseases, and cancer. In 1974, Bumpus recruited Jack R. Battisto, Ph.D., from the Albert Einstein College of Medicine to head this department. His research focused on the immune response and immunological tolerance. He was joined by James Finke, Ph.D., who worked with cytotoxic cells. To round out immunology, he recruited Max Proffitt, Ph.D., from Harvard and Bert Del Villano, Jr., Ph.D., from the Scripps Institute to focus on leukemia; and, as a link to clinical efforts, Claudio Fiocchi, M.D., a gastroenterologist and expert in inflammatory bowel disease.

In 1981 the department's name was changed to Molecular and Cellular Biology. After Michael J. Caulfield, Ph.D., and Martha K. Cathcart, Ph.D., joined the staff, it was renamed Immunology and Cancer. In 1986, Bumpus became acting chairman, and with the addition of research laboratories unrelated to immunology, the name was changed to the Department of General Medical Sciences. Recently, it has reverted to Immunology.

In November 1985, Bernadine P. Healy, M.D., became the first woman to chair the Division of Research. A cardiologist (who, like Page and Dustan before her, had been president of the American Heart Association), experienced research investigator, and expert in science policy and funding issues, she was eager to carry on the tradition of biomedical research that was highly interactive with clinical care. To better reflect this type of collaborative investigation, she proposed that the division be renamed the Cleveland Clinic Research Institute.

An active and involved leader, Healy's philosophy was simple: impressive talent and continually better results would mean greater success in obtaining grants and other outside funding.[13] She felt that having a superior group of interactive scientists would create an exceptional corps of experts who could provide knowledgeable contributions to many clinical research projects and, eventually, to inventions and other patentable procedures and mechanisms. But like Page, Healy emphasized the need to translate this activity into improvements in patient care.

Healy encouraged the pursuit of creative efforts within the areas of the Clinic's priorities and greatest strengths. This, she felt strongly, would not only result in competitive work of the highest

---

[13] Healy's philosophy of recruiting was to look for young or well-established investigators with "fire in the belly" who would constantly "elevate the mean."

Bernadine P. Healy, M.D., Chairman, Research Institute, 1985—1991

quality, but would also produce interdisciplinary programs worthy of philanthropic investment.

Among her top priorities for the Research Institute was to increase its fundamental science base, particularly in molecular and cellular biology. During her chairmanship, Healy recruited Amiya K. Banerjee, Ph.D., to chair the newly established Department of Molecular Biology. Major reorganization of the Research Institute also included expansion of the Department of Heart and Hypertension Research under the leadership of Robert Graham, M.D., recruited from Harvard; the creation of a new Department of Vascular Cell Biology and Atherosclerosis under Paul DiCorleto, Ph.D.; a new Department of Cancer Biology, directed by Bryan Williams, Ph.D., who came from the University of Toronto; and the combination of two departments (Artificial Organs and Musculoskeletal Research) into a consolidated Department of Biomedical Engineering and Applied Therapeutics, under J. Fredrick Cornhill, D.Phil., from The Ohio State University.

This was a time of major expansion for the Research Institute, both in promising young as well as established senior research talent, reflected in substantial growth in competitively awarded research grants.[14] NIH funds more than doubled, from seven million dollars in 1985 to over 17 million dollars by 1991.

Recognizing that endowment funds would provide a flexible investment for the future, Healy helped the Clinic work toward a half-billion-dollar endowment by the year 2000. A centerpiece of her stewardship was to be the Research and Education Institute, a 305,000-square foot complex of research and education facilities encompassing laboratories, offices, conference areas, and a state-of-the-art library/telecommunications/conference facility. The first phase, named the John Sherwin Research Building and built to house three of the eight research departments, opened in 1991.[15] The Research and Education Institute itself is scheduled to open in 1997 and will incorporate the Sherwin Research Building. To help ensure a steady stream of bright, highly motivated students, she seized the chance to formally affiliate with The Ohio State University (see Chapter 9). Healy's far-reaching ideas, dynamic personality, and outstanding professional reputation caught the attention of President George Bush, who appointed her first woman director of the National Institutes of Health in 1991.[16]

Banerjee, vice chairman of the Research Institute, was named acting chairman upon Healy's departure for the National Institutes of Health. During his vice chairmanship and acting chairmanship, he reached out to other academic institutions, improving relations with The Ohio State University and collaborating with Cleveland's Case Western Reserve University (CWRU) on virology projects. He continued to build his own strong program in molecular biology.

---

[14] Among them were two multimillion-dollar, multicenter trials: the Post-Coronary Angioplasty and Bypass Graft (Post-CABG) study and the Bypass Angioplasty Revascularization Investigation (BARI).

[15] John Sherwin, Sr., was president of The Cleveland Clinic Foundation from 1948 to 1957, chairman of the Board of Trustees from 1958 to 1960, and a trustee from 1930 to 1991 (see Chapters 5, 6, and Epilogue).

[16] At the time of Healy's appointment, the NIH was a 10-billion-dollar agency and the largest source of funding for research investigators in the U. S. and abroad. Her philosophy of performing public service gave her the impetus to endure public disclosure of many personal details as well as a lengthy appearance before a U.S. Senate committee before being confirmed. At the NIH, she established the Shannon awards for NIH intramural investigators and created the intramural program for the Human Genome Project, recruiting a major laboratory headed by Francis S. Collins, M.D., Ph.D. She inaugurated the Women's Health Initiative and developed the first strategic plan for the NIH [*Investment for Humanity: A Strategic Vision for the National Institutes of Health* (1993)]. Following a change in administrations, President Bill Clinton accepted her resignation. She returned to the Clinic in 1993 as senior health policy advisor to the Page Center for Creative Thinking, a magnet for intellectual discussion about biomedicine among physicians and researchers. In 1995 she became Dean of The Ohio State University College of Medicine, but continued her ties with the Clinic's Page Center.

In 1992, the Board of Governors named George R. Stark, Ph.D., chairman of the Research Institute. A molecular biologist of international repute, Stark was trained at Columbia University and first employed at Rockefeller University, where his work centered on protein chemistry. He then went to Stanford University, where he worked on enzyme mechanisms and developed two important methods in molecular biology known as the northern and western blotting techniques. In 1983, he joined London's Imperial Cancer Research Fund, where he focused on gene amplification and intracellular signaling pathways used by interferons.

Stark's chairmanship signaled an even greater emphasis on building depth of expertise in molecular biology. However, he firmly believed in the need to recruit excellent staff in all levels and in all fields, as well as to maintain interaction between the clinical and basic sciences staffs. With these goals in mind, he formed the Department of Neurosciences in 1992, incorporating staff from the former Department of Brain and Vascular Research. It represented the culmination of 15 years of efforts to establish research programs that linked the basic and clinical sciences to address the underlying mechanisms and treatment of nervous system diseases. From the outset, the program brought together clinicians from neurology, neurosurgery, neuropathology, and neuroradiology with cardiovascular neurobiologists, immunologists, and molecular biologists.[17]

Stark also established formal avenues for Research Institute investigators to create bridge programs with physicians in the Cancer Center, Mellen Center for Multiple Sclerosis, Center for Digestive Disease Research, and other clinical entities. He foresaw the Research and Education Institute as a key to interdisciplinary collaboration, and continues to work toward its completion.[18]

The current philosophy of the Research Institute, like that of the rest of The Cleveland Clinic, emphasizes research, education, and patient care. A major goal is to advance the means of prevention, diagnosis, and treatment of disease. The research staff are first-rate

---

[17] Stark's encouragement of new efforts that combined basic and clinical sciences included technology transfer. In 1994 this led to the Research Division's first free-standing spin-off company, BioSeiche Therapeutics, Inc., which was built on Robert H. Silverman, Ph.D.'s technique of using a new class of drugs called 2-5A antisense to target and destroy disease-causing RNA in virus- or tumor-causing cells.

[18] In order to stimulate cooperation with researchers outside the Foundation, Stark reached out to nearby CWRU to establish the "Joint CCF-CWRU Working Group." Comprised of the heads of basic science departments, this group quickly expanded to include Cleveland State University, MetroHealth, and University Hospitals, and was renamed "Biomedical Research Cleveland." Its goal is to establish major city-wide research programs and fund them with monies from the state and federal governments, major foundations, and local businesses.

scholars, supported by peer-reviewed and competitively awarded external grants, the majority from the NIH. They are mentors to graduate students, postdoctoral fellows, medical students, and interns, and they maintain close academic ties with The Ohio State University, Case Western Reserve University, and Cleveland State University.

The long tradition of creative scientific interaction and innovation continues. Recent discoveries made in the division include the factor myotrophin, which affects cardiac hypertrophy (Subha Sen, Ph.D.); the novel enzyme human chymase, which helps regulate blood pressure (Ahsan Husain, Ph.D.); a gene involved in the formation of Wilm's tumors (Bryan Williams, Ph.D.); a novel signaling mechanism used by interferons (George Stark, Ph.D.); and a new method that selectively eliminates specific proteins from cells (Robert Silverman, Ph.D.).

Excellent progress has also been made on many fronts, including the understanding of the key regulatory enzyme nitric oxide synthase (Dennis Stuehr, Ph.D.); how cells respond to growth factors (Alan Wolfman, Ph.D.); the mechanisms leading to atherosclerosis (Paul DiCorleto, Ph.D., Guy Chisolm, Ph.D., and Paul Fox, Ph.D.); and the development of a total artificial heart (Hiroaki Harasaki, M.D., Leonard Golding, M.B., B.S., and Raymond Kiraly, M.S., M.E.)

Every attempt is made to encourage scientific interactions between departments: Biomedical Engineering, chaired by J. Fredrick Cornhill, D.Phil.; Biostatistics and Epidemiology, chaired by Michael Kutner, Ph.D.; Cancer Biology, chaired by Bryan R.G. Williams, Ph.D.; Cell Biology, chaired by Paul E. DiCorleto, Ph.D.; Immunology, with Thomas A. Hamilton, Ph.D., Acting Chairman; Molecular Biology, chaired by Amiya K. Banerjee, Ph.D.; Molecular Cardiology, chaired by Edward F. Plow, Ph.D.; and Neurosciences, chaired by Bruce Trapp, Ph.D. Interdepartmental Program Project Grants are tangible examples of this philosophy.

The Research Institute also fosters many interactive research programs with clinical departments. The largest of these are organized into "centers" which bring together the clinical and basic science investigators to study focused problems. Existing and planned centers include anesthesia, surgery, biomedical devices, thrombosis and vascular biology, digestive diseases, ophthalmology, precursor cell biology, molecular genetics, and structural biology. The Department of Biostatistics and Epidemiology and the Department of Biomedical Engineering collaborate extensively with clinicians in organizing clinical trials and research programs involving medical devices and imaging procedures. The Research Institute also presents a bimonthly lecture series that presents outstanding scientists whose basic research is of notable clinical interest.

From collaborations of the sort favored by Page have come major program grants linking Stark as principal investigator with staff from Cancer Biology, Immunology, Molecular Biology, and Neurosciences; and DiCorleto as principal investigator with staff from Cell Biology and Immunology.

The Research Institute is poised for significant expansion. A strategic plan has been formulated to guide new developments that will combine scientific excellence with clinical relevance. The new Research and Education Institute will provide a functional environment for discussions leading to this activity. The recruitment of excellent department leaders and scientific staff will continue to build a worldwide reputation while earning necessary financial support.

The principles under which the Clinic was founded have continually been renewed by those who have headed research activity: Crile understood the importance of research in providing better patient care; Page emphasized the link between basic and clinical investigation, and the importance of training the next generation; Healy's wise planning and budgeting and her personal impetus energized the initial stages of the Research and Education Institute, increased outside funding and endowment, and attracted outstanding talent; and Stark expanded these approaches and encouraged collegial and effective joint activities to strengthen the current and future base of science talent. These leaders have ensured that the Research Institute will remain on the forefront of innovation and discovery well into the next century.

TWENTY

CLEVELAND CLINIC FLORIDA

A road that does not lead to other roads
always has to be retraced unless the traveller
chooses to rust at the end of it.

— *Tenyi Hsieh, 1948*

The Cleveland Clinic began its sixth decade in 1981 as the largest non-governmental employer in Cleveland. The city, however, was in deep recession and losing population. Although the Clinic was a successful institution, regional economics and the expected effects of medical reform posed a mild threat to its continued growth. But the opportunity accompanying this threat rested in the Clinic's main strength — the uniqueness of its organization as an integrated, academic group practice-based delivery system. The Clinic's leaders recognized the opportunity to expand beyond Cleveland, and they began a period of exploration.

They examined sites locally, regionally, and nationally. Because the Clinic's international reputation was strong, they also looked abroad, visiting locations in Europe, Africa, and the Far East at the invitation of local institutions or governments. They also gave serious consideration to Morocco and Singapore, where stable governments offered substantial financial and hospital support. In the end, however, the logistics of staffing and running a clinic on another continent proved impractical, and the idea of overseas expansion was set aside.

Attention continued to focus on the United States, and specifically Florida, where migration patterns from the Midwest and Northeast are strong. Marketing studies indicated that Tampa and Fort Lauderdale would be the best locations for specialty care, but

Carl C. Gill, M.D., Chief Executive Officer 1988–, and
Harry K. Moon, M.D., Chief of Staff 1991–, Cleveland Clinic Florida

that the Cleveland Clinic enjoyed the greatest name recognition in the southern part of the state, where Fort Lauderdale is located.

At that time, a growing number of patients from South America were seeking care at The Cleveland Clinic, where many physicians from these countries were training. Clinic leaders felt that a clinic in Florida might appeal to the large number of patients coming to the U. S. from Central and South America and the Caribbean through Miami. Therefore, southeast Florida, regionally known as "South Florida," became the most desirable location. To add to the attraction, no true multispecialty group practices existed in the area despite a population of four million, and no significant medical education or research was being done outside the University of Miami.

Coincidentally, the same broker who had worked on a bond issue for The Cleveland Clinic had also issued one for Fort Lauderdale's North Broward Hospital District. Learning of the Clinic's interest in the area, he introduced the two parties. The District's chief operating officer invited The Cleveland Clinic to consider a joint venture: the District proposed to build an outpatient building for the Clinic adjacent to Broward General Hospital. Specialty care staff would be recruited jointly and supplemented by Cleveland Clinic staff. Clinic leaders and District officials signed a letter of agreement. Unfortunately, when the medical staff at

Broward General Hospital learned about the agreement, they became infuriated and demanded that the offer be withdrawn. It was.[1]

Encouraged by Broward County's business leaders, however, Clinic leaders were confident that the new group practice would be welcomed by the public and the business community, and they decided to pursue opening autonomously. Demographic studies of South Florida (a single metropolitan area encompassing Broward, Dade, and Palm Beach counties) showed that a location in west central Broward County where the primary road from Florida's west coast ("Alligator Alley") crossed a major north-south highway on the east coast was within a two-hour drive of more than six million people. The Clinic purchased 320 acres of land in this prime location near the community of Weston.

The question of who would lead Cleveland Clinic Florida was addressed next. The Board of Governors appointed William A. Hawk, M.D., chairman of the Department of Anatomic Pathology, to the position of chief executive officer until the new facility opened. Hawk had played a key role in the construction of the Crile Building. He would be succeeded by Carl C. Gill, M.D., a respected cardiovascular surgeon who was on the Board of Governors and would serve as medical director until that time. James Cuthbertson, secretary to the Board of Governors, was appointed chief operating officer. Hawk and Cuthbertson moved to Florida in January 1987 to begin the process of building Cleveland Clinic Florida from the ground up. Gill remained in Cleveland a few months longer to start recruiting the medical staff.

As in Ohio, the corporate practice of medicine in Florida is illegal. Therefore, special legislative action was necessary to allow the Cleveland Clinic organizational structure to exist there. Moreover, the Florida licensure law requires physicians who have passed licensing examinations other than Florida's more than ten years earlier to take the Florida FLEX examination. This process is lengthy and arduous for mid-career physicians, especially specialists. In order to open in Jacksonville, the Mayo Clinic had successfully worked for the alteration of both statutes. In fact, the legislature passed a new statute, similar to that for Florida's medical schools, that permitted Florida to license wihout examination 25 Mayo Clinic physicians licensed in other states. The specificity of this law to Mayo was pred-

---

[1] Paralleling events in Cleveland nearly 70 years before, the response to the joint venture between the North Broward Hospital District and The Cleveland Clinic was so vehement that the physicians threatened to withdraw from Broward General Hospital if the agreement was signed. This hostile tone was carried over into future negotiations for cardiac surgery privileges at the public hospital.

Cleveland Clinic Florida outpatient facility

icated on the size of the mother institution and the amount of financial support provided for education and research, and, thus, excluded all other institutions. Therefore, in order to establish Cleveland Clinic Florida, both laws had to be altered again. With the help of a friendly and powerful delegation of Broward County legislators and cadre of lobbyists, the legislature passed the needed changes on the last day of the legislative session in June 1987.

The Clinic's leaders intended to establish a campus that included an outpatient clinic, hospital, research, and education facilities. In Florida, however, hospital beds cannot be occupied without approval from the Department of Health and Rehabilitative Services through the certificate of need process, which is strenuously monitored and defended by established institutions. In March 1987, the Clinic filed an application to build a 400-bed hospital. After a series of delays, revisions, and resubmissions, the Clinic's bid was rejected in January 1989 on the grounds that Broward County already had too many unused hospital beds. The Clinic decided not to appeal the decision at that time.

Expecting the approval and building process to take several years, the Clinic had made arrangements for temporary outpatient and hospital facilities. Even before the statutes regarding licensure were altered, construction began on a 76,000-square-foot outpatient building 10 miles northwest of downtown Fort Lauderdale. With the expectation it would be occupied for three years, it was designed to accommodate a staff of 40 physicians in a multispecialty setting.

Gill began recruiting staff in January 1987, but made little headway until the Florida statutes were changed in June. His first goal was to recruit the nucleus of a comprehensive clinic staff that could provide the majority of adult services. These physicians had to be of the highest quality available — mature clinicians with significant patient care experience. Preference would be given to Cleveland Clinic staff and graduates as well as physicians trained and recommended by Clinic alumni. He looked for physicians with strong backgrounds in research and education. He recognized that these qualities, combined with energy, collegiality, and a dedication to excellence in patient care, would help Cleveland Clinic Florida mature the culture and maintain the model of medical practice that had always distinguished the parent organization from other institutions. This transfer of culture was expected to be one of the most difficult aspects of building Cleveland Clinic Florida.

As previously noted, Latin America had been identified as a primary source of international patients, and Gill was committed to recruiting a staff that would attract these patients as well as the diverse population of South Florida. The Clinic planned to recruit local physicians as well, expecting that their local contacts would enhance specialty care referrals. Little did they know that the opposite would occur. Meanwhile, a search was under way for a hospital where Clinic physicians could admit patients.

From the start, local physician opposition to the Clinic was vicious. In order to prevent Cleveland Clinic physicians from applying for privileges, several hospitals closed their staffs — an action which later led the Federal Trade Commission to investigate for restraint of trade. However, Health Trust, Inc., the owner of North Beach Hospital, a 150-bed for-profit institution located across the street from the beach, invited Clinic physicians to admit their patients there. With a small active staff and a dangerously low census, they had everything to gain by locking in a steady source of admissions. After needed upgrades to the hospital had been agreed upon, the Clinic made North Beach its primary hospital.

Cleveland Clinic Florida opened its doors on February 29, 1988, almost exactly 67 years after the opening of the parent institution in Cleveland.[2] The first patient was admitted to North Beach Hospital

---

[2] Cleveland Clinic Florida opened with a staff of 28. The majority were Clinic physicians and former Clinic residents.

the following day. On April 8, Cleveland Clinic Florida was officially dedicated. Gill became the chief executive officer and Hawk retired to his home in Naples. Cuthbertson remained as chief operating officer.

Although North Beach Hospital was satisfactory for most patients, it lacked the facilities and certificates of need for invasive cardiology procedures and cardiac surgery. Only five hospitals in Broward County were approved to perform these services. One was Broward General, which had lost its primary team of cardiac surgeons to a competing hospital in nearby Palm Beach County. When Cleveland Clinic Florida cardiac physicians applied for privileges at this public hospital, Broward General Hospital's Medical Executive Committee postponed a review of their applications for three months. Finally, the applications were rejected as a group, and this action was supported by the hospital district's Board of Commissioners. Confronted with the illegality of its action, the Board reversed its stand in January 1989 and asked the Clinic to assume control of the cardiac surgery program at Broward General. However, the Medical Executive Committee still refused to grant privileges to the Clinic physicians. On April 27, the Commissioners were forced to import a committee of physicians from outside the state of Florida at taxpayers' expense to review the Clinic physicians' applications. They passed easily, and Gill performed Cleveland Clinic Florida's first open heart operation at Broward General on May 15, 1989, without incident, over a year after the fledgling organization's opening. Shortly thereafter, the majority of Cleveland Clinic Florida physicians obtained privileges there.[3]

The struggle for privileges at Broward General made many local physicians more determined than ever to drive The Cleveland Clinic out of Broward County. Their animosity was annoying but tolerable until it began to interfere with patient care. Local physicians who interacted with Cleveland Clinic staff received threats that referrals from their non-Clinic colleagues would stop unless they severed all relationships with the Clinic. In early 1989, a terminally ill Clinic patient needed a consultation with a pulmonologist, a specialty that Cleveland Clinic Florida did not yet have on staff. Incredibly, no pulmonologist in Broward County would see the patient![4] This despicable and unethical behavior was the last straw,

---

[3] In 1994, a cardiac catheterization laboratory was opened at North Beach Hospital, by then owned by the Clinic and renamed Cleveland Clinic Hospital, and an application for a certificate of need for open heart surgery was filed the same year. The final decision will not be made until after this book is published.

[4] The needed consultation was eventually provided by a pulmonologist from Miami, who was given temporary privileges at North Beach for this purpose.

Cleveland Clinic Florida Hospital

and the Clinic filed a $1 million anti-trust suit against the offending physicians.

Although the suit was eventually dropped, it caught the attention of the Federal Trade Commission. Agents began investigating selected Broward County hospitals and physicians for anti-trust activity in August 1989. Sixteen months later, armed with abundant evidence, they accused local doctors of attempting to restrain trade. At the insistence of the chief of staff at Broward General Medical Center, most physicians initially resisted the commission's order to admit wrongdoing and sign a consent decree. But faced with the consequences, by May all had signed except the chief of staff. Not until faced with criminal charges did he reluctantly back down in January 1992, ending the overt hostility and the ugliest chapter in the early history of Cleveland Clinic Florida.

Practicing side-by-side with local physicians at North Beach Hospital was beneficial to Cleveland Clinic Florida during these troubled first years, for it helped Clinic physicians assimilate into the community while providing the hospital with a growing number of admissions from both groups. Extensive renovations had turned North Beach into an attractive, modern hospital, and the census had climbed dramatically. The Cleveland Clinic purchased North Beach Hospital in 1990 and began to merge its operations with those of the Clinic in September 1992. On January 1, 1993, its name was changed to the Cleveland Clinic Hospital.

During its first seven years, Cleveland Clinic Florida made a remarkable impact on the face of medicine in South Florida, which was dominated by solo practitioners. Led by Gill and Harry K. Moon, M.D., appointed chief of staff in 1990, Clinic physicians quickly demonstrated the benefits offered by a multispecialty group practice to patients and physicians alike by providing expert diagnoses and sophisticated treatments not widely available. They began performing clinical research and publishing their findings. By September 1995, 221 projects had been approved, and almost 400 articles published the previous year alone. A basic research program began in 1994 with the recruitment of biochemist and molecular biologist Susan R. Abramson, Ph.D.

Cleveland Clinic Florida physicians initiated weekly grand rounds in 1988. Community physicians were invited to participate. Larger continuing medical education programs offered throughout the year attracted a large audience of local, regional, national, and international physicians.

Cleveland Clinic Florida's colorectal surgery residency program was the first in the state to be approved by the American College of Graduate Medical Education (ACGME) and now has two residents a year. Clinic residents and fellows from the Cleveland campus in a variety of specialties rotate through services at Cleveland Clinic Florida, and a residency program in internal medicine — now held jointly with The Cleveland Clinic — has been approved by the ACGME for Cleveland Clinic Florida alone beginning in 1996.

The need for educational materials to support residents and staff physicians led Cleveland Clinic Florida to open a medical library in 1990. The funds to purchase books, periodicals, and computer services are raised through donations and special events. Now known as the A. Lorraine and Sigmund Goldblatt Medical Library in honor of its major benefactors, it is open to anyone who wishes to use it.

By 1995, the Clinic staff had grown to nearly 100 physicians in the full range of adult specialties, and the recruitment of selected pediatric specialists was under way.[5] Although the outpatient build-

---

[5] Young patients were seen in several outpatient departments and treated regularly by the child and adolescent psychiatrists since Cleveland Clinic Florida's early years. Plans for a comprehensive pediatric specialty program began in late 1995 when the Children's Cancer Caring Center, Inc., a 30-year-old charity that raises funds to cover the cost of children's cancer treatments, moved their base of operations to Cleveland Clinic Florida. Pediatric hematology/

ing had been quickly outgrown and an additional 53,385 square feet leased in adjacent buildings, inadequate space was becoming a handicap to the rapidly growing institution. Furthermore, Cleveland Clinic Hospital's small size, location far from the outpatient clinic, and lack of sophistication presented a growing problem. Therefore, Cleveland Clinic Florida remains committed to building a complete medical campus and hospital in Weston and adding an outpatient clinic across the state in Naples, Florida. The superior quality of the Clinic's brand of medicine continues to support its growth, and the population of South Florida is the beneficiary.

---

oncology, neurology, and gastroenterology were the first specialties targeted, and invaluable assistance in recruitment and temporary manpower was provided by Douglas Moodie, M.D., the Clinic's chairman of Pediatrics in Cleveland, and his staff.

EPILOGUE

SOME AFTERTHOUGHTS

*History never looks like history when you are
living through it. It always looks confusing and
messy, and it always feels uncomfortable.*
                                    — John W. Gardner, 1968

TRUSTEES AND GOVERNORS

The Board of Governors was established in 1955 and subsequently assumed increasing responsibility for the direction of the Foundation. We have recounted the stories of the four chairmen of the Board of Governors, each of whom made lasting contributions to the institution during these four decades. Dr. Fay A. LeFevre served from the beginning of the Board of Governors era through 1968, and then Dr. Carl E. Wasmuth succeeded him, serving through most of 1976. The third chairman was Dr. William S. Kiser, who served until 1989. He was followed by the present chairman, Dr. Floyd D. Loop. The challenges, issues, and opportunities of each administration characterize these periods of leadership as do the personalities of the leaders themselves.

If the establishment of the Board of Governors has generated an evolving theme, it is the role of increasing managerial responsibility assumed by the Board, which represents the professional staff. The trustees have necessarily maintained legal accountability, but they have delegated many responsibilities to the Board of Governors. However, the ultimate responsibilities of defining institutional purpose, acquiring and selling property, staff compensation, and budgetary approval still rest with the trustees.

245

After forty years of operation, one can look back with some amazement at the success of the plan of organization as developed by the Planning Committee in 1955. During the early years of this period only minor changes were made. The original plan stated that the chairman must be a voting member of the Board of Governors. With the recommendation of the staff, this was amended so that any member of the staff could become chairman. From its inception the Board of Governors was able to unite a group of bright, highly trained professionals so that they could work together unselfishly. This achievement can be attributed largely to a democratic system of

Table 1: Elected Members of the Board of Governors		Table 1: Elected Members of the Board of Governors (continued)	
Name	Term(s)	Name	Term(s)
Fay A. LeFevre	1956–1960	Bruce H. Stewart	1977–1981
W. James Gardner	1956–1959	John J. Eversman	1978–1981
William J. Engel	1956–1959	Antonio R. Antunez	1978–1982
George Crile, Jr.	1956–1958	George C. Hoffman	1978–1982
	1962–1966	Jess R. Young	1979–1983
E. Perry McCullagh	1956–1958	Caldwell B. Esselstyn, Jr.	1979–1983
A. Carlton Ernstene	1956–1957	Eugene I. Winkelman	1980–1984
	1959–1963	Froncie A. Gutman	1980–1984
Irvine H. Page	1956–1961	Donald G. Vidt	1981–1985
Howard S. Van Ordstrand	1958–1962	William M. Michener	1982–1986
	1965–1969	Lester S. Borden	1982–1986
Stanley O. Hoerr	1959–1963	Maurice R. Hanson	1983–1987
	1965–1969	Thomas L. Gavan	1983–1987
Roscoe J. Kennedy	1960–1964	Mehdi Razavi	1984–1988
John B. Hazard	1960–1964	Joseph F. Hahn	1984–1988
Guy H. Williams, Jr.	1961–1965	Fawzy G. Estafanous	1985–1989
Robert D. Mercer	1963–1967	Carl C. Gill	1985–1988
Charles H. Brown	1964–1968	Carlos M. Ferrario	1986–1990
Donald B. Effler	1964–1968	D. Roy Ferguson	1987–1991
Leonard L. Lovshin	1966–1970	Jack T. Andrish	1987–1991
Ralph A. Straffon	1967–1971	John D. Clough	1988–1992
	1973–1976	Gregory P. Borkowski	1988–1992
Thomas F. Meaney	1968–1972	Floyd D. Loop	1988–1989
James S. Krieger	1969–1973	Muzaffar Ahmad	1989–1993
William L. Proudfit	1969–1973	Robert Kay	1989–1993
Ray A. Van Ommen	1970–1974	Melinda L. Estes	1990–1994
Donald F. Dohn	1970–1974	Victor W. Fazio	1990–1994
William A. Hawk	1971–1975	Paul E. DiCorleto	1991–1995
William S. Kiser	1972–1973	Wilma F. Bergfeld	1992–1996
Ray W. Gifford, Jr.	1973–1977	Bruce W. Lytle	1992–1996
Richard G. Farmer	1974–1978	Edgar Achkar	1993–1997
Shattuck W. Hartwell, Jr.	1974–1975	Zeyd Ebrahim	1993–1997
William C. Sheldon	1975–1979	Susan J. Rehm	1994–1998
F. Merlin Bumpus	1975–1979	Alan R. Gurd	1994–1998
Alan H. Wilde	1975–1980		

selecting governors. The following tables list all who have served on the Board of Governors up to the time of this writing (June 1995). Table 1 lists elected members, and Table 2 includes those serving on the Board by virtue of their office.

Table 2: Non-elected Members of the Board of Governors	
Name	Term(s)
Fay A. LeFevre (Chairman)	1955–1968[1]
Walter J. Zeiter (Executive Secretary)	1955–1963
Janet W. Getz (Recording Secretary)	1955–1971
Carl E. Wasmuth (Chairman)	1969–1976
William S. Kiser (Vice Chairman)	1974–1976
(Chairman)	1976–1989
James Lees (Executive Secretary)	1973–1980
(Chief Administrative Officer)	1989–1991
Gretchen Z. Belt (Recording Secretary)	1973–1979
Shattuck W. Hartwell, Jr. (Head, OPSA[2])	1977–1987
Elaine Clayton (Recording Secretary)	1979–present[3]
John J. Eversman (Chief Operating Officer)	1982–1989
James Cuthbertson	1982–1987
Ralph A. Straffon (Chief of Staff)	1987–present
Thomas Bruckman (Executive Secretary)	1987–1990
Carl C. Gill (Cleveland Clinic Florida)	1988–present
Floyd D. Loop (Chairman)	1989–present
Daniel J. Harrington (Chief Financial Officer)	1989–present
Gene D. Altus (Administrator[4])	1990–present
Frank L. Lordeman (Chief Operating Officer)	1992–present

Table 3 lists chairmen of the Board of Trustees and Table 4 lists presidents of the Foundation (the president serves as chairman of the Executive Committee of the Board of Trustees) from the time the organization was founded.

THE PROFESSIONAL STAFF

Despite the many fine physical facilities the Clinic has assembled over the years, the main asset of the Foundation is the people who

---

[1] Elected to a 5-year term in 1955.

[2] OPSA = Office of Professional Staff Affairs. Hartwell's predecessor in this office was Leonard Lovshin (1959–1976), but he did not sit with the Board of Governors except during his elected term (1966–1970).

[3] "Present" = as of this writing, June 1995.

[4] Title of this position changed from executive secretary to administrator in 1990.

Table 3: Chairmen of the Board of Trustees of The Cleveland Clinic Foundation	
Chairman	Term(s)
Henry S. Sherman	1942–1944[5]
John Sherwin, Sr.	1956–1961
George F. Karch	1966–1968
James A. Hughes	1969–1972
	1975–1984
Arthur S. Holden, Jr.	1973–1974
William E. MacDonald	1985–1990
E. Bradley Jones	1991–1992
Ralph E. Schey	1993–present

Table 4: Presidents of The Cleveland Clinic Foundation	
President	Term(s)
George Crile, Sr.	1921–1940
Henry S. Sherman	1941–1942
Edward C. Daoust	1943–1946
John Sherwin, Sr.	1948–1957
George F. Karch	1958–1965
George E. Enos	1966–1968
E. Tom Meyer	1969–1972
Elton Hoyt, III	1973
James A. Hughes	1974
Harry T. Marks	1975–1980
E. Bradley Jones	1981–1982
	1990
William E. MacDonald	1983–1984
E. Mandell DeWindt	1985–1989
Arthur B. Modell	1991–present

work here. At the core of this is the professional staff. These physicians and scientists have been carefully chosen by their peers, and over the years have come to represent one of the finest collections of professionals in the world. The Clinic attracts them by offering the opportunity to practice their profession in an academic setting which, unlike many other academic settings, maintains a collegial, collaborative atmosphere stemming from the spirit of group practice.

The present members of the professional staff are a culturally and ethnically diverse group representing the best physicians who could be recruited from the United States and 26 other countries.

---

[5] This office was unfilled from 1945 to 1956 and from 1961 to 1966. The Trustees' Executive Committee, chaired by the president, functioned in place of the chairman during those periods.

Table 5: Presidents of the Staff			
President	Term	President	Term
Robert D. Taylor	1949–1950	Charles B. Hewitt	1973–1974
Leonard L. Lovshin	1950–1951	Thomas L. Gavan	1974–1975
Donald B. Effler	1951–1952	Ralph J. Alfidi	1975–1976
John R. Haserick	1952–1953	Eugene I. Winkelman	1976–1977
George S. Phalen	1953–1954	Caldwell B. Esselstyn, Jr.	1977–1978
Robin Anderson	1954–1956[6]	Jess R. Young	1978–1979
Richard N. Westcott	1956–1957	Froncie A. Gutman	1979–1980
James S. Krieger	1957–1958	Royston C. Lewis	1980–1981
Robert D. Mercer	1958–1959	William M. Michener	1981–1982
Roscoe J. Kennedy	1959–1960	Thomas E. Gretter	1982–1983
Charles C. Higgins	1959–1960[7]	Russell W. Hardy	1983–1984
Charles H. Brown	1960–1961	Howard Levin	1984–1985
William J. Engel	1961–1962	Phillip M. Hall	1985–1986
E. Perry McCullagh	1962–1963	John D. Clough	1986–1987
Ray A. Van Ommen	1963–1964	Ronald L. Price	1987–1988
James I. Kendrick	1964–1965	Wilma F. Bergfeld	1988–1989
David C. Humphrey	1965–1966	William R. Hart	1989–1990
Donald E. Hale	1966–1967	George B. Rankin	1990–1991
Arthur L. Scherbel	1967–1968	Kenneth E. Marks	1991–1992
Robert E. Hermann	1968–1969	Gita P. Gidwani	1992–1993
Harriet P. Dustan	1969–1970	Sebastian A. Cook	1993–1994
Lawrence K. Groves	1970–1971	George H. Belhobek	1994–1995
Victor G. deWolfe	1971–1972	Herbert P. Wiedemann	1995–1996
Alfred M. Taylor	1972–1973		

The staff is governed under a set of bylaws, which are administered by the chief of staff (an officer of the Foundation, who sits on the Board of Governors, Medical Executive Committee, and Administrative Council), and a set of elected officers (see table 5 for a listing of staff presidents). Since 1989 the Board of Governors has required that each new staff member be board-certified in his or her specialty, either by a recognized American board or the international equivalent. Most of the physicians who joined the staff prior to 1989 are board-certified as well. All staff members are periodically recredentialed by the Office of Professional Staff Affairs for the services and procedures they perform, and each staff member undergoes a detailed annual professional review of performance in the areas of patient care, research, education, administrative service, national prominence, leadership, and collegiality.

---

[6] Anderson served as president for two years during work on the Plan of Reorganization.

[7] Both Kennedy (president) and Hazard (vice president) were elected to the Board of Governors during their terms as staff officers (see table 1). They were replaced by Higgins and Brown.

Ralph E. Schey, Trustee 1980– , Chairman, Board of Trustees, 1993–

The details of the staff's activities in their various areas of expertise are outlined elsewhere in this book, but the group has been increasingly recognized in the lay media for its excellence. Eight specialties have been cited for excellence by *U.S. News & World Report* and many individual staff members have been recognized as among the best physicians in the country by *Good Housekeeping, The Best Doctors in America* (first edition 1992-93, second edition 1994-95), *Town and Country,* and other publications. Furthermore, many of the staff have served as officers of their specialties' national organizations. At one time in 1993, The Cleveland Clinic staff included 13 presidents of national subspecialty societies! Nothing approaching this has been achieved by any other institution in the state, and it is a powerful endorsement of the Clinic's approach to group practice.

The Clinic's orientation to subspecialty medicine began in earnest in the 1950s with the formation of a number of subspecialty departments in internal medicine, continued in the 1960s with the elimination of the obstetrics service, and accelerated in the 1970s when many of the medical subspecialty boards were organized. In one of his "State of the Clinic" addresses, then chief executive officer William S. Kiser told the staff that it was of great importance that

The Cleveland Clinic campus looking toward downtown Cleveland

they become "technocrats." The staff had already embraced this concept with wild abandon, and by then the only pocket of primary care remaining in the organization was the Primary Care Department, which was responsible for delivering care to Clinic employees under the Cleveland Clinic Health Plan.

In the mid-1980s, however, the health care scene began to change. Cost-based reimbursement of hospitals received a knockout blow from the Health Care Financing Administration in the form of Diagnosis Related Group (DRG) reimbursement for Medicare patients. Managed care had emerged on the west coast in the 1920s and had reached Cleveland in the late 1960s in the form of Kaiser Permanente. Business was footing most of the bill for health care of their employees (and increasingly of their retirees as well) and was beginning to get uncomfortable with its escalating cost. Managed care, with its primary care orientation and gatekeeping methodology, seemed to offer a reasonable possibility of controlling these costs by keeping patients away from specialists and technology, and this movement was gaining momentum. As health care costs continued to rise, it became apparent that this approach, driven by the marketplace and accelerated by potentially disastrous but ultimately

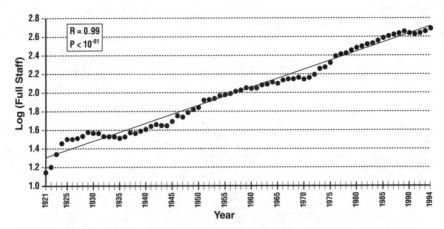

Figure 1: Exponential growth of the Cleveland Clinic's staff since the grand opening in February 1921. The ordinate shows the logarithm to the base 10 of the number of full staff on the roster at the end of each year indicated on the abscissa.

abortive federal attempts at health care reform, would change the delivery system. One of the most important results of these changes would be the emergence of the primary care physician as the central player in the new order; specialists would be relegated to a supportive role. Chapter 9 describes the Clinic's response to these forces.

The modest beginnings of the organization have been described earlier in this book, but since then the staff has grown at a constant, more or less inexorable rate to the present complement of more than 600 members. Figure 1 shows the exponential nature of the growth of the staff. Like a huge bacterial culture or a myeloma, it has followed predictable kinetics, with a doubling time of 15.6 years. Both *in vitro* and *in vivo*, constraints of space and nutrients normally cause such exponential growth curves eventually to plateau; the Clinic, however, has simply built more space each time things got tight. Though slight deflections have occurred (*e.g.*, downward with the Great Depression and the Clinic disaster in 1929, upward with the end of World War II and the introduction of antibiotics in 1945), the closeness of the adherence to the regression line has been remarkable over the past 74 years. For those who enjoy mathematics, the estimated staff size at any point in time can be expressed by the equation:

$$\log_{10} y = .0191x + 1.301$$

where y is the number of full staff and x is the number of years after 1921, the year the Clinic opened. This equation predicts that the

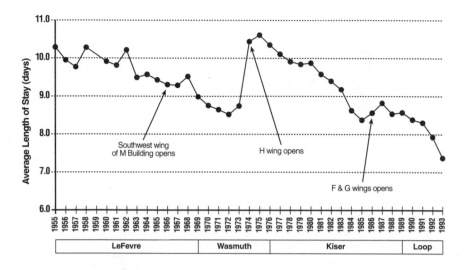

Figure 2: Average length of stay in The Cleveland Clinic Hospital shows a downward trend with increases each time a new wing was opened.

number of full staff will reach 1,000 members ($\log_{10} y = 3.0$) in the year 2010, 89 years after the doors first opened.

Another important trend during this tumultuous period has been the pressure to deliver increasingly complex services in the outpatient setting and to restrict hospital length of stay for those services that still require hospitalization. If we look at the Clinic's average length of stay over the years (figure 2), an interesting sawtoothed pattern appears, each "tooth" appearing at the time of hospital expansion.

Length of stay has declined still further with the addition of the Kaiser Permanente patients in 1994 and obstetrics in mid-1995. Until the marketplace applied pressure to reduce length of stay, the Clinic's own space restrictions did it fairly effectively.

The Clinic's staff has repeatedly shown its adaptability to adverse conditions over the years. Since the Board of Governors era began in 1955, this adaptability has continued. It will be tested mightily as reform of the health care delivery system, whether market- or government-driven, occurs over the next decade. So far the group has met the challenge and has every right to look to the future with confidence. As Loop has said, "Those who think our best years are behind us are looking in the wrong direction!"

INDEX

C. V. WEED, Administrator
Estate Dr. H. J. Wood
380 PEARL STREET

HOURS. **Exhibit A**

To Professional Services Rendered,

1 all brown mare
1 all sorrel horse
1 horse
1 buggy

1 one set in car
1 Horse shoe tus
1 horse clutc
1 wall as
1 bug pad
1 rugs
1 croscope
1 ruges
1 metal speculum
1 celluloid speculum
1 speculum
1 speculum
1 hand sp forcep
1 ears dressing forcep
1 Pairs dressing for
1 Throat mirror
1 trocar an

Brown Jerg & Roselu
Duke
Roy

To **Drs. Weed, Bunt**
380 PEARL STR

TELEPHONE 1812.
OFFICE OPEN AT ALL HOURS.

4

Room 1   Bedstead and bed
           2 Chairs
           Wash stand
           Dresser
           Whatnot
           1 whit

                In Com
           ry   and sundry
                   day sold
                   All the go
                   articles
To Professi   farm, in
1 Large Glass
1 Pocket batt